PELICAN BOOKS

A800

GENETICS AND MAN

Cyril Dean Darlington has pursued the study of chromosomes and heredity for over forty years and it has led him
to inquire into several sciences and to travel in many
countries.

Darlington was born in Lancashire in 1903, educated at
St Paul's School in London and at Wye College in Kent.
At Wye he learnt about agriculture and about genetics.
At twenty he went to the John Innes Horticultural Institution, for long the home of genetics in England. There he
stayed for thirty years. In 1939 he became Director and
in 1941 an F R S.

Darlington's books are equally devoted to plants,
animals and human beings, mostly flavoured with history,
and always controversial. Among them are *Cytology*,
The Evolution of Genetic Systems, *The Conflict of Science
and Society*, *Darwin's Place in History*, *Chromosome
Botany*, and with Professor Mather, *The Elements of
Genetics*, and *Genes, Plants and People*.

Darlington is married and has five children. For twelve
years he has been Professor of Botany in Oxford. Gardening is his recreation.

C. D. DARLINGTON

Genetics
and
Man

Penguin Books

Penguin Books Ltd, Harmondsworth, Middlesex, England
Penguin Books Pty Ltd, Ringwood, Victoria, Australia

—

The Facts of Life first published by Allen & Unwin 1953
Genetics and Man first published by Allen & Unwin 1964
Genetics and Man published with minor revisions by Penguin Books, 1966
The Facts of Life copyright © Allen & Unwin, 1953
Genetics and Man copyright © Allen & Unwin, 1964, 1966

—

Made and printed in Great Britain
by C. Nicholls & Company Ltd
Set in Monotype Times

This book is sold subject to the condition
that it shall not, by way of trade or otherwise,
be lent, re-sold, hired out, or otherwise circulated
without the publisher's prior consent in any form of
binding or cover other than that in which it is
published and without a similar condition
including this condition being imposed
on the subsequent purchaser

God yeve me sorwe! but, and I were a pope,
Not only thou, but every mighty man,
Thogh he were shorn ful hye upon his pan,
Sholde have a wyf; for al the world is lorn!
Religioun hath take up al the corn
Of treding, and we borel men ben shrimpes!
Of feble trees ther comen wrecched impes.

Chaucer: *The Monkes Tale*

Quel monstre est ce, que cette goutte de semence, dequoy nous sommes produicts, porte en soy les impressions, non de la forme corporelle seulement, mais des pensements et des inclinations de nos peres? cette goutte d'eau où loge elle ce nombre infiny de formes? et comme portent elles ces ressemblances, d'un progrez si temeraire et si desreglé, que l'arrière-fils respondra à son bisayeul, le nepveu à l'oncle?...

... Qui m'esclaircira de ce progrez, je le croiray d'autant d'aultres miracles qu'il vouldra: pourveu que, comme ils font, il ne me donne en payement une doctrine beaucoup plus difficile et fantastique que n'est la chose mesme.

Montaigne: *Essais*, II, 37

The perfect equality of men is the point in which the extremes of democracy and despotism are confounded.

Gibbon: *Decline and Fall of the Roman Empire* (ch. xliv)

Their Notions relating to the Duties of Parents and Children differ extremely from ours. For, since the Conjunction of Male and Female is founded upon the great Law of Nature, in order to propagate and continue the Species; the *Lilliputians* will needs have it, that Men and Women are joined together like other Animals, by the Motives of Concupiscence; and their Tenderness towards their Young, proceedeth from the like natural Principle: For which Reason they will never allow, that a Child is under any Obligation to his Father for begetting him, or to his Mother for bringing him into the World; which, considering the Miseries of human Life, was neither a Benefit in itself, nor intended so by his Parents, whose Thoughts in their Love-encounters were otherwise employed.

SWIFT: Gulliver's Travels I. 6

Contents

CONTENTS

CONTENTS

PART FIVE. THINKING AND KNOWING

Preface

THE present volume is a revised edition of *The Facts of Life*. This book was published ten years ago and was intended as a history of man's genetic understanding of himself. It was based on a Herbert Spencer Lecture, given in the University of Oxford in May 1950, and entitled 'The Coming of Genetics'.

Owing to the rapid expansion of the subject – in scope and detail – I have had to abridge the old text. I have removed the last two chapters, the appendices and some topical comments in order to make room for the new matter set out below.

C. D. DARLINGTON

Magdalen College
Oxford
May 1964

NEW OR EXTENDED SECTIONS

Chapter 6. Morgan's Fly Experiment. The Chemical Code.
Chapter 7. Myxomatosis.
Chapter 8. Smoking and Lung Cancer. Damage by Atomic Radiation.
Chapter 10. The Evolution of Heredity.
Chapter 13. Twins.
Chapter 14. Malaria and the Blood Genes. The Medical Dilemma.
Chapter 15. Chromosome Mistakes in Man.
Chapter 16. Cousin Marriage. Homosexuality.
Chapter 17. Instincts and Morals. Religious Teaching.

Illustrations

chromosomes and the great range of shapes entailed by the variation in crossing-over

Photo by Hubert Rees × 2400

4. Chromosome complement of a woman

From Ford, Jacobs and Lajtha, 1958
(*Nature*, 181 : 1965) × 3000

TEXT FIGURES

TABLES

TABLES

PART ONE

CLEARING THE GROUND

Our first task is to see where common observations and simple analogies led our ancestors, what beliefs they formed about the facts of life and how far those beliefs were distorted by interest and prejudice, by the confusion of moral and natural law, and by the general imperfections of religion and of science. The use of the microscope and the theory of evolution removed ancient errors in the study of reproduction and heredity but, as we can now see, they introduced other new errors.

1

The Old Ideas

ADAM'S SURPRISE

IN the year 1785 at Geneva there appeared an account of *Experiments to serve as a History of Generation in Animals and Plants*. The author of this celebrated book was a certain Lazzaro Spallanzani, a Jesuit priest and a Professor of Natural History at the University of Pavia. His work was translated by a Swiss evangelical divine and fellow experimenter, Jean Senebier. In introducing his subject, M. Senebier also introduces the history of genetics and the study of life:

The birth of a man, of an animal, of an insect, the appearance of a plant which pierces the earth to cover it with verdure have [he writes] certainly provided all thinking men with a problem whose solution should singularly engage their curiosity. When the first man, six thousand years ago, saw his existence so pleasingly doubled by the birth of his first child; when he saw it develop little by little to present itself at last as a being like his father; when new children arrived and proved to be still the same object of tenderness, of astonishment and of admiration; when his descendants informed him with emotion that they, like him, had the happiness of being fathers; he sought without doubt the causes of this phenomenon so constant yet so obscure: perhaps he saw no further into its cause than the union of the sexes; certainly two hundred generations have succeeded one another with no greater enlightenment. In vain a host of ingenious and profound men have gathered together their observations on this important matter. In vain the boldest minds have analysed this capital fact. The succession of centuries presents only a succession of errors. And, while the thickest shadows have always hidden the secret of generation from intelligent physiologists, others, who prided themselves on having explained the facts of life, gave us nothing but the most incredible ideas, the most flagrant contradictions, the most incoherent travesties of Nature.

We have to begin talking about heredity in this simple and general way for a very good reason. If we were describing chemistry to the world at large it would be enough to tell the story as modern science has revealed it, to tell it simply, plainly and in straightforward fashion. For, although it is not a new story, it has no forerunner and no competitor in the public mind. This way of proceeding is not enough for anything that concerns life. Everybody already knows much too much about it. The infant sucks up its first ideas about heredity with its mother's milk. Moreover, these ideas are not all true. The physics that a child learns before the age of ten (whatever it may learn afterwards) is apt to be good physics. The biology that it learns (which may be all it ever does learn) is apt to be bad biology.

The problem which, in the age of enlightenment, the learned and even the ecclesiastical world thought might 'engage the curiosity of all thinking men' became in the following century a dangerous subject divorced from polite conversation as tending towards atheism, obscenity and sin. A gulf was fixed between the secluded specialists who discussed these matters in profound or at least technical language and a public who were educated on moral principles laid down 2,000 or more years ago.

Modern education is often attempting to bridge this gulf. But it is doing so under great difficulties. Discovery is proceeding at a great pace. Those engaged in it are very deeply engaged in it, often to the exclusion of wider public or cultural interests. The fact that the advances of the last fifty years require a new thinking-out of our social, moral and intellectual ideas has therefore almost escaped notice. The system of teaching, even in the most advanced centres, is inevitably twenty or thirty years behind-hand in facing this problem. Educated men and women are therefore by no means ashamed of professing an ignorance of the discoveries which should determine their conduct. They are content to use the ideas of life, heredity and society which have done service since Old Testament times.

How recent is the notion of heredity in our minds is shown by the fact that the word was imported into the language of science only during the last hundred years. Before that time we (in common with other European nations) used the same word to describe, on the one hand, the chattels we received from our parents by process of law and, on the other hand, the inborn character we received from them by the processes of reproduction and growth. To Darwin, who still spoke of 'natural inheritance', the subject had the novelty of a new world. 'The whole subject of inheritance is wonderful', he wrote in 1868. It was more wonderful than he guessed. The study of heredity has indeed required us, step by step, to explain life. This has often had to mean, not only what men knew of life, but also what they *thought* they knew. For, where the fundamental properties of life are at issue, no clear division could be made between fact and theory or between theory and superstition.

There is, however, an easy way of telling what people know (or think they know) in this apparently abstruse field of thought. It is to look at what our forefathers, the educated ones who could read and write, said on the matter. We can indeed learn a great deal of the problem, and of the kinds of evidence that we can make use of in studying it, by taking a glance at the old Stone Age beliefs which have come down to us in one way or another. We can also in this way learn how far such beliefs are still held today and still determine our behaviour.

FIRST QUESTIONS

If we look at the literary evidence of ancient beliefs on heredity we are struck by the large proportion of ideas which run clean contrary to all the evidence we have today. Of what we now believe to be the true principles very little is said. But we know, or can infer with certainty, whether from Hebrew, Greek or Latin writers, that the facts of life were understood in a simple way. Reproduction resulted from intercourse between the two sexes. Intercourse took place only between individuals of a like kind or, as we should say, of the same species. Both the male and the female made some contribution to heredity.

These were rules but they were rules to which exceptions were all too frequent. Men were puzzled and often bewildered – as they still are today – by an apparent diversity in the means of reproduction. This diversity we know to have been superficial, but to them it was utterly misleading.

The first difficulty arose from the fact that, while in the higher animals the sexes were separate (whence indeed the word *sex*), in the higher plants, if there was such a thing as sex at all, the two sexes, the pollen and the eggs, were usually united on the same individual. And then again, in some animals the young were born alive, while in others they hatched from an egg, either at once as with some snakes and fishes, or after an interval as with birds and frogs and those insects where an egg had been seen. But, as to the insects, yet another trouble arose; for some, so it seemed, produced a grub directly which grew into an egg later. What we call the butterfly's pupa or chrysalis, or the ant's 'egg', for example, was the result of growing backwards into an egg, so they thought, for they did not know that the grub or caterpillar hatched from one egg before it grew into the other. And where an egg had not been seen, none was supposed to have existed. Again, while a bird's egg reveals no apparent structure, our own young are born half developed. And even the ripe seeds of plants contain a well-formed embryo.

Beyond this understanding and misunderstanding of reproduction what was there? We may take, as examples, first Aristotle and the Bible as a basis for considering man and animals, and later Theophrastus and Virgil as a basis for considering plants.

Aristotle, with regard to facts, is usually critical of what he will believe. He makes a stand, although not a very brave stand, against the superstitions with which the ancient world abounded, against the old wives' tales. He would not swallow, as others did, the fable that the weasel brought forth young by the ear, while the raven had sexual union only by the beak. He probably rejected the story that armed men sprang up where dragon's teeth had been sown by Jason, but he accepted the most widely-believed, and therefore the most dangerous, of such stories. He accepted the notion that less-advanced organisms like worms and snails and mere plants could spring from decaying matter of all kinds. He believed, that is, in the spontaneous generation of life – a theory whose history we shall be following down to the present day.

Aristotle is much concerned, as many others have been, with the relative contribution of male and female parents in heredity. He repeatedly asserts that the female provides the *matter*, while to the male is due the *motion*. This is the first attempt to distinguish between material and immaterial elements in heredity, a distinction which was to dominate controversy on the subject at the beginning of the twentieth century.

One of the more fanciful arguments in support of the view that the female contribution is unequal to the male is that the female need not have pleasure in sexual union. Lucretius, the Epicurean poet, uses a similar argument in suggesting that the contributions of the two parents in heredity are determined by which seed 'prevails', that is by the proportion of the emotional interests of the two parents in the matter. The idea that the seed of one parent should prevail no doubt seemed to be justified by the evident fact that children sometimes resemble one parent and sometimes the other. Such arguments show us the gap between the analytical processes of thought and the crude analogies which are used by the same writers. This gap was due to their leaving out parts of the argument – a practice which was even easier in ancient times than it is today.

Yet another subject that interested Aristotle was sex determination. This is a problem that has baffled men and women since very early days. He quotes Empedocles as suggesting that the heat of the womb may determine the sex of the offspring. This, Aristotle feels, was a very reasonable view for one who did not know that the same womb might give birth to twins of opposite sex. Again, he quotes Democritus, whose opinion he prefers, as saying that the sex, like other properties, follows the parent whose generative particles or seed prevails. It is to Anaxagoras, however, that he attributes the most far-reaching of all these doctrines. For this philosopher says that the embryo is already formed and its sex determined in the seed of the male parent before sexual union; those offspring derived from the right testis are male, those from the left are female. This is the theory of *preformation* and it is again a theory whose repercussions are still felt around us today.

All these learned arguments notwithstanding, Aristotle feels, like many modern scientists, that he must pay attention to the practical man. And to the working shepherd (for whom the proportion of the sexes in his flock was a bread-and-butter matter) the heat theory was the only one of any practical value. If you want ram lambs, says the philosopher, put your ram with the ewes when the north wind is blowing. To make doubly sure take care that the animals when tupped are facing north. If it is ewe lambs you want (in order to increase your flock) face them south. 'So small a thing', he reflects, 'will sometimes turn the scale and cause cold or heat.' These things were believed with certainty in England only a few hundred years back. Today probably they are still argued over a mug of ale.

There is one original contribution, perhaps the only one, of intellectual interest in the whole of Aristotle's discussion of reproduction and heredity. Aristotle declares that he believes that:

children are born with a likeness to their parents not only in congenital but also in acquired characters [and he goes on to quote] the case at Chalcedon where the father had a brand on his arm and the letter was marked on the child – only confused and not clearly articulated.

De Generatione Animalium

This is the simplest possible theory of heredity, a theory whose history through the centuries may be followed wherever written records remain. It is what we may call the direct theory. The parent passes on to his offspring a representation of himself as he is at the time of begetting the offspring. But how can this representation, this up-to-date model, be made? The Hippocratic writings had proposed what still seems to be the only possible explanation. The suggestion was that all the parts of the body contributed some germ, or humour, or essence, to heredity. And these materials, if they are materials, are collected in the seed of the male or female parent. The seed thus comes to epitomize the parent's body part by part, by *pangenesis*.

This theory is necessary in some form, it would seem, to any assumption of the inheritance of characters acquired by the action of the outside world on the several parts of the parent's body. Yet Aristotle, having assumed the inheritance of acquired characters, rejected the necessary explanation. Perhaps it was that the suggestion of material inheritance through the male offended him. His devotion to essences and humours, principles and purpose, and the eternal rightness of nature, may have turned him away from anything so squalid as matter in the male contribution to heredity. Whether for this reason or not, he set his face against pangenesis and used against it the best weapons that he could lay his hands on. The result is an excellent argument.

First, Aristotle says, children resemble their parent in such parts as hair and finger nails, voice and gait. This is undeniably true. Now, he says, no one can suppose the semen is collected from the hair or from the voice. The notion that hair or voice might have a material and living basis did not occur to him.

Further [he continues] children are like their more remote ancestors from whom nothing had come, for the resemblances recur at an interval of many generations, as in the case of the woman in Elis who had relations with the Ethiopian; her daughter was not an Ethiopian but the son of that daughter was.

To us this seems not only an acute observation but also a sound argument, for we now have the explanation of such reappearances of ancestral characters and the explanation (as we shall discover) is radically inconsistent with pangenesis.

And, finally, Aristotle says that the same thing applies also to plants. For the seed inherits the properties of its parent in regard to the formation of fruit. Yet the seed is produced before the fruit is ripe. So it cannot carry hereditary or representative particles derived from the ripe fruit.

Thus in certain negative respects we find Aristotle right. But in being right he has to be inconsistent. When we come to positive ideas on the other hand, we get nothing beyond the female matter and the male principle of movement. And this is a little less than the man on the land knew in Aristotle's own time – a little less because Aristotle's first principles prevented him from facing the awkward facts of stock breeding and agriculture.

THE BIBLE AND HEREDITY

The Bible candidly reveals both points of view. On one side it examines the crude facts of cattle-breeding and seed-raising as they concern the farmer earning his bread or meat by his knowledge and cunning and the sweat of his brow. On the other side it expounds the views of divers seers and sages on inheritance in man, a matter of no less practical importance, but bound up also with deep questions of morality. Both views of heredity have influenced European thought for 2,000 years and continue to do so.

What strikes us first is the biblical attitude towards the same problem of the inheritance of acquired characters, the direct and obvious theory of heredity which had interested the Greeks. It is related to the highest religious doctrine. When we are told that

God will 'visit the sins of the fathers upon the children to the third and fourth generation' (Exodus xx. 5; xxiv. 7) we have to understand that the effects of the bad habits of parents are expressed in their remote descendants. Now they can be expressed only by way of heredity, bad heredity. Indeed, the classical example of this effect is to be found not in Exodus, but in Genesis, for the effect of Adam's original sin there recorded is inherited, as we know, by the whole of mankind. St Augustine (the Bishop of Hippo, not of Canterbury) makes this clear when he compares the effect of Adam's error with what was then regarded as an hereditary mutation, that of a cultivated and innocent olive into a wild and guilty one. For 'inasmuch as his sin was so great, that by it his nature became commensurately changed for the worse, he converted the entire race of man into a wild olive stock' (*Marriage and Concupiscence*, from Zirkle, 1946).

It is obvious that the threat of hereditary punishment is likely to have a certain moral use as a deterrent against sin. Such a threat may be needed in the absence of a belief in hell or an effective enforcement of moral law by public opinion. It was cultivated equally by the official mythology of ancient Greece and of Israel; but enlightened men, equally among Greeks and Jews, deplored its use. Hence we find a revulsion of feeling expressed by the prophets at a time when the punishment of the Jews for their past sins seemed altogether too great. 'Everyone shall die for *his own* iniquity', cries Jeremiah. 'Every man that eateth the sour grape, *his* teeth shall be set on edge', declares Ezekiel. In future therefore every man will pay as he earns. Retribution shall be direct, not deferred or inherited. Many later Greek and Latin writers took this more humane view. But both opinions were based on moral rather than on scientific grounds. Between the two opinions, both the prophets and the people have halted now for 3,000 years.

As the centuries have followed one another little of any substance has been added to the argument. To be sure it has been noticed that mutilations are remarkably little inherited. Lambs have had their tails cut off for a hundred generations, but they still continue to be born undiminished in this respect. For a much longer time certain religions have required male human babies to be similarly mutilated, yet Mohammedan and Jewish boys are still born uncircumcised. There are exceptions, but they are no more frequent now than in the days of Moses.

It was once believed that the black races derived their colour from the curse which Noah uttered upon his son Ham, from whom they are said to be descended. For Ham had seen Noah (as the Book of Genesis records) asleep, drunk and uncovered, and had fetched his brothers to share his wicked amusement. More sophisticated people probably still believe, as Ovid did, that the colour is there because the ancestors of black peoples were scorched by the sun – either suddenly on one very hot day, or over a long time. And no doubt many will continue to believe this. But while waiting to examine the evidence let us remember that in the tropics – and even in the same island of Ceylon – there are pale and black races of men who have lived in the same latitude for thousands of years. Under the same sun the pale remain pale, the black remain black. Let them cross and their offspring will be brown. Heredity determines their colour and the sun does not alter their heredity.

The length of the experience, and the weight of the evidence, against the inheritance of acquired characters in no way reduces, it would seem, the strength of the belief. It is a belief which rests not on observation but on desire. As things *should* be, so they *must* be. Antonio Zara writes in 1615, according to Zirkle, that the evil effects of a certain heinous crime (that of *lèse majesté*) is inherited by the children of the evil doer, and not only those born *after*, but also those born *before*, the crime was committed! Here at last moral fervour has completely subdued reason, and superstition has stolen the place and name of science.

Let us turn now from high religious doctrine to low practical interest. One of the most popular of all acquired characters to be inherited is what is called the 'maternal impression'.

The earliest documented instance of the effects of a maternal impression is found in chapter xxx of the Book of Genesis. Jacob has agreed with his uncle (and father-in-law) Laban the son of Nahor that he shall take as his hire for tending the sheep and goats of Laban all the striped and coloured offspring that shall be born in the flock. Jacob then sets to work to increase the proportion of such offspring. He takes rods of hazel which he has peeled in stripes; he holds them in front of the ewes when they come down to drink and are likely to mate and to conceive. Finding his design successful – 'the flocks brought forth ringstraked, speckled and spotted' – Jacob then improves upon it by holding his peeled rods only in front of the stronger ewes and she-goats, leaving the feebler ones to conceive unaided by his trick. The stronger therefore bring forth striped offspring for Jacob; and the weaker bring forth white offspring for Laban. Hence Jacob ensures that Laban shall have some lambs and kids but they will be of the weaker sort. This account is not the one Jacob gave to his wives, Leah and Rachel (who were, after all, the daughters of Laban), but it is the one which he reported to the Recording Angel.

The story of how Jacob got the better of Laban is a legend. It is evidence not of what actually happened but of a belief as to what should happen: a belief that the impression of the expectant mother – particularly at the very moment of conception – influences the character of her offspring. It is not a moral belief so much as a magical belief. This belief still exists all over the world today. It has been held by such important and diverse literary figures as Tristram Shandy (that boundless source of contemporary biological learning) and Sarah Gamp. But it has no foundation in the authentic records of science.

The story of Jacob and Laban is, however, at the same time evidence of a belief in the effectiveness of a genuinely scientific principle, that of selection in breeding. By choosing the stronger mothers Jacob also secured the stronger offspring, the better breed, for himself. The understanding of this principle had been the origin and basis of crop and stock improvement some thousands of years earlier. Without it the New Stone Age men could never have established agriculture.

To the Hebrew prophet and the medieval thinker, whether it was a question of high doctrine or base practice, there was no clear distinction between biology and magic or between biology and morals except that magic and morals came first and were more useful. In general, what should happen, did happen. Those who study life by laborious experiments today are prone to think that this is the view of a world devoted to superstition and now long dead. As we proceed in our story we shall find, however, that the line between biology, morals and magic is still not generally known and admitted. Even among the most advanced and sophisticated peoples of our own time it is generally obliterated by the pleasant fancies to which we may apply the name of vitalism.

VIRGIN BIRTH

A second important field of thought in which biblical teaching has reacted on the theory of heredity was in relation to virgin birth or parthenogenesis. The oldest of Greek legends tells us that 'The Earth . . . bare also the fruitless deep without the sweet union of love', and the idea of a virgin birth was continually recurring in the literature, first of the mythology and then of the natural history, of ancient peoples. Many kinds of animals, including harmless ewes and fearful tigresses, were reported by various authors, including Aristotle (and are recorded by Zirkle), as having been impregnated by the wind.

Two genuine sources of confusion existed. In the first place Aristotle, correctly as it so happens, believed that drone bees arose without copulation and thus by virgin birth. But it so happens also that he believed the queen bee, the only bee that lays eggs, to be actually a male – the 'king' as he called her – so that his opinion on both matters could only have been a guess. In the second place when the domestic fowl was introduced into the Levant (about the time of Nebuchadnezzar) it was seen that the hen would lay eggs without having been trodden by the cock. What was more natural than to suppose that the spring breeze, Zephyrus, blowing gently from the warm west had fertilized the birds! Not everyone was able to notice, as Pliny did, that these eggs were infertile.

What was true of ewes and hens, and was widely believed of mares, was naturally not thought impossible of women. Accordingly the belief that women might conceive through eating some special herb or fruit, or merely through bathing in the sea, was applied by the Greeks to their goddesses and by the Arabs and the Chinese to whole populations of remote and inaccessible Islands of Women.

In this state of confusion it was natural that the early Christians should adorn their lovely legend with the story of a virgin birth. There were two ways of defending it. Some were satisfied with Tertullian that it was certain because it was impossible. Others looked round for what evidence they could lay their hands on to promote belief in the doctrine they had adopted. Thus St Augustine says (*De Civitate Dei, 21* (5)):

Sceptics keep demanding that we shall explain these marvels to reason and because we cannot do so, inasmuch as they are above human comprehension they suppose we are speaking falsely. These persons themselves therefore, ought to account for all these marvels which we either can or do see. ... In Cappadocia the mares are impregnated by the wind, and their foals live only three years.

Nearly 1,000 years later that enterprising Oxford chemist, Friar Bacon (in his *Opus Majus*) uses the same argument:

The human mind can be induced to accept the truth of the virgin birth because certain animals remaining in a state of virginity conceive and bear young, as for example, vultures and apes. ... Aristotle maintains in the second book on Vegetation that the fruits of the female palms mature from an odour coming from the male trees.

The problems of heredity are difficult enough as they are presented to us by nature. As they are presented to us by the masters of ancient thought they are much more difficult. Their labours had cleared a little ground at the expense of barring every way out from the clearing. They had made themselves a cage. To us it seems obvious that plants are often fertilized with the help of the wind but that animals are not. To them the contradiction was fatal. To us it seems obvious that the moral value of original sin has no bearing on the physiological evidence for the inheritance of disease. To them the moral and the physiological problems were the same: what *should* happen, *would* happen. To us it seems obvious that the mule is half-way between the horse and the ass, whichever is the father, and that the contributions of the male and the female to heredity must therefore be the same. To them the difference between the work done by the two sexes in reproduction was so great it was impossible to think that the work done in heredity was the same.

It was possible for a shrewd sceptic, like the French-Jewish philosopher Montaigne, to see and express the problem of heredity quite clearly. The organic connexion with his father, the material out of which he was built, was a mere drop of water. This structureless fluid conveyed to Montaigne his father's propensity to stone in the bladder. But not to his elder brothers. His father's propensity was not expressed until twenty-five years after Montaigne was born. And Montaigne himself did not show it for forty-five years. Explain this to me, he says, and I will believe as many more miracles as you like – provided, of course, that the explanation is not (as it usually turns out) more complicated than the facts.

No one could answer Montaigne's problem at that time with reason and in consequence superstition was called upon to fill the gap.

Hence, from these early centuries of argument, as M. Senebier says, what was learnt proved to be the most incredible ideas, the most flagrant contradictions, and the most incoherent travesties of nature. Our next business is therefore to discover how in the last 300 years with new tools, new ideas, and new methods of organized inquiry man has in the end found out how to tackle the problem.

2

The New World of the Microscope

WHEN the new way of finding out about things, which we call scientific method, grew up in the seventeenth century the state of belief on the facts of life, on reproduction, heredity and development, was very much as Aristotle and his successor Theophrastus had left it. The great problems of spontaneous generation and virgin birth, of the influence of the male and the female in heredity, of the inheritance of acquired characters, of the theory of pangenesis, all these problems were still being settled by invoking a magical or a moral superstition. But occult qualities and moral attributes were no longer enough to answer the arguments of inquiring people. Now a few doubters began to suggest observations and experiments. And, in some countries at least, they were able to undertake, and discuss, and publish such observations and experiments without fear of a Papal Bull or a Holy Inquisition.

For these tasks a new and powerful instrument was crying out to be used – the microscope. As that ingenious artificer, Robert Hooke, an architect as well as a microscopist, put it with missionary fervour in his *Micrographia* (1665):

By the help of *Microscopes* there is nothing so *small* as to escape our inquiry; hence there is a new visible world discovered to the understanding

– an opinion which anyone who looks down a microscope today can well confirm. This new world, however, came into view only by glimpses. Hooke and those of his time caught the first glimpse. Their simple and compound microscopes, magnified 100 or 200 times, with a distortion of shape and colour which increased with the magnification. But they revealed many new things. Thereafter men had to wait for better lenses to see anything more. They waited 160 years. And during this time they naturally argued about what they had seen. It mainly had to do with the higher animals. This aspect of the problem was in the forefront of men's minds throughout the eighteenth century and with it we must begin.

IN SEARCH OF THE EGG

That the testes must be the essential organs of reproduction of the male had been known since ancient times, indeed, presumably, since the New Stone Age, when castration produced the first eunuchs. The testes must either produce or, at least as some said, collect the generative fluid. With the female the situation was not clear till later. The Alexandrians had discovered by the dissection of monkeys that females had what we call the egg-producing glands, the ovaries. They thought the ovaries were like the testes and produced some kind of seminal fluid which united with the male fluid to generate the offspring: that is, to induce or stimulate the formation of an embryo.

So the story remained for nearly 2,000 years. The observations on which our modern knowledge of reproduction is based were made by two inquiring Dutchmen, both of them living at Delft in the time of the painter Jan Vermeer. It was in 1672 that the first of these, Régnier de Graaf, a young surgeon who died the very next year, showed what it is that the female has to contribute. He found that, before conception, there were small watery lumps on the surface of the ovary. He found them first in rabbits, then in ewes, and finally in women. Further, in the rabbit, these lumps, one to four of them on each ovary, were partly replaced after conception by little yellow bodies which a few days later could be seen to agree in number with the small embryos developing in each limb of the womb. De Graaf's observation made it very likely that each of these lumps, which we now call Graafian follicles, contained some kind of generative particle; this particle must be something like a hen's egg, and not at all like the male semen; further this particle had somehow made its way from the ovary to the womb and had become itself the beginning of the embryo. The release of this 'egg', its journey, and its development to form a foetus, de Graaf concluded, had been stimulated by the *aura seminalis*, that is to say, by the pungent vapour of the male secretion.

Thus an extraordinary mystery was in part resolved. No one had seen the egg in these cases. But it now appeared beyond doubt that female mammals, including women, produce eggs like the ones laid by birds or fishes with which everyone was familiar. Who would have imagined what was now brought to light! That the larger quadrupeds produce smaller eggs than the insects; that these eggs float from the ovary to the vessels which carry them to the womb, free and unprotected in the belly – or abdominal cavity, as it is now politely called; and that they make a part of this journey unassisted by the innumerable canals and conduits with which, for relatively trivial uses, and sometimes for no use at all, the animal body is so amply provided.

From these surprising discoveries or conjectures arose a wave of enthusiasm for the newly acknowledged egg. Why should not the egg contain within it the sole and universal principle of heredity in all life? Those who supported this view – the egg enthusiasts – became known as *ovists*. But from the very beginning their view was challenged by the zealous adherents of an opposite doctrine.

It was only three years after the revelation of the egg, or rather of its movements, by de Graaf, that there came the even more momentous discovery of his fellow townsman, Antony van Leeuwenhoeck. This enterprising man, having made a competence by selling linen, gauging wine and surveying buildings, was able to devote himself to pure research. He occupied himself with glass-blowing, grinding lenses, making simple microscopes or rather what we should call magnifying glasses. With these he searched for everything small that he could examine with them, very much as enthusiastic amateurs still do today. There was a difference however. He surpassed the rest of mankind in what he saw. Whether it was by the cunning of his fingers or the sharpness of his eyes – genetic properties in which men vary enormously – or by a more mysterious ingenuity, we shall never know. The 272 microscopes he left on his death have mostly disappeared and his contemporaries and immediate successors were unable to repeat his most remarkable discoveries. Certain it is that he applied his gifts indefatigably and with prodigious and unquestioned success. Amongst other things he looked at the seminal fluid of various animals, including man. Imagine his astonishment when he found that it was not, as Montaigne and everyone else had supposed, a mere fluid. Swimming about in it there were little tailed creatures like tadpoles but with heads only a ten-thousandth of an inch across!

Without undue delay Leeuwenhoeck wrote an enthusiastic letter to the newly founded Royal Society in London describing the discovery of what he called his 'animalcules'.

Here, he thought, just as de Graaf had thought, was the material connexion between parent and offspring, the long-imagined foundation of heredity. Modestly he begged the Society to suppress the information if they found it repugnant or scandalous. But the secretary replied that it pleased them very much – as well it might. Indeed, they very shortly, in 1680, elected him a Fellow of the Society.

To us it would seem that only enlightenment would come from these marvellous discoveries of de Graaf and Leeuwenhoeck. But their consequence for long years was nothing but strife and confusion. The technical means for carrying the discoveries on to a full understanding of reproduction were lacking. The fusion of sperm and egg had not been seen. Indeed, the egg itself was still a conjecture; no specific structure had been found under the microscope.

The fearful problem of heredity still yawned at men's feet and they wanted a quick answer. They wanted a final solution such as Newton at that very time was able to give them in physics. They leapt upon the easiest explanation, or rather, the two easy explanations. In the same year that de Graaf had discovered his follicles, Malpighi in Italy wrote to the Royal Society describing a young germ he had seen in a hen's egg, recently laid. It seemed to him that the egg (which must have been incubated for a day or two) contained a young embryo, a replica of a hen in miniature. Could it be that the egg contained a minute model of the parent just as a bud contains the next year's flower already preformed? Could it be that heredity was merely development and that development was merely an unfolding of something already there? That heredity was not only predetermined but preformed from the beginning?

This tremendous notion was expounded by the party of the ovists. But Leeuwenhoeck, fresh from the discovery of his spermatic worms, his animalcules, took up the challenge. In a letter to Sir Christopher Wren (*IX Kal.* Feb. 1680) he writes:

having found spermatozoa in the male seminal fluid of animals, birds, fishes, and even insects, I assert much more certainly than before that man arises, not from the egg, but from the spermatozoa in the male semen; and especially as I recollect having seen in the semen of a man, and also of a dog, two sorts of spermatozoa. Seeing this I pictured to myself that the one kind was masculine, the other feminine.

Strangely enough, we now know that there are indeed two kinds of sperm. But Leeuwenhoeck could not see them; for even we cannot see them with microscopes ten times as strong. With him the wish was father to the thought. Others of a Calvinistic persuasion were prepared to go to even greater lengths in the interest of predestination. Another Dutch microscopist published a sketch of what the little model man, the homunculus, inside the sperm head *might* look like. The world at large, not knowing either the size of the sperm head (one ten-thousandth of an inch across), or the hazy limits of magnification, took the drawing for gospel truth. And a hundred years later one might still find the homunculus in the pages of *Tristram Shandy* which, like the original, was a work of fiction. This was perhaps the first instance of the difficulty in microscopic studies, which still exists today, of drawing the boundary between observation and invention.

THE BOX THEORY

Now the battle could be fully engaged. On one side were the ovists. They were supported by the authority of Aristotle and the observations of de Graaf. On the other side were the spermists. They were supported by the obvious visibility and the obvious vitality of the spermatoza, the microscopic embodiment of the principles of life and movement. Each school imagined that the material of heredity lay in its own favoured type of germ cell; the other agent, the spermatic vapour or the egg albumen, as the case might be, merely providing the physical stimulus or the chemical pabulum.

The possibility that two equal homunculi contributed by opposite sexes might fuse in fertilization to give a double product was hard to imagine and was never suggested. The fact that the pip of an apple contained a structure, an embryo – discovered by Malpighi and admirably described by an English microscopist,

Nehemiah Grew – which was in no sense a model of an apple tree, was disregarded. On the contrary, the doctrine of preformation began to unfold in wonderful detail. It culminated in the Box Theory, the brightest jewel to be worked by the philosophers of this age.

If the germinal particles, whether male or female, were to be supposed to contain within them the preformed homunculi of the next generation merely waiting the call to grow, develop, or unfold, it was only too easy to go a step further. It was only natural to suppose that these germs themselves, or those at least of the favoured progenitive sex, should contain the germs of another generation within them, and so on *ad infinitum*. Adam – or Eve as the case might be – would contain, packed within his or her generative organs, the whole of the future human race like boxes within boxes. At one stroke the Creator had done it all. Such was the theory put forward by Jan Swammerdam of Leyden.

This highly predestinate view of human history put the doctrine of original sin on an apparently scientific basis, a basis that anybody might apprehend. And, when Leibniz took the matter up and pointed out that souls as well as bodies might be packed, the Box Theory began to contribute to the theological fervour with which, in that very theological age, preformation was sustained by some sects, and opposed by others. The smallnesses involved were inconceivable, but no more so than the largenesses revealed at the same time by astronomy. And there was (so some said) a spiritual satisfaction to be obtained from stretching the organs of credulity and conceiving what others found to be inconceivable.

This was not very far from religious mania and it was like a mania that it caught on. By 1699 Leeuwenhoeck, now well on in years was writing to the Royal Society:

Now if we know which way the Fishes do increase, that it is not done by intermixing of the Male and Female Seeds [this was a sad mistake] and likewise we do know the great Mystery that is included in the small seed of an Apple; why might we not then assert that *a whole intire Man is contained in an Animalcule of the Masculine Seed*, and that Animalcules of the Male Seed are all descended from the first created Man.

Some practical minds, however, were more familiar with apple seeds:

I cannot but think [writes the botanist Patrick Blair twenty years later] Mr Lewenhock [*sic*] has been much put to it for Answer to those pinching *Questions*, when he was obliged to use such Subterfuges, which are mere Hypotheses and no ways demonstrative.

The utter inconsistency of the Box Theory with chemistry could not be obvious for 150 years when atoms set a limit to the subdivision of seminal as well as of other fluids. But the genetic implications were at once obvious. Preformation was utterly at variance with the inheritance of acquired characters. Indeed, as Swammerdam saw the matter, one of the virtues of the Box Theory was that it explained why a man who has lost an arm does *not* have one-armed children. This was no disadvantage. But unhappily an equality of contribution of the two parents in heredity was also excluded by the Box Theory. And this was where, in good time, the opposition made a breach in the doctrine.

LICE AND FROGS

Preformation and packing if devoutly accepted, offered a short cut to certainty and understanding. It hid away from prying eyes, in the smallest of those Chinese boxes, at the end of an infinite series of diminishing homunculi, the painful need of explaining heredity. However, since there were two opposing factions, the matter was not allowed to rest there. They had to support their views by engaging in experiment. The results were not always what the experimenter had hoped.

The problem of virgin birth, as we have seen, greatly exercised the ancient world, its philosophers, no less than its herdsmen. It was Leeuwenhoeck, now, as we have seen, a fanatical spermist, who, twenty years after his animalcule letter, first made a proper experiment to find out whether sexual union was always needed for the fertile reproduction of animals. He chose what was for him an unlucky example. Among plant lice, or aphides, growing on blackcurrants he could find no males. Which is easy to remember by paradox since the French for a louse, *puceron*, is exclusively masculine. None the less the females continued to multiply very fast. Leeuwenhoeck took single females of all sizes. He found that they all brought forth young, as many as nine in twenty-four hours. And inside every one he could discover embryos of all sizes. But never a male could he find. This is something (he wrote in 1700) that is found in no other creature. 'They bring little ones into the world without mating with the male.' And later an admirable French investigator Charles Bonnet (who was fortunately an ovist) with tender solicitude raised nine generations of lice living on a plantain, raised them without the intervention of a male, and without the intrusion of a spermatozoon into the long succession of virgin mothers. A single maiden mother may indeed, if we give her the chance, bring 100,000,000 fatherless little ones into the world in one year.

The fantasy of the ancients thus proved true – not of vultures or mares or women – but of the miserable louse. The fact of parthenogenesis was there. No one, we should suppose, could any longer imagine that the spermatozoon was privileged, and alone privileged, to contain the model of the man (or the louse). Yet Leeuwenhoeck, brushing aside his own discovery as an exception, continued to believe that the sperm was the prime and predominant agent of heredity.

The experiment of the opposing party was made with larger animals. Already in 1683 (in another letter to Sir Christopher Wren), Leeuwenhoeck had explained how male fish squirt the milt over the newly laid eggs to fertilize them – and indeed we can all see mating frogs do the same. Yet, in spite of this, the wildest notions continued to hold belief through the eighteenth century. The great Linnaeus held that female fishes accomplish their own fertilization by swallowing the milt of the male. He found the notion that fertilization could take place (as it certainly does take place) outside the body altogether repugnant to his sense of the fitness of things. And some even found it easier to believe that the animalcules in the seminal fluid were artefacts, mere bubbles, such as might be seen in beef juice or urine or cabbage water.

It was in these circumstances that the Abbé Spallanzani took the matter up. He prepared certain experiments which he hoped would resolve the issue once for all. He decided to interfere in the 'amours', as he put it, of the frog. At mating time, he did up his male frogs and toads in silk knickers (*petits caleçons en taffetas ciré*). After this precaution he found that the eggs that were shed by the females remained sterile. They did not grow. Continuing the experiment, he strained the seminal fluid collected in this way through filter paper. He then found that the fluid which came through had no effect in fertilizing the eggs. They, too, died without growing.

Thus it was not the vapour, the *aura seminalis*, nor even the fluid itself, it was the animalcules, the spermatozoa, that set things going. At least so one would suppose – and so we do suppose today. But Spallanzani was a veteran of the ovist camp. To yield that point would have been to yield everything. Like Leeuwenhoeck, in the opposite camp, therefore, he shut his eyes to the obvious conclusion. He made every kind of trial, and played every kind of game, with the fluid, diluting and dividing it, so as to allow himself to continue believing that it was the juice and not the germs that did the trick; the real matter of heredity, he felt, must reside solely in the egg.

MULES AND MULATTOES

The preformationists, ovists and spermists alike, based their views largely on microscopy and moral feeling. In the first respect they correspond with the cytologist of today. There was, however, a smaller and, it must be admitted, a more intellectual school, who based their views of heredity on what they saw of breeding. They took into account the origin and properties of hybrids, above all of the mule and the mulatto, both of which had been open to observation for a long time.

The evidence of known crosses or hybrids of species had been considered 150 years earlier by Leonardo da Vinci, that great sceptic. It had convinced him of the equality of the male and female contributions to heredity. As he put it in his *Notebooks*:

The black races of Ethiopia are not the products of the sun: for if black gets black with child in Scythia, the offspring is black: but if a black gets a white woman with child, the offspring is grey. And this shows that the seed of the mother has power in the embryo equally with that of the father.

Cited by Zirkle

This method of reasoning based on experiment should have sufficed to wipe out both ovism and spermism and both the errors of Aristotle: the inequality of male and female contribution and the inheritance of acquired characters. Two difficulties, however, stood in the way. At this time men still believed in a host of fairy-tales about hybrids that never existed. The philosopher John Locke knew very well that Lucretius had denied the existence of centaurs and chimeras, monsters and hybrids of all kinds. But when he came to write his *Essay concerning Human Understanding* (in 1690) he left the austere Lucretius on one side and followed rather where Ovid might have directed his steps. Having solemnly related (book III, chapter vi) that women were known to have conceived by baboons ('if history lye not') Locke proceeds to tell us that he 'once saw a creature that was the issue of a cat and a rat, and had the plain marks of both about it'. It is not surprising in these circumstances that, as Zirkle says, physicians in this age of scandal as well as enlightenment commonly attributed the deformed appearance of miscarried or stillborn embryos to an animal paternity, on the analogy of Pasiphae's misguided passion for the bull.

The other difficulty was that genuine hybrids were almost unknown, while the one widespread, authentic, and easily observed example, the mule, was itself stuffed with mythology.

We may recall that Anah, a grandson of Esau, 'found the mules in the wilderness as he fed the asses of Zibeon his father' (Genesis xxxvi. 24). The mules of the *Iliad* and the *Odyssey* were likewise, it seems, born wild and the first mules may well have been natural hybrids born by straying mares. The ancient Hebrews were enjoined by the Mosaic Law not to interfere with Nature by breeding mules but they must have possessed them, for it was a mule that bore King Solomon when he rode on his way to be anointed.

Now anyone who knows the mule first, and forms his opinion afterwards, is bound to agree that it is half-way between its two parents. The *true mule*, where the mare is the mother, is a bigger and better animal than the *hinny* where the she-ass is the mother, naturally so, since it has a better start in life. But in other respects the influence of the two parents is equal whichever way the cross is made. Indeed this is the general rule for crosses between different species of animals and plants.

To the ancients, however, this was not at all evident. Had not Aristotle asserted the very contrary: 'in size, looks and vigour the foal resembles the dam rather than the sire' (*Hist. Anim.* vi. 23)? And the virtuosi, at least the ovists, of the seventeenth century were inclined to think the same because they could not explain the matter any other way: they could not imagine a fusion of two heredities.

DEVELOPMENT BY TRANSFORMATION

With the evidence that both sides contributed something material to the fertilized eggs, and conversely that the fertilized egg, as revealed in the offspring, had obtained something material from both sides, the difficulties of the ovists and the spermists mounted. It became necessary to ask how this inheritance from both parents could come about.

The only alternative to preformation was transformation. One had to suppose that the seed of an organism, the animalcule from which it sprang, the coalesced semen of male and female, or whatever its first beginning might be, was something altogether simpler than what it was to grow into; in other words that something relatively plain and homogeneous became complicated and heterogeneous; that development was a process by which the parts became different; one thing following another quite different thing; so that starting perhaps with a heart, other things were added until the mature differentiated creature emerged. This was indeed what Aristotle believed. William Harvey, who discovered the circulation of the blood, and others tried to understand things in this way but nobody could make a model of what might be supposed to happen. The word *epigenesis* could be given to the idea of development by transformation but words that would express it in familiar terms were not to be found.

So difficult indeed was the matter to understand that when the solution was found no one could see that it had been found – a common paradox with great discoveries. The evidence was that development takes place, not by simple expansion and unfolding as in a bud, but by a series of transformations, revolutions, and turnings inside out. A certain Caspar Wolff, working in St Petersburg at the Academy of Catherine the Great, published a book in 1759 which revealed the secret. It was called the *Theoria Generationis*. Here Wolff showed the utterly unpreformed way in which the chick embryo develops from an invisible germ. Out of the structureless fluid a solid mass appears. It swells and hardens, thickens and folds, so as to form gutters and passages and ultimately the tubes and fibres and fluids and other tissues of which the body is made up. Thus it grows from a speck to a leaf, a veined leaf, and from a leaf into a solid body.

Nobody took any notice of Wolff's work, any more indeed than they took notice of the fact that an acorn certainly contained no model of an oak tree. People insisted, as they so often do, on asking their questions in the wrong order. What they wanted to know was – not *how* the steps took place, but *why* the goal was reached. Which is the very last thing we can know.

In this pursuit, the forefathers of genetics in the eighteenth century fell back on the old idea of pangenesis. They imagined a condensation of invisible determinants from the whole body into the generative fluid of both the male and the female. This was the only way (the way rejected by Aristotle) in which the French naturalist, the Comte de Buffon, could conceive of biparental heredity. But in doing so he had to admit the genetic doctrine which had been excluded by preformation – the doctrine of the inheritance of acquired characters. The views of those who took up this opinion can be understood, as we shall see, only in relation to the theory of evolution.

But before we attack that problem we have to see what progress had been made from the study of sex in plants.

SEX IN PLANTS

Although the primary notions of heredity and reproduction came first from the seeds of plants, philosophers, concerned in their higher thoughts with man, have been inclined to disdain the vegetable forms of life. As Aristotle had said, plants are something between animals and the lifeless earth. Those who have studied plants have therefore been only too happy, as a rule, if they could modestly propose an analogy with animals. The students of animal life, on the other hand, have regarded these interpolations as irrelevant to the loftier theme of their own inquiries. Our history, however, has brought us to the point at which we have to admit something more than relevance: we have to acknowledge unity of principle between animals and plants.

The Babylonians knew that there were two kinds of date palm. One had only the pollen-dust in its flowers; the other was capable of bearing seeds. They also knew that the pollen had to be shaken on to the fertile flowers if they were to bear fruit. Later, any number of practical and observant naturalists recorded this fact and drew the correct conclusion: trees of many species, they said, were of two kinds, one bearing fruit and the other barren. The fruitful were usually called female, the unfruitful male. Theophrastus explains the matter as follows:

With dates it is helpful to bring the male to the female; for it is the male which causes the fruit to persist and ripen ... when the male palm is in flower they at once cut off the spathe on which the flower is, just as it is, and shake the bloom with the flower and the dust over the fruit of the female. ... In the date ... there is a union of the sexes.

But, if the nature of this union was unclear in animals, in plants it was still more so. Anatomists like Malpighi, who described the embryos of plants and their pollen grains, rejected the idea of a sexual union. Systematists like Linnaeus, who used the flowers in naming the species, largely ignored the question. Finally an experimenter like Spallanzani, obsessed with the sovereign power of the Ovum, by omitting the necessary precautions in his experiments, was able to prove to his own satisfaction that in plants, just as in animals, there was no fertilization of an egg by a sperm.

The credit for putting things right belongs to a whole line of thinkers, observers and experimenters. Of these the first was Nehemiah Grew. In a lecture given to the Royal Society in London on 9 November 1676, Grew considered that every plant was 'arrhenothelus' or hermaphrodite; as we should say, both male and female. This, he assures us, 'may the rather be believed in that snails and some other animals are such'. Further, Grew suggested that the small particles of 'Spermatick Globulets' or 'Vegetable Sperme' fall from the 'Thecae' or stamens upon the 'Seed-Case or Womb', 'and so touches it with Prolifick Virtue'. It does not necessarily do so, however, by means of 'Gross Substance' but only, he tell us, 'by some subtle and vivifick Effluvia to which the Visible Body of the Semen is but a Vehicle'.

It was nearly twenty years later that Camerarius (or Kammerer, in the vulgar tongue), a professor of Tübingen University, published a letter *Concerning the Sex of Plants*. Here he says that he has read the views of 'those two British Lights, John Ray and

Nehemiah Grew', on the reproduction of plants. He has therefore made experiments and shown in maize and other plants that the pollen is necessary for the setting of seed by the female flowers. This was in 1694, almost the same year that Leeuwenhoeck was unwillingly proving the opposite event of parthenogenesis, or reproduction without sperm, in animals.

What had, however, been proved was merely Grew's theory, a theory which is not very far from the theory of the ovists on the animal side. Equally in plants and in animals causal relationships were assumed to work on the same foundation of immaterial substances as Aristotle had assumed. What was this Prolifick Virtue? Still in 1720 we find Patrick Blair arguing not unreasonably that the solid particles of farina or pollen cannot pass down the style into the ovary and (by a singular inspiration!) that single pollen grains cannot be supposed to fertilize single seeds.

It was not, therefore, until Geoffroy in Paris and Bradley in Cambridge had confirmed the experiment, not until Thomas Fairchild in Hoxton had actually made hybrids, crossing the sweet-william and the carnation, and not until Logan in Philadelphia, Philip Miller at the Chelsea Physic Garden, and Arthur Dobbs of Castle Dobbs in County Antrim had worked out the details – introducing the world to the notion that bees did something important in carrying the pollen from flower to flower, and repeating the experiments with such refinements as removing the stamens of hermaphrodite flowers and enclosing them in muslin bags to keep away the bees – it was not until all these things had happened and half a century had passed that the idea of a material pollen began to get a foothold in the learned world.

To carry conviction to the higher levels of society it was necessary for an accomplished impresario to repeat the practice of the Babylonian peasant and to repeat it before a royal and academic audience. In 1749 from the Botanic Garden of Leipzig the pollen of a male date (which now, under the system of Linnaeus, bore the name of *Palma dactylifera*) was brought in a box by coach a distance of over thirty leagues to the palm house in Berlin, where a female date had long lived and flowered in unfruitful solitude. When the female parts of the flowers were dusted with the pollen they grew and ripened with good seed. The President of The Prussian Academy of Sciences, the versatile de Maupertuis, was thus able to present his patron, Frederick the Great, in due course with a harvest of unaccustomed fruit.

The laborious results of crossing species obtained by Koelreuter (who had followed Camerarius at Tübingen) were published soon afterwards, and left no doubt that plants derived their heredity from two parents, male and female, in equal measure.

But before the new knowledge of reproduction had been accepted, new problems and new difficulties had arisen. We must clear them out of the way before we can return again to the direct and obvious road of discovery.

3

Evolution Takes Charge

DOES LIFE CHANGE?

NOT long after the time of Leeuwenhoeck, the idea of the changeability of living organisms began to colour the study of heredity and reproduction. Those who held with the Box Theory were not likely to suppose that one species could beget another, a different one. But the idea of change had come into the heads of observant people, at many times and for many reasons, both the right ones and the wrong ones.

Weeds will often come up where a crop has been sown but has failed to germinate. It is probably owing to this observation that puzzled farmers since the earliest times have been led to suppose that one species could be transformed into another. The replacement is especially deceptive since the weeds that infest crops in primitive agriculture are often those most like them. As Virgil pointed out in the *Georgics* (i. 153–4) we find rye with wheat, darnel with barley, wild with cultivated oats, and so on. What was easier than to suppose that the wild plants were the result of degeneration from their superior relatives?

It is for such reasons that correct observation came to be mixed with, and confused by, false inference. For example Theophrastus says:

the stones of the olive give a wild olive and the seeds of the sweet pomegranate give a degenerate kind ... so also is it with pears and apples.

These observations are true. But he goes on to describe the opposite change:

There are also modifications due to feeding and attention of other kinds which cause the wild to become cultivated, or again cause some cultivated kinds to go wild, such as pomegranate and almond.

Here he is using the same observations of the changed character of seedlings and drawing an inference as to the *cause* of the change.

45

He is assuming the inheritance of a character acquired in reaction to a change in conditions, an inheritance for which we have (and presumably he had) no experimental evidence.

Again, Theophrastus says bergamot turns into mint (unless often transplanted) and wheat turns into darnel. These are transformations of species and quite impossible transformations. There are limits to what he will believe, but unfortunately, they are the wrong limits, for he says it is not possible to turn a wild olive, pear, or fig, into the cultivated forms; yet this is just what his ancestors had done! They had done it, to be sure, too slowly and too long ago for anyone to remember. He adds that 'Some say that wheat has been known to be produced from barley, and barley from wheat.' There are indeed people who will say this. 'But', he adds, 'these accounts should be taken as fabulous.' And here his opinion, to which we must return in a later chapter, is entirely in keeping with ours.

The modern attempt to sort out what could be believed from what could not be believed, in the way of transformation, came from the need to classify plants and animals. The first man to see this need and to expound the necessary methods and theories was John Ray. This man was the son of a blacksmith, who, having been expelled from the University of Cambridge for his religious scruples, took a main part in founding several sciences.

Ray saw that, among the welter of diverse and often unstable forms that nature presents to us, there were certain signs of constancy, and certain limits to inconstancy. He was the first to recognize such great plant families as the grasses, and the pulses. In other words he noticed the relationships of large groups. But he also grappled with small groups. These are the ones that have a close bearing on the principles of heredity. They were represented by what he chose to call species.

Species, in Ray's opinion, were groups of plants and animals within which sexual reproduction occurred. Members of the same species could mate together. They did not as a rule give offspring outside the range of differences known to exist within the species. This did not mean that members of each species always bred true when sexually reproduced; on the contrary they usually varied but they bred true within their own limits: they showed what Ray called *distincta Propagatio ex Semine*. The whole of living plants and animals could thus in Ray's view be allocated to species whose description and naming provide the basis of classification. And in his *Historia Generalis Plantarum*, which appeared in 1686, he described nearly 20,000 of them.

These species are not, Ray thought, fixed throughout time but are liable to undergo gradual transformation. Apart from the existence of infertile hybrids and their derivatives, which appear occasionally in nature but more frequently in domestication, Ray's definition agrees with the view we take today.

Indeed it is the view that would have been taken ever since Ray, had it not been for the overwhelming personality and immeasurable labours of his successor, Linnaeus – and also of the followers of Linnaeus. These devoted men have toiled during two centuries in the tremendous task of classifying plants and animals. For them classification has become an end in itself: indeed the be-all and end-all of existence. It seems that very early, following the example of their prophet, they became overcome with the importance of the species which they were naming and describing. Importance suggested durability and durability suggested fixity. So that they began to think that their labours and those of the Almighty were coexistent and coeternal. So many species there were, declared Linnaeus, as God made in the beginning. And so many there would remain, as a rule with the name of the great man attached to them.

These Linnaean views break down whenever they are tested by experiment, and as a theory of life they fell to pieces a hundred years later They are perpetuated today merely in the teaching of botany and zoology to children.

They have also, however, had a good effect. They have called attention to their own absurdity. Good people believed that all the species of plants and animals – not so many were known and named in those days – had come out of the Ark. Noah's Ark. But as the truth unfolded itself many puzzling questions came to be asked. Why was a set of plants found in America (including potatoes, tobacco and maize) entirely unrepresented among those living in the part of the world where the Ark had actually come to rest? If new species were born and old species died, and the new arose from the old in different parts of the world, these things could be understood. But a preformation of species

47

became almost as difficult to believe in as a preformation of individuals. And the two ideas rose and fell together.

HEREDITY TO MEASURE

As the belief in fixity of species developed in the minds of both Linnaeans and of theologians, it had the effect of stimulating elsewhere an opposite belief, a belief in their changeability. The idea grew that plants and animals were descended from simpler ancestors and even common ancestors. At first the principle was known as *transformism*: later it became known as evolution.

Explaining heredity, the likenesses of parents and offspring, without knowing for certain the facts of reproduction, had been hard enough. But it now became necessary to explain something more than heredity. It became necessary to account for variation: that is, for the differences between parents and offspring, as well, and at the same time. Some assumptions with regard to heredity had to be introduced if any theory of the transformation of species was to be developed. Now, since the laws of inheritance were unknown, and since experimental means of discovering them were also unknown, these laws had to be invented to fit the theory of transformation that was adopted. They had to be invented *ad hoc* and heredity had to be made to measure.

This situation was inevitable because evolution was not forced on men's minds by their observing the variations within families bred experimentally, or within races or species – variation to whose study we owe our present knowledge of heredity. On the contrary, the idea of evolution was forced on the world by the study of life on a grand scale, by the study of the whole panorama of nature with its vast range of species, their peculiar geographical distributions, their arrangements in large groups which showed a relationship of form and therefore suggested a relationship of descent.

There was the similarity of the four limbs of frogs and lizards, birds and men. There were even more striking similarities of development when it was found that even the human embryo had (at a few weeks old) a blood system which fitted the gill slits of a fish. And then there were the strange but regular sequences of forms revealed in more and more detail by the fossil animals dug up in successive strata of the rocks. All these considerations drove men to assume some kind of orderly system of change and to invent some kind of theory of heredity and variation to make the whole story more plausible and more coherent.

In a word, the unknown heredity had to be deduced from the supposedly known system of change in heredity. This was putting the cart before the horse. The result was a confused and disorderly movement. Let us see how it developed.

LAMARCKISM

The men who gave the new idea shape were Lamarck, who invented the word *biology*, Herbert Spencer, who introduced the term *evolution*, and Charles Darwin, who propounded the theory of *natural selection*.

Among those who first took up the idea of transformism in the eighteenth century, de Maupertuis, Buffon and Erasmus Darwin, the principle of direct inheritance, and therefore an inheritance of acquired characters, seemed an indispensable and even an unquestionable assumption. It was Lamarck, however, who at the end of the century thrust the whole question into the forefront of ideas, making the problem of heredity itself an explicit one. He did so by the audacity with which he carried his principles to a logical conclusion. He still managed to believe in ovism and in the *aura seminalis*. He disregarded the facts and braved the ridicule which ensued. In consequence his name has never failed to be the catchword of opinion. What was his theory?

Lamarck founded his theory on a basis of spontaneous generation. Men, he said, had gone too far in denying it. The simplest gelatinous plants and animals were probably due to the direct action of 'nature'. And 'nature' for Lamarck was an expression of overwhelming significance. It was in fact interchangeable with the *Auteur suprême de toutes choses*. Thus:

The will of God is everywhere expressed by the execution of the laws of nature. ... Nature is a power which produces, renews, changes, displaces, in a word, makes and unmakes the different bodies which constitute the universe.

On this foundation of divine purpose two forces were working:

first, there was a principle of progress, an innate tendency, to improvement, elaboration and multiplication of parts, determining the great movements of change. Secondly, there was the environment, determining as a rule only the details of change.

On plants the environment acts directly through nutrition: whence the improvement of cultivated plants, as most gardeners since Theophrastus, have willingly supposed.

All botanists know [he writes (1809)] that the plants they bring from their native places into their gardens to cultivate them there undergo, little by little, changes which make them unrecognizable. . . . These effects of changed conditions are so well recognized that botanists do not like to describe plants from gardens unless they have been newly brought into cultivation.

On animals, however, the environment acts only through creating new needs, and hence new efforts, on the part of the individual.

Man is left out of the picture for a special reason:

If man were distinguished from the animals only by his organization, it would be easy to show that the properties of organization which we use to make man and his races a group apart are all the products of old changes in his actions and of habits which he has assumed and which have become peculiar to individuals of his species.

Phil. Zool., ch. xi, 1809

In other words man could be supposed to have arisen from a monkey by the inheritance of effects of use and disuse were he not known to have arisen in a different way, i.e. by special creation, and in respect of his immortal soul. Lamarck shrank in 1809 from the step Darwin was to take in 1872.

The doctrine of Lamarck thus has two parts. The major part is what we may call *perfectionism*. It is a sort of dynamic version of the doctrine of Leibniz, that everything is for the best in the best of all possible worlds. It supposes that everything is getting better and therefore will be for the best. This view has had its adherents in all ages. Indeed it is so commonplace that it has been utterly obscured by the daring fantasy of the minor part of Lamarck's views. It is this minor part which is the excuse for what we usually call Lamarckism. This is how he expresses it:

Everything that nature has caused individuals to gain or lose owing to the influence of the circumstances to which their race has been for long exposed and hence owing to the influence of the predominant use of one organ, or disuse of another; she conserves it in the new individuals which arise by reproduction, provided that the acquired changes are common to the two sexes or to the progenitors of the new individuals.

Phil. Zool., 1809

Thus Lamarck took the ancient theory of the inheritance of acquired characters. Then he separated plants from animals, as a good vitalist should, and reduced the principle to the inheritance of the effect of use and disuse, so far as animals were concerned. And, finally, he grafted it on to a general faith in the ameliorating power of 'nature' or a beneficent creator. The result was plausible as literature but unsatisfactory as science. And some of the examples he chose for illustrating the effects of use were unlucky. Having pointed out that anger directs the body fluids of stags to their heads and leads them to secrete horns, he explains how the giraffe meets the challenge of his environment:

We know [he writes] that this animal, the tallest of mammals, dwells in the interior of Africa, in places where the soil, almost always arid and without herbage, obliges it to browse on trees and to strain itself continuously to reach them. This habit, sustained for so long, has had the result in all members of its race, that the forelegs have grown longer than the hind legs and that its neck has become so stretched, that the giraffe, without standing on its hind legs, lifts its head to a height of six metres [nearly, as he adds, using the antique measure, twenty feet].

Phil. Zool., 1809, ch. 9

Instead of carrying conviction this argument sent a ripple of laughter running down the nineteenth century, ending its career in the comic journals of Paris (Figure 1).

The position of plants was hardly more satisfactory than that of animals. How has the supply of nutrients led those first cousins, the cabbage and the turnip, to meet the requirements of the same environment in such different ways? And how has the same environment led to the divergence of flax and linseed, two forms of the same species?

A still deeper question arose later: namely, how could the evolution and adaptation of reproductive mechanisms of plants and animals have been brought about? When Lamarck says that anger makes the horns of a mating stag grow the physiologist can

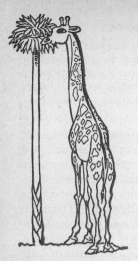

— Dis donc, papa, *pourquoi* que les palmiers sont si grands ?

— C'est pour que les girafes puissent les manger, mon enfant, car...

... si les palmiers étaient tout petits, les girafes seraient très embarrassées.

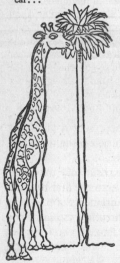

— Mais alors, papa, *pourquoi* que les girafes ont le cou si long ?

— Eh bien ! c'est pour pouvoir manger les palmiers, mon enfant, car...

...si les girafes avaient le cou court, elles seraient encore bien plus embarrassées.

only smile. But why should mating have developed at all? It does no good to the individuals who indulge in it. Is it the kicking of posterity in the womb of time? Why do we not all multiply by budding like plant lice? Only the poetic imagination can find a Lamarckian answer for this penetrating question.

But for Lamarck this question could not arise: he did not even realize that heredity was biparental. It was odd that he should have inferred the principle of heredity from the supposition of evolution, discovering the unknown through what will always be more unknown. But it was even odder that he should do so in ignorance of such of the principles of reproduction as were understood in his own time. The views of Lamarck were, however, excusable at their time. They were even, we may argue, justified by their purpose. Lamarck wanted to awaken the world to the possibility of interpreting the whole of nature, the whole range of plants and animals, as the result of evolution. He was right in thinking that evolution was a process whereby the complexity and diversity of the forms of life increase; and that they do so through change in the heredity received from simple common ancestors in the course of great spaces of time.

Lamarck's theory of heredity was inferred from this assumption of evolution. The mode of reasoning at the time was almost inevitable. It is, as we shall see, not a mode of reasoning to be justified today when we have the results of experiments and the facts of reproduction in both gross and minute structure. Nevertheless, ever since Lamarck, there have been people with great experience of some aspect of nature, such as animal breeding, or gardening, herbarium botany or the study of fossils, or some kind of medical research, anthropology or sociology, but unaware of the facts of life as a whole and of the experimental evidence, who have taken the Lamarckian view of heredity and taken it entirely as a matter of course. To them the direct inheritance of all the individual or personal properties of the parent by the offspring has seemed not an assumption but an axiom, something altogether self-evident. Let us now see how Darwin faced the difficulty.

Figure 1
The problem of Lamarck's giraffe faced by the challenge of the environment as seen 100 years later by the cartoonist Caran d'Ache in *Les petits pourquoi de M. Toto* (*Album de Caran d'Ache*: Plon, Paris)

DARWIN'S SOLUTION

Darwin was forced to accept the idea of transformism by his observations of plants and animals, chiefly in South America, during the voyage of H.M.S. *Beagle* between 1831 and 1836. He had noticed that plants and animals were nearly all of different species in the Old and the New World. But the larger groups were the same. Each large group, whether it was the ferns or the frogs, was represented on both sides of the world. Moreover, small islands like the Galápagos Islands often had species of their own – ten species for ten islands – although a vast area of a continent might have only one. All this was to explain on the view that the species of animals had all come out of the Ark. And it was hard to explain even as the result of special creation by a wise creator.

These were the facts that pushed Darwin over the edge from believing in fixity to believing in transformation. When he returned from his travels, therefore, there was little doubt in his mind about the fact of evolution. But how was the fact itself to be explained? The ridicule that had attended Lamarck's theory had driven the inheritance of acquired characters, for the first time in history, into general, albeit momentary, disrepute. Darwin had to find some other driving force to account for the change and the diversity of change which together he called the Origin of Species. This force he found, two years after his return to England, in an observation of the mathematician Malthus (another of those parsons and priests who creep into our history). Malthus pointed out that there was a 'struggle for existence'; more children are born than ever live to become parents; indeed a proportion of each generation have always died before maturity. This obvious generalization, coupled with another obvious generalization, that farmers and breeders are continually altering various races of domesticated plants and animals by selecting the ones they liked best for breeding, gave Darwin the idea of *natural selection*.

This conclusion was evidently a necessary one, for it was reached independently at the same time, on the same basis of Malthus, by Alfred Russel Wallace, an English naturalist engaged on collecting insects in the East Indies. Their views were presented together to a meeting of the Linnean Society in London on 1 July 1858.

If hereditary differences occur within wild species of plants and animals, as they normally do in domesticated forms, then, Darwin argued, nature will eliminate some and thereby select others for breeding. The character of the race will change. The focus of the problem thus again shifted from evolution itself to the nature of heredity. And how did heredity work? Here Darwin accepted the dominant view of the day. When two species were crossed many hybridizers had now discovered that the qualities of the two parents were blended in the offspring. Darwin therefore assumed the principle of what was called 'blending inheritance'. Heredity did not vary by jumps but by imperceptible gradations. It did not sort itself into atoms or particles but ran together in an infinitely divisible fluid or essence.

There were other properties of heredity that fascinated Darwin, the properties of what he called 'prepotency' and 'reversion'. Prepotency was the name given by the modern breeder to what the translators of Aristotle had called the prevailing of the seed of one parent over that of the other. And reversion was the name given to the appearance of some undesirable character in an individual which was supposed to have been shown by its ancestors but carried hidden for many generations. These peculiarities of inheritance baffled as well as attracted Darwin. They might have suggested particles or jumps but he put them on one side for the time being.

A storm of indignant refutation greeted the appearance of the *Origin of Species* in December 1859. But when the storm had died down, lying among the wreckage could be found one valid and weighty criticism. In 1867 a certain Fleeming Jenkin of Edinburgh, a professor of engineering, pointed out (and it is a remark of more consequence than any mentioned by his biographer, Robert Louis Stevenson) that any new variation that arose, crossing, as it must do, with a normal brother or sister, would have its peculiar character reduced in each successive generation. It would indeed be wiped out before nature could decide whether it was worthy to survive. If blending inheritance were admitted, therefore, natural selection would not work: some other engine must be found to drive the evolutionary machine.

To combat this danger Darwin had no weapon of his own in his hands. He therefore very prudently retreated into the lines prepared for him by Lamarck. In the following year 1868, in his *Variation of Animals and Plants*, he adopted (without acknowledgement to Lamarck or Jenkin or any other of his predecessors) the doctrine of the inheritance of acquired characters. Indeed, not content with reverting to the ancient doctrine, like Lamarck he felt he had to offer a theory of how it happened. His theory was not of course taken from Lamarck. It was a complete up-to-date physiological theory taken from Herbert Spencer and offering acknowledgements to Spencer, Buffon and a number of others. This was, it turned out, a version of the ancient theory of pangenesis, which had been rejected on such ample grounds as we have seen by Aristotle, and to which he added two things: the name, which Aristotle would no doubt have understood, and the once-again fashionable idea of particles. Let us see how these ideas had taken hold of Spencer.

SPENCER AND PANGENESIS

Herbert Spencer was the third thinker to deduce the principles of heredity from a belief in evolution. Having retired from the construction of the London and Birmingham Railway in 1846, already, in 1852, he had published an essay on the *Development Hypothesis* and in 1855 had espoused the view that ideas, the most obviously acquired of all characters, became heritable and led to the development of the mind. Thereafter the whole of his life was given to arguing and urging the Principle of Evolution.

Spencer's enthusiasm makes his *Principles of Biology* unreadable today. But it was not so in its day. His freedom from superfluous traditional learning enabled him again and again to introduce phrases which have contributed to the understanding of life, phrases generally adopted except by Darwin. They are phrases which we remember by their verbal compulsion as much as by their intellectual legacy: Evolution, Heredity, the Survival of the Fittest, and the Physiological Unit. Evolution in place of transformism was his slogan. Heredity reminds us that, before Spencer, the distinction between natural or organic and civil or legal inheritance was never made explicit. The Survival of the

Fittest dangerously completes the trilogy of which the two other members, Struggle for Existence, and Natural Selection, had been given to the world by Malthus and by Darwin. But of the Physiological Units there is much more to be said. For it was they which grew in the twentieth century, as the atoms grew in the nineteenth, into the shape of a new science. This revolution in thought they worked after the death of their inventor, to make an idea greater than the rest of his inventions.

To both Darwin and Spencer variation seemed to be founded on a kind of uncertainty in the principle of heredity although not co-extensive with it. But, while Darwin was baulked by heredity itself, Spencer extracted the right principle. 'The laws governing inheritance are quite unknown', wrote Darwin in 1859. In 1863 Spencer pointed out: 'A positive explanation of Heredity is not to be expected in the present state of Biology.' But he went on:

The power which organisms display of reproducing lost parts, we saw to be inexplicable except on the assumption that the units of which any organism is built have an innate tendency to arrange themselves into the shape of that organism. . . .

Thus Spencer saw in the maintenance of a specific character in a tissue, when it is regenerated, a property of specific self-propagation of certain *physiological units* which was analogous with heredity. After Spencer's time the pre-eminence of the theory and technique of sexual reproduction distracted attention from what we may call Cell Heredity – the genetic permanence of lineages of cells making the permanent character of tissues. Today, as we shall see, the constancy of tissue cultures and transplanted tumours has shown us the effectiveness of cell heredity and the validity therefore of Spencer's point of view.

Quite in harmony with this conclusion [Spencer continues] are certain implications since noticed, respecting the characters of sperm-cells and germ-cells. We saw sundry reasons for rejecting the supposition that these are highly-specialized cells and for accepting the opposite supposition, that they are cells differing from others rather in being unspecialized. And here the assumption to which we seem driven by the *ensemble* of the evidence, is, that sperm-cells and germ-cells are essentially nothing more than vehicles, in which are contained small groups of the physiological units in a fit state for obeying their proclivity towards the structural arrangements of the species they belong to. . . .

We must conclude that the likeness of any organism to either parent, is conveyed by the special tendencies of the physiological units derived from that parent. In the fertilized germ we have *two groups* of physiological units, slightly different in their structures. These slightly-different units, severally multiply at the expense of the nutriment supplied to the unfolding germ – each kind moulding this nutriment into units of its own type.

Principles of Biology, 1863

Darwin never knew whether he ought to accept the Cell Theory or not. But Spencer had found it entirely acceptable. As an engineer he was probably less suspicious, or more understanding, than Darwin of the consequences of using a high-powered microscope.

On this basis, therefore, Spencer was led to discuss 'segregation', hybridity and the adaptation to cross-fertilization in relation to his 'survival of the fittest'. Obviously he could not go very far. And beyond a certain point he was bound to be led astray. His units of heredity were derived from the observation of constancy in tissues and hence from differentiation. They were therefore subject to the effects of the environment. It was in this way that he was led to assume the inheritance of the effects of use and disuse. This in turn inspired Darwin to give Spencer's factually static Units a fictitious circulation and to call them Pangenes – so that both together fell into the Lamarckian pit.

Let us see how Darwin presented the ancient theory of pangenesis in 1868:

I assume that cells, before their conversion into completely passive or 'formed material' throw off minute granules or atoms, which circulate freely throughout the system, and when supplied with proper nutriment multiply by self-division, subsequently becoming developed into cells like those from which they were derived. These granules for the sake of distinctness may be called cell-gemmules, or, as the cellular theory is not fully established, simply gemmules ... the gemmules in their dormant state have a mutual affinity for each other, leading to their aggregation either into buds or into the sexual elements. Hence speaking strictly it is not the reproductive elements, nor the buds, which generate new organisms but the cells themselves throughout the body.

Animals and Plants under Domestication, 2: 374

Here we see the theory of pangenesis, as understood by Aristotle, being expressed in the terms understood by the nineteenth century. But how strange are the assumptions that Darwin has to rely on! In sexual reproduction he assumes that many sperm or many pollen grains are necessary to fertilize one egg. He assumes that irregular distribution or contribution of pangenes will account for 'reversion' and 'prepotency'. He also assumes that 'sexual reproduction, does not essentially differ, as we have seen, from budding or self-division'. And finally he assumes that the pollen may influence the colour of the hybrid fruit and that the sperm of one mating may influence the progeny of a later mating of the same mother.

All these assumptions we must, one by one, examine and test.

CONTAMINATING THE STOCK

The strangest argument that Darwin was led to use in support of pangenesis he derived from the notion that the progeny from one mating might be influenced by the male parent of a previous mating, influenced, as we may say, by its deceased stepfather. To this notion, the German zoologist, Weismann, later gave the name of *telegony*.

After quoting an example reported of a horse in 1821, Darwin concludes that:

Similar cases have so often occurred that careful breeders avoid putting a choice female to an inferior male on account of the injury to her subsequent progeny which may be expected to follow.

Somehow or other, the breeders thought, the stock had been contaminated. The confusion would be all the easier since practical men have never distinguished between a supposed inheritance of disease and a true inheritance of *susceptibility* to disease. And Darwin, who had an exaggerated respect for the practical man, was inclined to think they must be right.

In antiquity the nearest thing to the idea of telegony is probably where Aristotle alleges that if a mare or a she-ass is used for breeding mules regularly, she will go sterile. No question of a change in heredity arises here but only of damage to the mother from carrying a hybrid embryo. The belief is a part of the mythology of mules.

Can there be any truth in telegony? Among the thousands of

mice and rats which have been sired by a second spouse under controlled experimental conditions during the last sixty years no evidence of telegony has ever been reported. Among human beings where a widow has borne children to a second husband the influence of a previous mate has occasionally been suggested; but it has never been confirmed. And, since the evidence indicates that the sperm in the womb which fail to effect fertilization die in about twenty-four hours, their influence, some years later, one would expect to be powerfully lacking.

There are, we may guess – and it is only a guess – two reasons why the belief in telegony is maintained. One is theoretical, the other practical. Many have believed in the idea of pangenesis, that heredity is collected in germs from all parts of the body by a process akin to infection. For these it is easy to suppose that such infection may be reversed, and the foreign semen may infect the body of the mother, and so return to determine the heredity of a later offspring. Reversing the argument, as Darwin actually did, the occurrence of telegony would help his own arguments in favour of pangenesis and the inheritance of acquired characters. It is perhaps from this belief that the English statute draws its sanction whereby a man who seduces the wet-nurse of the heir apparent is presumed to have corrupted the blood royal and thereby becomes guilty of high treason.

The practical reason for keeping up a belief in telegony is that it helps to prevent the crossing of pedigree stocks of animals. It is on the foundation of a belief in telegony that today English breed-societies concerned with sheep will strike off the register – as they state in their published rules – any female of their breeds who is mated outside the breed. She is permanently corrupted in the sight of men. Up to thirty years ago the pig breeders did the same.

The belief in telegony is common, not only among the more ignorant breeders, but also among those who wish to protect the markets in which they sell their pedigree stock. It will also help to protect privileged classes or races of men. It is said to be common, no doubt for this reason, where two races live together in severe segregation, as in the Southern United States and in South Africa. There, it is bound to help the segregation by discouraging the intercourse of the two races.

These rules, like all superstitions about heredity, have no foundation except in the misunderstanding of the complicated possibilities of normal heredity.

THE DEAD END

Thus Darwin clothes the wrong conclusion, the inheritance of the effects of the environment, with a garment pieced together of the superstitions of his day. He even adopts the showiest of the old arguments of the inheritance of the effects of use and disuse, which he does without mentioning the disreputable name of Lamarck.

We may wonder how such an absurd notion with such a wealth of imaginary detail, could still be taken seriously – as it undoubtedly was – in the nineteenth century. The answer is that it explained not only the inheritance of acquired characters but the whole business of heredity, and development, reversion and prepotency, as well as regeneration or the lack of it. And it was put forward with the authority of the leader of biological thought. Deprived of the support of preformation, men clutched at any straw of explanation. No one had the least idea how all the details of an animal's or a plant's body and above all of a man's intellect and temperament and mere habits – as Darwin expresses it so forcibly in the same book – how all these things can be carried and propagated by microscopic germ cells unless these germ cells had themselves been inspired by all the parts of the body which were to be reproduced in the offspring. They were in the dark just as much as Montaigne had been. Pangenesis offered a glimmer of light. It was a formal *ad hoc* solution. There was no evidence for it. But there was no alternative to it. That was the position as most people saw it in 1868.

Lamarck and Darwin, as we have seen, were bound to be wrong because they deduced heredity from the assumed principle of evolution. For them, everything else could be deduced from evolution, so why not heredity as well? But in fact the principles of heredity can be reached only from the study of heredity.

Heredity can be demonstrated only by experiments in breeding, by observing the processes of breeding, especially the microscopic processes, and the results of breeding. Observations of this kind, inquiries based on the assumption of inheritance by single cells, were in fact being pursued unbeknown to Darwin in his own lifetime. But since he says 'it would be presumptuous in me to express an opinion' of the cell theory, it is obvious that for him that theory had come too late.

BLENDING INHERITANCE

His first assumption of blending inheritance drove Darwin into his second assumption of the inheritance of acquired characters. This in turn drove him into his third assumption of pangenesis. Now when he had to rake together all possible arguments for his pangenesis he bethought himself of the mysterious property of reversion. Ancestral characters might, after many generations, suddenly reappear. The gemmules or pangenes, which could themselves hybridize, would account for this:

> The sexual elements of hybrids will include both pure and hybridized gemmules; and when two hybrids pair, the combination of pure gemmules derived from the one hybrid with the pure gemmules of the same parts derived from the others would necessarily lead to complete reversion of character.

In this statement, Darwin admits that he is following the French hybridizer, Naudin, who had specially studied reversion. But what do we see? Instead of making the great discovery which he seems to be on the verge of making, Darwin is just tying himself into a knot. The pangenes, which he has introduced to make good the defects of blending inheritance, he is now using to account for the occurrence of what is, *par excellence*, non-blending, or particulate, inheritance.

If we now jump forward sixty years we may record the judgement of history on Darwin's dilemma. In 1930 R. A. Fisher, in his illuminating work, *The Genetical Theory of Natural Selection*, went into the whole Darwinian theory with analytical rigour. Fisher concluded that indeed blending inheritance can provide a basis for evolution by natural selection but only with outside help. It needs either, as Darwin had realized, the auxiliary motor of directed Lamarckian change in heredity; or, with undirected change, it needs such change on a scale many thousandfold what it needs with the assumption that inheritance does not blend.

We may turn back now to the proper order of discovery and see how the principles of heredity at last came to be understood.

4

Particles or Essences?

CELLS AND NUCLEI

BY the middle of the eighteenth century the struggle between ovists and spermists had advanced man's understanding of reproduction, heredity and development very little. Plants and animals, in these primary respects, seemed to be much alike. They both multiplied by sexual reproduction which was assumed to follow the principles of ovism or spermism. They both existed as species and races whose individuals grew, reproduced and, within limits, bred true, thereby showing heredity and development. But beyond this, in the structure and working of their bodies they did not seem to have much in common. Plants showed, at least in their pith and wood, a structure like the cells of a honeycomb. Animals on the other hand revealed vessels and vesicles, corpuscles and fluids and even animalcules of a more various character. Their tissues had flesh and bone with a certain homogeneity, like that of jelly, cheese, or horn rather than any delicate fine texture like that of a honeycomb.

It was into this world that improvements in the microscope began again to bring a better understanding. Its influence was extremely slow, for then, as now, only a few of those who talked about the processes and structures of animals and plants knew what the microscope had already revealed about them. Caspar Wolff's discovery of what happened in the development of the animal egg was therefore only gradually understood. Development, he had shown, was not direct but revolutionary, not laid down in the beginning but appearing as a succession of events, not preformed but *epigenetic*.

This view was repugnant to his own generation of naturalists and it did not mean anything to Spallanzani or Lamarck. But, as it came to be accepted by younger men, it demanded an explanation. How was the succession of foldings and the differentiation of tissues determined? The explanation took the whole of a hundred years to be expressed. And when it did come to be expressed it covered a great deal more than development.

Gradually it appeared that the spheres or vesicles of Wolff, the globules and bladders of others who dissected animals, were the same things as the compartments seen in the pith of plants and called *cells* by Robert Hooke in 1665. Slowly it dawned on the microscopist that the animalcules or spermatozoa in the semen were derived from vesicles or cells in the testis by a process of shrinkage or concentration. Slowly they saw that the eggs in the ovary were the result of an opposite process of puffing out a minute globule with an enormous body of food or yolk. Even the corpuscles in the blood could be seen to arise from cells in the bone marrow. And then again, could not the animalcules or infusoria that were found in pond water, the protozoa, be just single units corresponding to the parts, the single cells, of the larger organisms?

As the nineteenth century advanced, microscopy – whose centre both of manufacture and utilization had now shifted to Germany – became more and more discriminating. The idea germinated and grew that all animals and plants were made up of the same elements; that these elements (vesicles or cells or whatever else one chose to call them) were the units of growth, of development, and of activity. Later, too, it began to appear that, just as life did not arise out of the mud, so no cell arose by mere crystallization out of the living jelly or protoplasm but always from a previous cell; by a division of one cell into two: a process which was actually seen in plants in 1827. Hence the cell had a progenitor and it had progeny. It was a unit in a succession of units. It was therefore a unit, perhaps the unit, of reproduction. And, if it was the unit of reproduction, was it not also the basis of organization as well as the means of permanence in that organization? Was it not, in a word, the ultimate particle in life?

This theory, the *Cell Theory*, slowly gained acceptance during the first part of the nineteenth century. We saw that Darwin did not know whether to accept it or not. But he was one of the last to suffer from this dilemma. Now everyone accepts it. The ideas of homogeneity and fluidity are now as difficult to understand or believe as was formerly the idea of cells. But that does not mean that everyone understands the theory they accept. On the contrary, ever since its two authors, Schleiden speaking for plants and Schwann speaking for animals, put it forward in 1840, the world has been trying to grasp its meaning.

To begin with, nobody knew what was meant by a cell and that, curiously enough, is probably the last thing we shall be able to settle. And again there were several dark patches in the record of events which connected sperm and eggs with the embryo. What happened when the prolific virtue or fertilizing principle of the animalcule made itself felt? It was only later that the microscope provided the answer.

Already in 1827 Karl Ernst von Baer had found that there are microscopic specks of jelly inside the Graafian follicles on the surface of the ovary of a rabbit. He had also found that there are similar specks in the oviduct entering the womb. He had rightly concluded that these specks, these potent specks of matter, one two-hundredth of an inch across, which happen to be the largest cells in the body, were the female germ cells. They were the eggs long ago imagined by de Graaf. But it was only in 1854 that a sperm was seen making its way into the egg of a frog; and only in the following year that the same process was seen in various pond weeds or algae.

So sexual reproduction depended on the fusion of cells, the germ cells, sperm and egg, of opposite sexes. And it happened in the same way in plants and animals. This process now began to be studied in great detail. In the first place an important organ had been seen inside living cells of plants by Robert Brown (working at the British Museum) in 1831. This body was what he called the *nucleus* or *areola* and it came to be seen more and more frequently in cells. Usually it was called the nucleus but in the animal egg old-fashioned people still refer to it as the germinal vesicle. The sperm consisted, it was found, of very little but nucleus. What happened to this nucleus in fertilization? Some, perhaps secret ovists, held that having accomplished its task of impregnation by entering the egg it simply went to pieces. But in 1875, Oscar Hertwig at Munich proved that the nucleus of the egg of a sea-urchin fused with the nucleus of the sperm. And it was only a single sperm that reached the goal. Two years later the same fusion was seen by Strasburger in a lily.

The story, the much debated story, of fertilization had now

been told. It was the same for plants and animals. For both it was an affair not of essences but of cells. And not merely of cells but of special organs within them, the nuclei.

THE CHROMOSOMES

These discoveries did for the study of life much what Kepler had done for astronomy and Galileo for physics. They did not constitute the Newtonian revolution that was yet to come. But let us look at the transformation they brought in their train.

In the first place, the new individual *began* at a particular point in space and time, at the fusion of the two parental nuclei. In the second place the origin and character of the new individual was *determined* by a particular piece of matter: by the new fusion nucleus acting in the fertilized egg. For it was soon shown that unless the fusion took place the kind of individual that grew, if anything grew at all, was quite different.

In all this there was a complete reversal of outlook. Instead of looking at the cell as a pretty detail in a tissue (a view which students still learn from books) it became possible to see the tissue and the organism as coming from the multiplication of cells. Wolff had thought of cells arising as spaces or holes or pores in a jelly. A new generation could look upon them as the active agents, the things that really mattered.

And how much substance was it that really mattered? Consider the living human population of England. All the eggs from which that vast body has grown could be contained in the space of one hen's egg. But the egg contains mostly water. The male sperm is a condensed form of the reproductive material. And the 40,000,000 sperm which have carried half our nation's heredity could all be carried in the space of one pin's head. Can we even now grasp the power of determination, the concentration of destiny, that this means?

This was not all. The stage was set for a deterministic analysis, not only of heredity, or development, or evolution, considered separately, but of life as a whole. In place of prolific virtues and generative principles there were cells and nuclei; in place of abstract forces, or vapours, humours and essences there was matter, visible and particulate, regular in its behaviour and

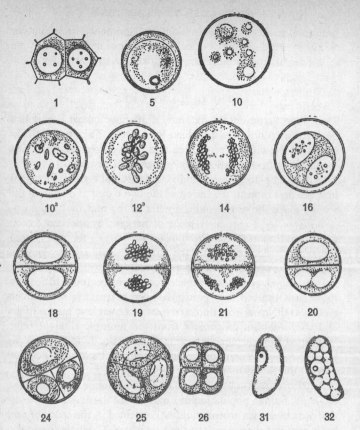

Figure 2

Some of the earliest drawings of chromosomes made by Hofmeister in 1848 from living cells of *Tradescantia virginiana*: 1 and 5, cells showing the nuclei; 10, nucleus alone in pollen mother cell; 10^3, 12^3, the paired chromosomes appear; 14, the chromosomes separate to the poles at the first division, forming (16) two daughter nuclei with (18) a cell wall between them; 19, the chromosomes appear again to undergo a second division visibly separating (21, 20) to the two poles in the lower cell; 24, 25, 26, a 'tetrad' is formed with four cells (only three visible in 24). The four cells grow and fall apart to give separate pollen grains (31, 32), each with its own nucleus.

Note: the first of all drawings of chromosomes was published by Nägeli in 1842 (Sirks 1952).

universal in its occurrence. Instead of the design of a supreme being or the purpose of a nature no less unspeakable and unquestionable, there were chemistry and mechanics, atoms and particles, to be spoken of and also to be questioned.

What was the material in the sperm nucleus? It was no longer an imaginary little man. The homunculus was dead. In its place was found (to use the words that had recently come into currency) a mixture of *protein* and *nucleic acid*. How did the cell divide? How did the nucleus propagate itself? These were questions that microscopes fitted with even more powerful new lenses that were being developed in Germany during the 1880s made it possible to answer.

In the very early days of the cell-theory it was already clear that when cells divide the nuclei divide with them. It was also becoming clear that they do so not by a mere splitting, as though cut by a knife or by a budding off from one side, but by a special kind of manoeuvre. Away back in 1848, Wilhelm Hofmeister, a twenty-four-year-old bookseller of Leipzig who was to be one of the leading figures of the new movement, had already seen what happened. We can examine his drawings of the nuclei of the mother cells which produce the pollen in the anther. He had shown how they resolve themselves into smaller bodies at the time the cell divides. These bodies which he sketched are what thirty years later became known as *chromosomes* (Figure 2).

During the years that followed their discovery it was found that the nuclei of any one plant or animal when about to divide always resolve themselves into the same number of these rod-shaped bodies. The means by which this happens is the most elaborate, and in principle the most uniform, piece of organization so far discovered by the microscope. For in all plants and animals, and even probably in bacteria, the same series of steps are seen with the same beautiful synchronization and succession.

Mitosis – for so we call it – is a symphony consisting of four movements: a beginning, two middles, and an end. The beginning is a slow contraction of the chromosomes inside the nucleus from long threads, each of which is already double, to form regular short coils or rods. Then there is a short minuet when these double rods, which may be two or two thousand in number, according to the plant or animal, arrange themselves in a single

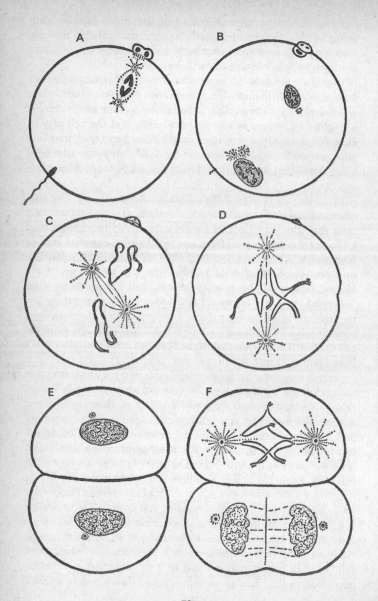

plane or plate. Next is a rapid moving apart of the half-chromosomes or daughter chromosomes to opposite sides of the cell. And the end is a slow re-forming of the two daughter nuclei by two equal groups of daughter chromosomes.

Thus the constancy of chromosome numbers is due to the fact that each of the chromosomes is divided lengthwise into halves which are exactly equal. And one half goes to each of the daughter nuclei and each of the daughter cells. Thus a cell with a nucleus having twelve chromosomes divides by mitosis into two cells each with a nucleus and each nucleus with twelve chromosomes like those of the mother nucleus. Further, between two mitoses, in the 'resting nuclei', the single chromosomes reproduce and become double, in preparation, as it were, for the next mitosis (Figure 3).

The two half-chromosomes are exactly equal. It seemed, therefore, that the process by which each single chromosome exactly reproduces itself and becomes double is the root of the whole problem of reproduction, of growth, and of heredity.

To put the matter in another way, there was a reproductive or genetic continuity in life. It joined together in unbreakable succession, not merely parent and offspring, and not merely cell and cell, but also nucleus and nucleus and ultimately chromosome

---

Figure 3

The beginning of an individual. A, the sperm enters the egg which is undergoing the second division of meiosis, and, B, losing its tail the head swells to form a nucleus containing a chromosome like that within the egg nucleus. C, the two nuclei move together, empty out their chromosomes, and a spindle is formed between them by organizers brought in by the sperm. D, the chromosomes each divide on the spindle and are pulled apart by the movements of their centromeres. E, the first mitosis of the embryo is complete. F, each nucleus undergoes a second division leading to the formation of four cells – all of them with two chromosomes, the *same* two chromosomes, one from the mother and one from the father. Compare Figure 15.

Note: The two divisions by which mother cells give rise to germ cells with the halved chromosome number are known as *meiosis*. The egg at meiosis divides to give three small cells which are pushed out of the fourth big one; but the sperm or pollen mother cells divide to give four equal nuclei at meiosis (see Figures 2 and 8).

and chromosome. And this unbreakable succession must have been going on since the beginning of cells, of nuclei and of chromosomes. For the new principle was step by step shown to be true of all plants and animals. Its universal truth was first understood and expressed in 1883 (by a German zoologist, Wilhelm Roux), and after the due delay of fifty years it came to be generally accepted.

By a few the idea of chromosome continuity and chromosome individuality was understood almost at once. The following year already Hertwig and Strasburger, the discoverers of fertilization, came to the necessary conclusion that the nucleus and the chromosomes it contains are the material basis of heredity and at the same time the material governing development. As Strasburger puts it:

molecular stimuli are passed from the nucleus to the cytoplasm which surrounds it, controlling the process of metabolism in the cell and giving a specific character to its growth.

And in 1893 we find Strasburger referring to the cell as the 'sphere of action' of the nucleus. At last, we may agree, the meaning of the cell theory was understood. It meant that localized and specific particles with localized and specific actions were responsible for heredity and development.

This view of the nucleus meant a revolution in the understanding of life and it was the second in a generation. But it was not the last. It opened the way for even more discoveries, or, shall we say, for even more speculation, which has come to be verified with the passage of time. For now it became possible to push back the study of heredity not merely to single cells, or even to nuclei, but to the chromosomes themselves, and what were the chromosomes? Minute they certainly were, but, under the microscope, visible. They were fibres and ferments bound in one. But chemically and physically they were still single molecules: monster molecules, perhaps, but still molecules; they had in themselves none of the structure which they must, at least in the opinion of a small body of enthusiastic microscopists, be supposed to determine. To preformationists they gave no hope at all. And others might be excused for finding it a bleak and unpromising prospect to take bodies which varied only in size and number to be the sole source of diversity, and bodies which were seen only when they were dead to be the ultimate vessels of life.

WEISMANN'S PHILOSOPHY

The study of the nuclear elements revealed, however, many surprising properties. These structures, although entering into every cell of the body, were in a sense cut off from, or independent of, the hazardous vagaries of day-to-day existence. The cells in which the nuclei lay might be fluid or fibrous, gland cells or germ cells, but they had the same eternal constancy in their outfit or complement of chromosomes. There was therefore an antithesis between the materials of heredity and their expression in growth and differentiation, between a protected germ and a body exposed to the changes of development and the chances of decay.

The first discoveries in the new field of work suggested generalizations on these lines. In part they were successful and have led straight on to the views we hold today. But in part they were sadly misleading.

It had been found that a threadworm named *Ascaris*, which dwells in the stomach of the horse, had enormous chromosomes. In a certain species, sperm and egg nucleus each gave *one* chromosome to the fertilized egg. The embryo nuclei therefore had *two* chromosomes in each cell at the first and at succeeding mitoses. If this were the case, how should the new animal come to form germ cells with only one chromosome in their nuclei?

For the solution of this problem we are indebted to the genius of August Weismann. This German zoologist after a long but not a very fruitful experience of microscopy was compelled by failing eyesight to give up the study of cells and nuclei. That was in the 1870s just when it was becoming most exciting. Turning from observation to reading he became the one man who was competent to interpret evolution to the cytologist and the chromosomes to the evolutionist. In his views on evolution he became more Darwinian than Darwin. But he believed in the cell theory. He therefore began to look for evidence in cell studies to explain the basis and character of heredity. Having found it, as he believed, in the chromosomes, he felt able to reject Darwin's backslidings on the inheritance of acquired characters. He then looked for evidence in cell studies to support this rejection. These three steps we can now follow in their somewhat dramatic sequence.

It was in 1887, while attending a British Association meeting at Manchester, that Weismann explained what happened to the chromosomes in sexual reproduction. He suggested that in the process of forming a germ cell the nuclei underwent a *reduction* or halving of chromosome number which would as it were undo the addition that takes place when egg and sperm fuse.

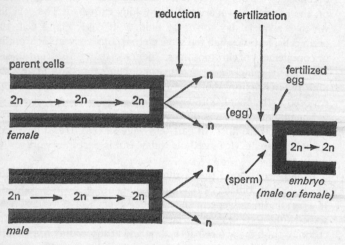

Figure 4

Weismann's theory that the alternation of reduction and fertilization is necessary for maintaining constant chromosome numbers with sexual reproduction: n and 2n represent the single and double (haploid and diploid) numbers of chromosomes characteristic of the species and seen in the lineages of dividing cells.

This prediction has since been confirmed for all plants and animals. At the time the process had not been seen and its mechanism was a matter of conjecture. Undeterred by this difficulty, however, five years later, in his Germplasm theory of heredity, Weismann suggested that what the mother and father had contributed to the chromosomes could be sorted out or separated at this reduction (Figure 5). In this way sexual reproduction would be the means by which the elements in the heredity of different individuals would be recombined in successive generations of their descendants. Or, as Weismann put it (p. 245):

The germ cells of one and the same organism must consequently contain very different combinations of . . . primary constituents from those which were present in its parents.

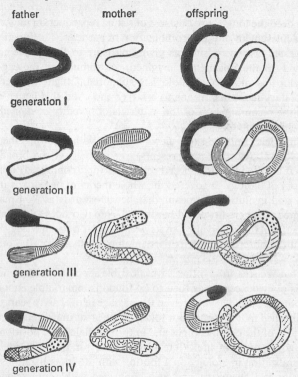

father   mother   offspring

generation I

generation II

generation III

generation IV

Figure 5

Weismann's view as to the way the materials (the ids) in the maternal and paternal chromosomes were added together and mixed in succeeding generations of an outbreeding species like man. The total length of the chromosomes added together at fertilization regulated themselves by a process of reduction. The ideas of mixture and reduction have been confirmed but the particular methods proposed gave rise to the erroneous notion that chromosomes paired end to end at meiosis. It should therefore be compared with Figure 8 in Chapter 6 (from *The Germ-Plasm*, 1893).

Hence it followed that:

> The dissimilarity between the children of the same parents . . . resulting from the halving of the germplasm [i.e. the chromosomes] in the process of 'reducing division', which takes place in a different manner each time . . . gives rise to a surprising number of combinations.

Indeed the long-range business of sexual reproduction might be the achievement of this recombination of particles. The functions suggested elsewhere, such as giving pleasure to the couple concerned (as the Epicureans imagined), or stimulating the egg to develop (as modern physiologists supposed), might be merely secondary incidents, means to a larger end. And this larger end was the recombination of the materials of heredity contained in the chromosomes.

Time has confirmed this view. Together with Darwin's theory of Natural Selection it represents, as we now see, the broadest generalization that had ever been made (and confirmed) in the history of biology. It covered the whole theory of heredity, variation and evolution. It meant that henceforward (as Weismann pointed out) heredity could be studied from two sides at the same time: from the observation of its *phenomena*, on the one side, and from the observation of its determining *substance*, on the other side.

That Weismann's synthesis was possible at all on such a slender basis of evidence as was then to be found is remarkable enough. But that it should have survived the passage of over sixty years undiminished in its cogency is a token of the great uniformity of behaviour of the chromosomes and in turn of their basic position in the government of life. Here was in fact, for the first time, a generalization in biology on a footing with the generalizations of physics and chemistry, and also connected with those sciences through the material of the chromosomes.

So important and so bold indeed was Weismann's statement that it is worth asking how he came to make it. We need not suppose that the order of his arguments was also the order of his reasoning as he presented it. It seems likely that the evidence of the continuity and controlling activity of the chromosomes on one side was equally balanced in Weismann's mind with the consequences of chromosome reduction and recombination as a basis of variations and of evolutionary change. The whole thing fitted together in his mind more coherently than he expressed it in words since reciprocal inferences of this kind cannot be expressed with corresponding symmetry: one argument has to precede another on the printed page.

Weismann's account is indeed by no means so clear as we have made it here. He insisted on clothing his twentieth-century ideas in an eighteenth-century costume. He prided himself on describing the hereditary materials as the Germplasm and Idioplasm, the chromosomes as Idants and their constituent particles as Ids. Weismann's ideas were new and revolutionary: his method of presenting them was old-fashioned and conventional. And the conventions of the time were exacting. They demanded Biophors, Plastidules and Micellae, whole worlds of little things now happily forgotten.

The novelty and importance of Weismann's ideas as well as the confusion created by metaphysical expression of them are well represented by an acute contemporary critic. Karl Pearson writes (*Grammar of Science*, 1st ed. 1892, chapter IX):

> It is not a continuity of the germ cells but of a hitherto unidentified substance contained in these cells. Cells, we know, nuclei, we know, with complicated networks of nucleoli, but what is *germplasm*?

Thus Pearson objects to Weismann's mystification of chromosomes. But he also objects to Weismann's materialization of them:

> There are still stronger metaphysical aspects in Weismann's doctrine. That a substance which possesses continuity and sameness should indefinitely reproduce itself ... and this owing to a definite molecular structure,

does not this notion, Pearson asks, quoting Weismann,

> compel us 'to suspend all known physical and physiological conceptions'?

Thus he also regards as metaphysical an assumption of properties which have in fact proved to be the physical foundation of genetics. In this he is merely the first of a long line of objectors.

Looking back seventy years we can now see that, wherever the idea of them might have come from, however mystical their name might be, and however uncertain their action was, nevertheless the Ids, the atoms of heredity, were seated firmly on the chromosomes. They were therefore well on the road to becoming what we call genes. And in the long pedigree of the gene, in spite of the highfalutin names that Weismann gave them, we may welcome them as the first respectable ancestors.

A FALSE CLUE:
DIFFERENTIATION AND THE GERMPLASM

Weismann's insight into the meaning of chromosome behaviour went so far ahead of his time that it is easy for us to forget how encumbered he was by the beliefs of his predecessors and the scanty knowledge of his contemporaries. If we study his difficulties we can measure the distance we have had to travel since his time. At the same time that he is representing his Ids as lying in the chromosome he is acknowledging their descent from the units of Spencer and the gemmules of Darwin. But they had an even more dangerous affinity, a connexion they could not shake off, with the preformed homunculus of the previous century. To be sure, each corpuscle of the blood could not be allowed its own forerunner or determinant: all the corpuscles together might perhaps have one. But these preformed determinants have to explain not only heredity and development but something else which we call differentiation.

In the course of development, a single cell, the egg, divides to become many cells and these cells are of different kinds: they make bone or brain, muscle or blood. If heredity is due to the chromosomes in the nuclei of these cells, and the chromosomes are always the same, how can the cells themselves become different? This was the problem which suddenly faced Weismann.

The first thing to explain was how the germ cells became different from the rest of the body. Here some sound ideas were already afloat. The distinction had already been noticed between what was permanent in heredity and what temporary in the body. Francis Galton, already in 1872, had suggested that the individual consists of 'two parts, one of which is *latent*, and only known to us by its effect on posterity, while the other is *patent* and constitutes the person manifest to our senses'. Eight years later a certain

Moritz Nussbaum had reached a similar view on quite different evidence: 'The reproductive cells of the higher animals represent the stock from which the individuals after a short existence detach themselves to die like the leaves falling from a tree.' In other words there is an unbreakable apostolic succession of recognizable and potentially immortal cells – the germ track – from which successive generations of breakable bodies are, as it were, budded off.

In the higher animals this distinction is crude and absolute. At an early stage in the partition of the egg among the dividing nuclei, each with a portion of cytoplasm which will make its own cell, those cells can already be recognized from which the testes or ovaries will be derived. And it is from these cells alone that the germ cells, the sperm and the eggs can develop.

Both Galton's and Nussbaum's opinions meant that heredity was not to be directly related to what happened in development. The whole of heredity was not expressed in the development of each individual body. And the whole of each individual, together with the accidents that happened to the body, should not be expressed in heredity. Weismann carried this view further. Heredity, which he called the germplasm, lay entirely in the nucleus, in the chromosomes. During the development of the body the unwanted parts of the germplasm escape into the cell. The nucleus unpacks itself and becomes a defective, limited, and specialized body-cell nucleus. Germplasm has become 'somatoplasm'. But in the germ track it remains complete and perfect and free from any developmental deterioration.

Weismann had himself studied simple animals in which the germ cells can be formed from quite ordinary body cells. He therefore refused to commit himself to the idea that the germ track was necessarily and visibly separated from the body in particular visible cells. It could be recognized as germ track only after the event. In view of a particular discovery made at this time, however, ambiguity and misunderstanding were inevitable.

The nucleus of the fertilized egg of the worm *Ascaris* had the double or diploid number of chromosomes for the species, which was two. These two chromosomes divided regularly in the first mitosis of the embryo to give daughter nuclei each with two. But, at the second mitosis of one of these nuclei, the chromosomes broke into twenty or more fragments, some of which were left on the equator of the dividing cells; the remnant, and it was only a remnant, made their way to the poles to form daughter nuclei. This process of 'diminution' repeated itself again and again in one of the products of the normal mitosis. Hence later, of sixty-four cells, sixty-three could be seen with fragmented and diminished chromosome complements; the sixty-fourth alone retained the full set of two large unbroken chromosomes. The perfect cell was found to be the one from which the sex glands, ovaries and testes, and hence the germ cells, were derived.

This remarkable series of events was discovered in the years between Weismann's prediction of chromosome reduction and his statement of the germplasm theory. He was bound to be impressed by it. Here, on the one hand, was a track of cell-history leading from the fertilized egg of one generation to that of the next without loss or damage, permanent and inviolable. On the other hand were the cells which gave rise to the perishable and differentiating body of the animal. And in these the chromosomes unpacked their contents, throwing away into their cells what they did not need – or perhaps what the cells did need. Thus Weismann writes:

We assume that the changes in the id of the germplasm during ontogeny [the development of an individual] consist in a regular disintegration of the determinants into smaller and smaller groups, until finally only *one* kind of determinant is continued in the cell, viz. that which has to determine it   1892, p. 63; and Figure 19

Thus it might seem that, in the two sides of this story, the independence and permanence of heredity, and the change and differentiation of development, were both of them revealed by the behaviour of the chromosomes and not only revealed but determined and, in a sense, preformed. The germ line was visibly separate from the body or soma and the evidence went to show that whatever might happen to the body the germ cells would be quite independent of it. If only this distinction and this behaviour had been universal the problem of how a fixed heredity and a changing development could be squared with one another, the great dilemma between preformation and epigenesis, would have been solved.

With the passage of time it became evident, alas that few if any other animals revealed a process of diminution or unpacking in the course of their development. *Ascaris* was almost unique. Its properties were, at the time, grossly misleading. Is there then any meaning we can attach to diminution? There certainly is. The loss of the chromosomes is not the cause of differentiation but an exceptional consequence of it. It is of interest as showing what the chromosomes *can* do, not as showing what they *must* do.

A more serious difficulty, however, was that differentiation in plants can never involve damage to the germplasm. In plants growth is potentially unlimited, and, as botanists did not fail to point out, their germ cells can arise from any stem or even sometimes from a root or a leaf. A germ track, therefore, and diminution in all parts outside the germ track, never could occur in plants.

Weismann himself realized that germplasm and soma or body were not visibly distinguished in plants and lower animals. He therefore assumed that there was a distinction, but it was invisible:

> The fact [by which he means the theory] that somatic idioplasm cannot give rise to germplasm serves as an additional support for the theory of the germplasm as here developed [i.e. of differentiation by loss]. In all cases in which such a transformation has apparently occurred [i.e. in plants] invisible or at any rate unrecognizable masses of unalterable germplasm must have been contained in the body cells.
>
> *Germ-Plasm*, ch. 6

Behind this confused statement is the unfortunate fact that in plants there is no genetic separation of germ-track cells and body cells: both contain a complete germplasm and the theory of differentiation by loss will not work.

THE TWO THEORIES OF HEREDITY

Disillusioned with these obvious errors people began to disregard Weismann's views, right or wrong, and to relegate them, together with his terminology, to a lumber room of ill-founded conjectures. Weismann's distinction between germplasm and body, however, like his theories of chromosome reduction and of sexual recombination, stands today. The distinction, as he realized, is not between the whole of the sex cells, the so-called germ track of earlier zoologists, and the whole of the body cells. It is – as now seems so obvious – between the nucleus with its content of chromosomes and the body of the cell with its content of what we call the cytoplasm.

The nucleus and its chromosomes are the basis of heredity, the permanent government of the cell, handed down from cell to cell, and from parent to offspring without diminution, adaptation or decay. The cytoplasm, the pabulum in which the nucleus lies, the basis of its propagation and the means of its expression, changes with every phase of growth. It gives the character to the tissue and, as it does so, loses (especially in the higher animals) the capacity for diversification and for indefinite growth: that is to say, unless it is the cytoplasm of a cell with the capacities of a germ track.

Weismann's theory of the separation and continuity of the germplasm, therefore, has a meaning today. It means what we mean by the individuality and continuity of the chromosomes. In addition it presents the clear issue between what we may call the two theories of heredity: the two theories which had existed side by side for over 2,000 years. They were the theory of direct transmission and the theory of successive determination.

The theory of *direct transmission* is the obvious, the naïve, the primitive, theory. It assumes that the reproductive essence or material, the germ or seed, is a contraction or condensation or abbreviation of the parent at the moment of begetting, a contraction which expands or unfolds or grows by a reverse process to give the mature offspring.

The theory of *successive determination* assumes that the germ or seed multiplies and, while it keeps enough of itself to provide the seed for the next generation, separates or buds off a body from itself whose character it determines. But whatever happens to this body has nothing directly to do with the germ which it is carrying within it (Figure 6).

Pieces of what was necessary for one theory or the other had hitherto been continually mixed up. They had been mixed up by Aristotle and by Darwin, both of them unconscious of the confusion. Lamarck had separated and assembled the mutually consistent elements of the first theory into one reasonably coherent system. It was the wrong system. Weismann assembled the elements of the other theory. His system, by contrast with Lamarck's, was the right system but he went too far. In trying to make heredity independent of development he tried also to explain the whole of development in terms of heredity. And while this was a necessary project, the undertaking was premature.

Weismann's error in proceeding so far, strangely enough, lay

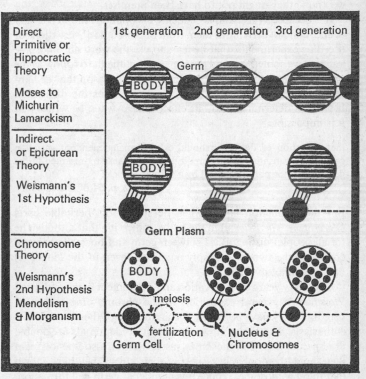

Figure 6

The two theories of heredity, showing the contrast between the *epitomizing* germ of Hippocrates represented by the name PANGENESIS, and the *determining* germ of Weismann in its crudest form (*middle*) and (*below*) as refined by modern genetics and cell-study.

where it lay with Lamarck and Darwin. Like them he was deducing his theory of heredity and even of differentiation, from his views on evolution. Nay more, he was deducing the properties of the chromosomes from his theory of heredity. Acquired characters, on Weismann's view, *must* not be inherited. Natural selection *must* be sufficient for adaptive change. The germplasm *must* therefore be independent of the body. Changes in the body *must* not change heredity. His premises were sound but (in the light of what we know) they ought not to have been premises.

It is because Weismann is deducing his opinions the wrong way round, and not arriving at them from microscopic observations or breeding experiments, that he fears to use the word chromosome and that we sometimes find his remarks as difficult to follow as the prophecies in the pyramids. It is also for this reason that he himself becomes, from time to time, confused. Thus the distinction between a determinant and its effect is clear when he writes that it is impossible

that a portion of the body should exhibit an independent variation capable of transmission [in heredity] unless it were represented in the germplasm [the chromosomes] by a special particle.

1892, p. 54 of translation

But the distinction lapses when he speaks of 'heritable parts (*Vererbbare Theilstücke*) in the body' indicating that although he (of all people) distinguishes between germ and body the habit of confusing the two is so deeply ingrained (even in the language) that he cannot avoid it.

Over sixty years of observation and experiment have vindicated Weismann's general exposition of the chromosome theory of heredity. They have borne out the arguments of the chromosome enthusiasts. They have shown that plants and animals are double in respect of their chromosomes, just as he (and also Spencer) said they should be double in respect of their units. They have shown that the chromosomes reduce this number at germ-cell formation. And they have shown that, after cross-breeding, plants and animals recombine their characters in the way Weismann foretold. With this unbroken success behind them, is it surprising that those who studied chromosomes, and thereby fulfilled the predictions of these philosophers, had no philosophical misgivings in following their clues? For the practical breeders, however, the followers of Mendel, who had scarcely heard of the chromosomes, the matter was far otherwise. It is their ideas we now have to trace.

PART TWO

THE FRAMEWORK OF LIFE

Only when attempts to explain evolution were put aside and microscopic and chemical methods and interpretations were combined with new experimental and statistical devices could the great problems of heredity, development and disease be sorted out and reduced to order. The order they showed was deterministic. The deterministic principle, however, works at different levels which were successively revealed in the search for (or against) spontaneous generation. Not only this but the course of life itself could be split into antagonistic parts within the cell: the host and the virus sometimes derived from it and often destroying it.

5

The Coming of Genetics : I

IS EXPERIMENT POSSIBLE?

WE have seen principles of heredity inferred and propounded from the desire to explain evolution and to make people believe in evolution. We have also seen such principles inferred from observations of cells, nuclei and chromosomes. The root of the matter could obviously be dug out only by experiment. Many people could see this and many had in fact tried it. The foundation must be in hybridization, in crossing different types of plant or of animal, either different varieties or different species.

When, in the eighteenth and early nineteenth centuries, men tried to make hybrids the results were various. Either they found a blending of different characters, or a mixed progeny with all kinds of different characters. Or again they found reversion or throwing-back to some supposed ancestral character. Or they found predominance of the characters of one parent. These things, as we saw, were noted by Darwin and his contemporaries with suitable exclamations of surprise. But of explanation there came none – unless the learned words atavism and prepotency which Darwin made popular could be said to explain reversion and predominance.

The practice of experiment had been developed largely with plants. Already, in 1717, Thomas Fairchild had made his cross of *Dianthus caryophyllus* by *barbatus*. But Koelreuter in his memorable experiments forty years later was the first man to set about making hybrids systematically in order to use them in testing the principles of reproduction and heredity.

Koelreuter showed that when mixed pollen was used only the plant's own pollen works; foreign pollen can hardly compete. Hence hybrids can be produced artificially, when the plant's own anthers have been cut out and the flowers covered, although they do not arise in nature. And when his crosses between different species of *Nicotiana* and *Dianthus* revealed that the influence of the two parents was equal – and equal whichever species was the female parent – he refuted the principles of ovism and spermism and the whole doctrine of preformation as thoroughly as, unknown to him, his contemporary Wolff was refuting them by examining the embryo of the chicken.

But there were limits to the distance that Koelreuter, or any of his time, could go by breeding experiments. They still thought that the prolific virtue of the pollen took effect in fertilization on the surface of the stigma. They still believed that the fertilizing materials were 'fluids', that is, something quite opposed to the solidity of particles. It was only natural for them, therefore, to attribute the advantage in competition enjoyed by the plant's own pollen to the operation of the 'harmony of Nature' rather than to the different properties of individual pollen grains.

It made all the difference in the world when in 1830 microscopists were able to see individual pollen grains hatch or germinate on the sticky stigma and their contents form tubes to grow down the style towards the ovule. These observations had to be known to the breeder, and the idea that indivisible units and materials were to be taken into account in reproduction had to take root in his understanding, before he could see the nature of the problem. That is why Darwin could not visualize it. And that is why Mendel, born a few years later, could do so.

MENDEL AND DARWIN

It was while Darwin was writing his *Origin of Species* at Down House that Gregor Mendel began his breeding experiments with peas in the Augustinian monastery at Brünn in Moravia. Mendel had been unsuccessful in his teacher's examinations in Natural History and had found some consolation in studying the weather, breeding mice, observing bees and growing vegetables.

The contrast between the first two of the great genetic discoverers that we meet, men who were personally unknown to one another, is of more than anecdotal interest. It reveals the interaction of heredity and environment. On the one side, Darwin was a world traveller and world observer. He was interested in vast generalizations of long-term processes. Most of his experiments were ineffective. His mind, while directed to the conclusions he hoped to reach or confirm, was contemplative and synthetic. His faith lay in the method of science and not in a supernatural revelation. And his work, published in 1859, achieved the most complete and immediate public success that scientific discovery is likely to afford.

On the other side, Mendel made trips to Vienna, Rome, Paris and London but his world was his monastery and its garden. He was interested in the minute determination of short-term processes. His mind was intense and analytic, and its bent therefore experimental. His beliefs lay partly, we must suppose, outside the scope of scientific investigation. His work, published in 1865, achieved as complete a public failure as it has been the lot of any discoverer to know: so much so that he gave up his inquiries in complete disappointment.

Mendel had two great advantages over Darwin. He was born later. And he lived in a country where microscopes were widely used and where the cell theory was widely accepted. He himself used a microscope and believed in the individual activity of cells. He therefore differed from Darwin in believing that single pollen grains fertilized single egg cells and he took the trouble to test it by an experiment. He therefore also felt that heredity must depend on these individual germ cells. And if a plant or animal had two kinds of offspring it was because it produced two kinds of germ cells. How could this principle be tested?

It was necessary, Mendel explained, to begin by taking a plant whose seeds were regularly fertilized by its own pollen. He therefore took varieties of the garden pea and found that, self-fertilized, they bred true for several generations. They were thus making germ cells all of one kind.

Then he crossed pairs of varieties. They differed, sometimes in one, sometimes in several, sharply distinct respects, respects in regard to which he could see differences among pea varieties in general: these are the Mendelian *characters* or, to be more exact, differences in character. But the offspring, the first filial generation, or F_1, as we call it, were always uniform. Examining them for each character in turn Mendel found that they always entirely resembled one parent or the other. A particular character was always *dominant* over its alternative which was recessive, or *vice versa*. There was no blending. Tall plants crossed with short gave only tall. Round-seeded plants crossed with wrinkled gave only round. This was true whatever other characters they might be combined with. It was also true whether the character was carried, or brought in, by the pollen or by the eggs: as we say, whichever way the cross was made. Each character, therefore, seemed to have its own individual properties, at least so far as the varieties of garden pea were concerned.

So far so good. Mendel now self-fertilized his first generation of hybrid peas. And in this second generation, the F_2, he found that the recessive characters of the first parents reappeared. The confusion of all his predecessors was now reproduced. But Mendel, undismayed, proceeded to count the progeny. He counted them plant by plant, and character by character. He found that for each pair of alternatives, one quarter of the F_2 plants showed the recessive character, three quarters the dominant: a 3 to 1 ratio.

He then found that, when self-fertilized, the quarter of recessives bred true, a part of the three quarters that showed the dominant bred true, and the rest of the dominants again split up. There were thus three classes: pure dominant, hybrid dominant and pure recessive. They proved to be in the proportion of 1 : 2 : 1. And this proportion, Mendel pointed out, was what would be expected if the germ cells, eggs and pollen alike, were of two types, carrying the dominant and recessive (say A and a) in equal numbers.

Thus:

$$(A + a) \times (A + a) = 1AA + 2Aa + 1aa$$

A pure-breeding plant, therefore, would arise when the eggs and pollen were 'of like character' (A and A or a and a). An impure or segregating plant would arise when the eggs and pollen were of unlike character. This conclusion Mendel then verified by making the crosses Aa female by aa male and *vice versa*. Both crosses gave a ratio of $1Aa : 1aa$. Finally, when two character pairs (Aa and Bb) were combined in one cross they recombined at random, for they gave two 3 : 1 ratios multiplied together, a 9 : 3 : 3 : 1 ratio. And, if n characters were recombined, the ratio would agree with the algebraic series: $(3 + 1)^n$.

Others before, indeed several English breeders forty years

earlier, had found dominance in pea seeds in a first generation, and reappearance in a second generation. But they had not counted the seeds and gone on counting them. Why did Mendel attempt this tedious task? He not only differed from his predecessors in believing in particles and causes. He understood something that no student of heredity had understood before him, namely, the inherent error of sampling. When you take a handful of peas from an evenly mixed heap where one quarter are of one kind and three quarters of the other, you will not find one quarter and three quarters of the two kinds in your hand, at least not exactly, and not usually.

To be sure most plant breeders before Mendel's time – and not a few since his time – would have been put off the recognition of the underlying ratio by the variation in sampling, the sampling of nature, when the seeds on individual plants were counted. Thus the first five of Mendel's plants gave round and wrinkled seeds (to take one pair of alternatives) in the ratios:

$$\frac{45}{12} \quad \frac{27}{8} \quad \frac{24}{7} \quad \frac{19}{10} \quad \frac{32}{11}$$

Each of these by itself was unconvincing. Taking them all together, however, 147 to 48 or 3·06 to 1, one could see the suggestion of a 3 to 1 ratio. When he had recorded over 7,000 seeds the ratio of 2·96 to 1 emerged, a ratio near enough to put the matter beyond reasonable doubt, and then he felt he had counted enough,

The essential statistical principle was still misunderstood when Mendel's paper came to be studied forty years later. Thus, when he had read Mendel in 1900, de Vries published an account of his own experiments; he then recorded not the numbers of individuals in the classes of his progenies but only their percentages. Thereby he showed that he had failed to grasp the meaning of Mendel's statistical method. For all mixed progenies are samples and the liability to error, of the ratios shown by the samples which we need to know, depends on the numbers of individuals in the samples.

RATIOS AND ELEMENTS

These ratios fascinated the Mendelians. They represented

something new in scientific method and they have, of course, played an enormous part in the development of all the later breeding work with higher plants and animals. It has therefore seemed very natural to regard the laws of recombination as primary laws. The ratio, having become the rallying cry in battle, became an end in itself.

Mendel is indeed known today to many students only through these ratios. The student is told a version of what his rediscoverer, Carl Correns, called Mendel's two laws. The first law is that hereditary 'factors' are derived in pairs from our two parents and are separated, or segregated, unchanged in the production of our germ cells. They do not blend. They do not alter one another, although they are carried together in every cell in the body. The germ cells therefore contain one of the two alternative factors responsible for, or connected with, each 'character' and are therefore 'pure' in respect of differences between alternative characters for which the parent may be hybrid or impure. The second law is that the members of different pairs of factors responsible for different characters are segregated and recombined independently in different germ cells.

True it is, of course, that these laws made it possible to throw a large part of the supposed common sense of mankind on the subject of heredity, and all the superstitions from Aristotle to Lamarck, on to the rubbish heap, as follows:

1. Pangenesis and the inheritance of acquired characters were left suspended in meaningless contradiction.

2. Blending inheritance was seen to be a misinterpretation. The mixing of characters left them entirely uncontaminated for posterity.

3. Prepotency was not a property of individuals, or of breeds, or of one or other of the sexes, but of a character-difference, or rather of something behind the character-difference.

4. The contributions of male and female were equal; reciprocal crosses were alike.

5. Everything in heredity was a property not of the parents but of their germ cells and thus had to be recorded statistically, and interpreted in terms of sampling.

6. Reversion was due to segregation. And recessive characters

appearing by segregation, although arising from something in the parents, need not have been inherited in the sense that any ancestor has shown them.

The most momentous of these last characters is sterility, and Mendel had shown how it could happen that all sterile plants and animals have had fertile parents. Their sterility is genetically determined but it is not inherited in the popular sense. What was to be hereditary in the future had not, therefore, necessarily been hereditary in the past. This last principle of latency had been perceived by Galton. But Mendel had explained it.

Singly these revelations were impressive. Taken together they were staggering. We may say that students of biology have never entirely absorbed them. But even together, although they are what we know Mendel's name by, they are only the subordinate principles of his discovery. They are applications of a primary law, or rather the primary law, of biology. This law was stated by Mendel as a hypothesis. The importance of the law is still as little apprehended by the student in his examination as by the philosopher in his treatise. It is that Mendel's segregation is due to the separation of things that *determine* not the differences of character between organisms but the whole character of each organism. There are determinants of development which, being carried from parent to offspring, are also the determinants of heredity. The rest of this book will be spent in examining and developing the consequences of this discovery.

MENDEL'S INFERENCE

The idea of determination Mendel was able to derive from his experiments because they were designed, as no experiments on heredity had been before, to simplify the relations of cause and effect between the germ cells of the parent and the character of the offspring. Mendel did not precisely explain this plan. Probably, as we shall see, he was not fully conscious of it. Consequently his successors missed the point altogether.

To us it is hard to realize how easy it was to miss the point. We have seen the chromosomes, both their constancy in development from the fertilized egg, and their reduction at germ-cell formation. Plants and animals have nuclei with two sets of corresponding chromosomes throughout their vegetative or body tissues. At the mitosis when reduction of the chromosome number takes place, in the egg or sperm mother cell, these chromosomes pair and the mates segregate at random to give germ cells with single sets. Thus a man or a mouse having chromosomes where the partners in each pair differ in one respect, *Aa, Bb, Cc, Dd*, etc., forms sperm *ABCD* and *abcd* from one mother cell, but *ABCd* and *abcD* from another, and so on to give all the possible sixteen combinations of the four pairs of alternatives.

The germ cells combine in fertilization again at random, one sperm fusing with one egg to give the double sets again. Thus the chromosomes do just what they should do if the partners carry corresponding factors which determine alternative characters. But how different it was for Mendel! He had to make experiments to prove that only pairs of germ cells fused, and he certainly had not heard of the chromosomes.

Mendel had to begin with his ratios. As, step by step, he described his experiments he confined himself to demonstrating the agreement in each experiment between the mathematical combination *series*, on the one hand, and the frequencies of individuals he actually found with different combinations of alternative *characters*, on the other. He was thinking in terms of probabilities when he examined his 9 : 3 : 3 : 1 ratio (Table 1).

TABLE 1

Mendel's 9 :3 :3 :1 ratio among 556 peas

Second generation from the cross:	315 Round and Yellow	or for *seed:* 423 Round 133 Wrinkled
Round *seed* and Yellow *cotyledons* × Wrinkled *seed* and Green *cotyledons*	101 Wrinkled and Yellow 108 Round and Green 32 Wrinkled and Green	and for *cotyledons:* 416 Yellow 140 Green

From this mathematical point of view determination could almost be overlooked. The character and what determined it could be equated, at least where the character was dominant. Thus, he says:

those characters which pass over quite, or almost, unchanged in the hybridization and therefore in themselves constitute the characters of the hybrid, are termed the dominant.

And again:

The hybrid-character resembles that of one of the parental forms. ...

Mendel's varying descriptions have evoked opposite opinions of praise and blame from his Mendelian successors. Here we have the comment of Bateson (1909):

Note that Mendel with true penetration, avoids speaking of the hybrid-character as 'transmitted' by either parent, thus escaping the error pervading the older views of heredity.

Haldane on the other hand, forty years later discovers:

the idealistic character of Mendel's formulation of his result. He spoke of the transmission from one generation to another of differentiating characters. ... A geneticist should not use such language. ... Mendel was presumably a Thomist. ...

The truth is that Mendel was less penetrating than Bateson supposes and less superficial than Haldane suggests. What he knew is not to be labelled in philosophical categories, since – horrible to relate – his views actually changed while he was writing the paper. One can only suppose that this unseemly development (which has not been remarked upon before) was the result of his examining the evidence!

Mendel did not speak of characters being 'transmitted' – the word was the translator's. He spoke of their *Übergehen* or 'passing over'. He did, however, speak of characters being dominant whereas (as we think) strictly it is the determinant that is dominant. But it was only in the discussion at the end of the paper that Mendel invented the determinant. How then could he have understood it at the beginning?

Throughout Mendel's descriptive pages he has spoken, sometimes prudently of the resemblance of characters, sometimes less prudently of the passing over of characters, or in some other way has evaded the question of determinants. At first he considers only the correspondence of a ratio with an algebraic series. Later he speaks of germ cells having this or that *composition* in respect of a character. Moreover, throughout the papers (and even in his later correspondence with the botanist Nägeli) he has described the three classes of individuals in an F_2 as A, Aa and a, evading the unproved doubleness of the 'homozygote' AA and aa classes. But when he comes to marshal the evidence, to consider his conclusions and to get to the bottom of his problem, like many great discoverers he begins to see a new light.

Dimly, at first, Mendel sees his new principle, because it is veiled, as it always must be, in the verbal habits of the past. But it is not veiled in idealism or Thomism. It is uncompromisingly deterministic. The development of the fertilized egg, he asserts, 'follows a constant law which is founded on the *material composition and arrangement* of the elements which meet in the cell to give a viable union'. This was in 1865, twenty-three years before the name chromosome was invented. He then refers to '*elements* of both germ cells which *determine* opposite characters'. These are held together throughout the life of the plant, and:

we must further assume that it is only possible for the differentiating elements to liberate themselves from the enforced union when the fertilizing cells are developed.

This was twenty-two years before Weismann predicted the occurrence of the segregation of chromosomes at the reduction division. And, in the end, he repeats:

The differentiating characters of two plants can finally only depend (*beruhen*) on differences in the composition and *grouping* of the elements which exist in the foundation cells (the fertilized eggs) of the same in vital interaction.

Thus we see, not merely material determinants, but their spatial arrangement and their segregation at germ-cell formation clearly foreshadowed.

It was in consequence of the clarity of Mendel's conclusion that his successors were able to make at once the next step and describe the classes of an F_2 as AA, Aa and aa, a step which Mendel himself would no doubt have made had he ever met a single person with whom he could seriously discuss his ideas.

There is more in Mendel's paper about material elements, determinants, and their fusion, separation and even interaction, which may be recommended to those anxious to see how scientific method can be made to work. They will then realize that though, in some senses, Mendel discovered less than what we call Mendelism, in other senses he discovered more.

Mendel lacked only one thing to enable him to go further. It was something which can come, as we know from our experience of scientific discovery, only from discussion and dispute with one's fellows. That was the confidence to develop the social attributes of a successful theory, the terminology required for its public description and explanation. How could he reconstruct the ideology of the Life Sciences on the basis of experiments which nobody who believed understood and nobody who understood believed?

PAUSE AND REDISCOVERY

Mendel's paper was read before the Brünn Natural History Society on 8 February and 8 March 1865, and published in its *Proceedings* a year later. It met with no response. Mendel's distinguished correspondent, the philosophical botanist Professor Carl Nägeli, who had a theory of heredity of his own, totally failed to see the point. What indeed could be the point of counting thousands of round and wrinkled peas! Mendel, disappointed in the success of his discoveries, found consolation in the absorbing duties of an Abbot of Brünn. He died just after Darwin, in 1884. In a botanical treatise on Plant Hybrids in 1881 a German hybridizer, Wilhelm Focke, mentioned his experiments fifteen times without noticing that he had drawn any conclusions from them. The prophet of Mutation, Hugo de Vries, probably saw it in 1899, realized its bearing on his own work, but quoted it only among the references in a paper of his own confirming Mendel's conclusions the following year. Mendelism was not therefore rediscovered until Mendel's results were confirmed and acknowledged by Correns at Tübingen and Tschermak at Vienna in 1900.

Thus it happened that by a strange accident, working not so many miles from Mendel's garden, but twenty years later, Weismann, and the German cytologists on whose work he built, were as ignorant of Mendel's achievement as he was of theirs. Independently, Weismann and Mendel had laid the twin foundations of the chromosome theory of heredity. For two men to have reached the same point, and by entirely different, indeed by opposite, roads in entire ignorance of what the other was doing, is unique in the history of discovery. The double foundations, equally foretold by Weismann and Mendel, gave the rediscovery of Mendel's work a double interest. Plant and animal breeders set to work hoping to confirm or confute the Mendelian ratios. Cytologists began to look at chromosomes as the possible agents in the new game – for it was something of a game – of Mendelian recombination. But before the union of the two techniques into one discipline was to be possible a few more obstacles had to be encountered.

BATESON THE IMMATERIALIST

To us it is now evident that the great revolutionary moment was when Mendel referred to 'elements which determine'. In Mendel's paper this idea was rigorously derived from the evidence of a designed experiment. Nevertheless the immense implications of Mendel's assertion, first for biology, and then for human thought as a whole, have not yet seeped through in the intervening hundred years.

The eclipse of all thought on heredity, including Mendel's, in the 1860s, and all except Galton's even in the 70s, was due to its being seen entirely in the *light* of evolutionary theory: that is to say, as Johannsen put it in 1922, in a very deep *shadow*. The great ideas of the struggle for existence, the survival of the fittest, and the descent of man, took the centre of the stage. And in the orchestra one heard the great theme of 'ontogeny repeats phylogeny' beating out its stately and compelling rhythm. Who then should notice the modest figure of heredity in the background quietly throwing the shuttle of life? To naturalists and to sociologists alike she appeared merely as a part of the decorative backcloth for the heroic realities in whose actions the drama of life and thought seemed to be working itself out.

When Mendel was rediscovered in 1900, therefore, what interested men was not the principles of heredity but the particulars of variation. To rediscover the whole of Mendel would perhaps have been too much. As Fisher said, each generation found in Mendel what it expected to find. Even a part-discovery created a burning crisis, the first of several in our story.

William Bateson of Cambridge read about Mendel's paper coming up to London, in the train, on 8 April 1900. He saw, at once, if not all its significance, at least a great part of it. It was Bateson who gave clarity to Mendelian theory by introducing such terms as 'heterozygote' for a Mendelian hybrid, and such notions as that of the purity of the gamete, meaning that it has to be either A or a and cannot be both. Bateson it was too who asserted, and worked and fought hardest to prove, the universality of the Mendelian theory in plants and animals. And it was he who gave the fitting name of Genetics to the whole study of heredity. It is to Bateson's missionary voice therefore that we look for the interpretation of Mendelism to the rising generation of the new century.

According to Bateson, however, Mendel's 'essential discovery' was not the elements-which-determine but the fact-of-segregation. Bateson would scarcely admit that there were elements which determined. Thus, although Mendel had taken the plunge, Bateson still shivered on the bank – where he remained for the rest of his life. To those who asked: Segregation of what? an answer had to be given, a word had to be conjured up – or rather several words. First there were Mendel's characters. 'Gametes', wrote Bateson in 1902, 'are differentiated in respect of pure characters.' But Mendel had used the word for the appearance of the plant and so did Bateson. Then there were 'unit-characters'. All Mendelian characters behaved as units and were therefore unit-characters. Again there were 'allelomorphs', alternative characters or, more strictly, alternative shapes. Ambiguity was complete. Were these characters or allelomorphs to be regarded as determinants in the gamete or appearances in the whole organism? The distinction did not exist. The separation that had been made by Mendel at the end of his remarks, the new generation refused to notice. The gap between determinant and determined opened by Mendel was closed again.

Two discoveries at last came to split the unit-character, to drive the determinant and the determined once more asunder. One was interaction, with which we must include dominance; the other was the 'genotype'.

Mendel had been quite unprepared to find that his elements might interact in determining a joint character. Indeed he had chosen his characters in the hope and belief that they were independent. Any degree of interaction would have muddled his experiment and defeated his analytic purpose. Suppose that two factor differences $A-a$ and $B-b$ are segregating in an F_2 such that both A and B are needed to show a visible difference from the double recessive *aabb*. Then instead of the $9:3:3:1$ ratio we saw earlier, the classes will be thrown together and we shall have $9:7$.

When Bateson crossed two strains of the white sweet-pea *Emily Henderson* and found in the F_1 that he had made a purple sweet-pea of the wild type he was surprised enough. It was, he said, 'entirely mysterious'. But when the coloured heterozygote was selfed and gave not $9:3:3:1$ but $9:7$, that is 9 coloured to 7 white, he was naturally even more surprised. Evidently here was no longer a unit-character but a 'complex character'. Two of something made a new thing that neither could make alone. What were these somethings? Their relations need not be so simple. If they help or hinder one another in other ways we might expect $9:6:1$ or $9:3:4$ or $12:3:1$ or $13:3$ or even $15:1$. Such ratios were found by Bateson's school in 1907. To judge by his notebooks and by one of his remarks, they probably had been found by Mendel himself in crosses of French beans and runner beans. But they must have been too much for him, for he said little about them.*

These ratios – and all possible combinations were later found – mean that the character and its determinant can no longer be identified: two determinants can go to make one difference of character. They interact. There is a process in development between the fertilized egg and the grown plant or animal. A gaping rent between cause and effect had once and for all been laid bare. Both dominance and interaction are examples of how one determinant interferes with another (allelomorphic or not allelomorphic) on the way to its expression in the appearance of the organism. Both made it necessary to think of how a cause carried in heredity acted to produce a consequence at the end of development. A word became necessary to express this cause, a second word. It came at once to mind. It was that very useful word *factor*. It was a word that Mendel himself had once used. To Bateson, the factor was invaluable because, as he said, 'it implied no hypothesis'. In fact

* Cf. frontispiece of *Genes, Plants, and People*, Darlington and Mather, 1950.

it implied the largest hypothesis in science and the first principle of genetics, the hypothesis of determination.

Now, in spite of Bateson, the question arose: was this factor of his a material body? Yes and no. On the one hand he had to admit (in 1914) that 'genetic factors are definite things, either present or absent from any germ cell'. But in the preceding paragraph he had safeguarded himself: 'it is unlikely that the genetic factors are in any simple or literal sense material particles'. In these equivocal circumstances, the distinction between the immaterial determinant and the undetermined character still failed to make itself felt and Bateson would still speak of 'dominant characters'.

The hypothesis of Presence and Absence was Bateson's contribution to resolving the problems of dominance, of interaction and also of the material nature of determinants. It supposed that the recessive factor was due to the absence of something whose presence constituted the dominant. The dominant factor was due to a presence of something absent in the recessive. In our eyes this hypothesis would seem to have had two merits, merits which it still partly retains. It was a minimum assumption, strictly according to William of Occam; and it implied the existence of material particles. But for Bateson it obviously had a third merit: it sounded immaterial. The philosopher Locke had described the soul as an 'immaterial substance' and Bateson wanted something from the same bottle. At the same time that he was advancing the Presence and Absence Theory, he was maintaining that the determinants depended not on 'materials' but on 'arrangements'. So that we were now two steps from crude matter. Alternative characters were due to 'allelomorphic factors' which were due to the presence or absence of arrangements. Arrangements of what? Perhaps alternative arrangements of molecules would have been immaterial while alternative arrangements of atoms would have been material? In those days such an indelicate question was not asked and now it need not be answered.

Bateson had no use for chromosomes – nor for Weismann either – but to any adherent of Weismann's chromosome theory the idea of determinants should have naturally commended itself. Yet, even in this quarter, the confusion of character and factor still prevailed. Thus the cytologist, Boveri, in 1904, while propounding the chromosome theory with great cogency, could suggest the possibility that an exchange of chromosome segments might give rise to crossing-over between 'characters' localized in chromosomes. Likewise T. H. Morgan, the American critic of Bateson, could still refer in 1909 to factors as 'alternative states of stability' and to 'paired characters that separate in the germ cells', thereby embracing Bateson's chief errors.

This refusal to face the assumption of material bodies in the germ cells, acting throughout life in determining the characters of the mature plant or animal, would astonish us if it had no antecedents. But when we recall the perfume of the palm trees and the *aura seminalis* which did the work of heredity equally for Aristotle, for William Harvey, and for Spallanzani, we are no longer surprised. Rather, having noted the persistence of the human mind in using preformation as a substitute for determination, we prepare to examine its consequences for the process of discovery.

With the leading Mendelian – and anti-Mendelian – thinkers in this state of confusion it is not surprising that the implications of the determinant were entirely unrealized. When Bateson had been lecturing to the troops on Mendelism in 1917 a soldier made the comment: this is *scientific Calvinism*. And Bateson reported the idea as something strange and novel – a flash of illiterate inspiration. For fifteen years the Mendelians of Europe and America had been making experiments and, lost in a thicket of ratios, they had slipped by the first principle of Mendelism without noticing it. Indeed they had covered it up with the unconscious facile fraud of the expressions 'unit-character' and 'factor'. Only the soldier saw how it worked.

JOHANNSEN AND THE GENE

The second step in the restoration of determinism was taken quite independently of the first. We owe it to the clear vision and mathematical simplicity of the Danish botanist, Wilhelm Johannsen. His ideas were expressed in two of the most important terms in genetics, the genotype and the gene, terms which he introduced in 1906 and 1909. Let us see how he arrived at these notions.

Johannsen's experimental method was even more austere than

Mendel's. He confined himself to examining the products of self-fertilization in a plant which, like Mendel's pea, was naturally self-fertilizing. He was concerned with the effects of the environment as well as of heredity. He was concerned to show how differences in such a fluctuating property as seed weight could be determined in one case by differences in heredity, in another case by differences in environment, and in a third by both.

Johannsen took beans, from commercial samples of the French bean, *Phaseolus vulgaris*, a plant which is regularly self-fertilized. He found, of course, that each of the plants which grew from them had beans of different sizes, according to the position and number in the pod and the order of development on the plant. But plants grown from the small beans had seeds of the same *average* size as those grown from the large beans on the same plant. And they continued to do so, year after year, as he grew them for six generations. Selection therefore had no effect. The differences between beans on the same plant, or even of different plants descended from the same ancestor by self-fertilization, were not hereditary. They were environmental. They were due to something outside heredity, sometimes outside the plant, but chiefly inside the plant, body effects arising in the development of the plant. Johannsen therefore called the self-fertilized progeny of one plant a *pure line*. And the differences between pure lines, between the average seed-weights of plants of different descent (which were very great) were genetic. They might also be environmental, if the conditions of growth were different, but the conditions could of course be kept uniform by good cultivation.

Thus Johannsen was able to show the difference between the effects of heredity and environment, the internal and external controls of life, when both were acting to cause variation in the same character, a measurable character. The internal control, the heredity, of an individual plant or animal, what determined its visible character, Johannsen called the *genotype*.

The genotype then was what was handed down unchanged from generation to generation. In reaction with the environment it gave the observed or external character of the organism. This visible character fluctuated from generation to generation with the soil and the sunshine, and even from one part of the body to another, but its fluctuations had no effect on the genotype. To this visible character of an individual Johannsen gave the name of *phenotype*.

This precise way of thinking was necessary for Johannsen and it was also, as the event has shown, necessary for genetics. Johannsen noticed, as we may, the likeness between his distinction of genotype and phenotype and Galton's antithesis of Nature and Nurture, or of Stirp or Stock and Person, and likewise Weismann's antithesis of Germplasm and Soma. They are different ways of looking at the same fundamental problem. For the chromosomes are the basis of genotype as well as of the stirp and the germplasm: and the soma is undoubtedly the substance of the person and the vehicle of the phenotype. But Johannsen's way of looking at these things and the terms he used to express it, arise from a rigorous experimental method that was his own.

Having clarified the relations of heredity, or the internal condition of life, and the milieu, the environment, or the external conditions of life, Johannsen proceeded to ask himself what the various words used for the units of heredity, the 'factor', or, in the German of Correns, the '*Anlage*', really meant. He saw that they were equivocal (or *mehrdeutig*). He recognized that there was something in the gametes and in the fertilized egg by which the character of the organism was determined (*bedingt* or *mitbestimmt*) and he proposed the word *gene* for it. In introducing his new term, he used the same words that Bateson had just been using in introducing the word factor:

The word Gene [he wrote] is fully free from every hypothesis; it expresses only the ascertained fact that at least many properties of the organism are determined by special separable and therefore independent 'conditions', 'bases', or 'materials' – in short what we shall call genes – which are present in the germ cells.

1909, p. 124

Thus to both Bateson and Johannsen determinism had ceased to be a hypothesis. This was not a Weismannian conjecture. It was an ascertained fact. But the matter determining was still a hypothesis: it might be merely a 'condition'.

The fathers of genetics could not, however, determine the fate of their children. In practice, while the genotype could not fail to be abstract, the gene was bound to be concrete and material. Indeed, by a paradox, genotype owed its importance to its

abstractness, gene to its opposite quality of concreteness. Johannsen did not want the gene to be any more concrete than a factor,
or to have any more substance than the genotype. He was pushed
into using the word because, as he said later, it was such a neat
little word; so precise and such a proper component of the thing
that to Johannsen really mattered, the genotype.

In this way several neat little equations became possible.
Heredity was the presence of similar genes in parents and offspring. The genotype was the sum of all genes, while the product
of the genotype and the environment was the phenotype.

Today it seems exceedingly strange that while Johannsen was
the one early geneticist to see clearly the importance of the distinction between determined and determinant, yet he loathed,
just as much as Bateson did, the idea of allowing this distinction
its necessary material basis and locating his genes in any visible
structure such as a chromosome. For Johannsen determination
did not imply matter and he loathed the assumption of a material
basis so much that he almost seemed to be disowning the gene
itself. Having conceded one half of the philosophical principle, he
wished to resist what we regard as the inevitable other half.

The determinants in the germ cells [he wrote] must be related with
'no kind of definite material or other representation' (1909) and 'The
question of the chromosomes as the presumed bearers of hereditary
qualities seems to be an idle one' (1911).

But the name of gene carried with it all the materialistic implications, all the dynamic hypotheses and ideas, which, willy-nilly,
opened our eyes to genetics in the course of the forty years that
followed.

Cytologists inspired by Weismann had long been interested in
heredity and had been quick to recognize the correspondence
between Mendelian segregation and the separation of the paired
chromosomes at meiosis. But their amiable advances were
received with stern indifference by the Mendelians who concentrated their gaze for the most part on higher (or larger) things
than chromosomes. The determinants or the *Anlagen*, the pairing
and the crossing-over, which appeared natural to observers of
chromosomes, were put aside. And, when the chromosome
theory was finally made to work, it was only after twelve years of

reluctance that the material and particulate term 'gene', which was the natural expression of the theory, came to be adopted. The future success of the genes was predetermined by the fitness of their name: but between conception and birth there was to be a long period of gestation.

Easy ideas do not easily die. But gradually in men's unwilling minds the determinants came to be separated from the characters they determined. Gradually not only the unit character but even the less inert word, factor, become inappropriate for the most potent particle in the world.

6

The Coming of Genetics: II

IN the years following the rediscovery of Mendelism, while Bateson and Johannsen were in different ways laying the foundations of genetics in Europe, and at the same time resisting the importunities of the oncoming chromosome theory, an equally far-reaching, although quieter, development was taking place in America. It depended again on the complementary roles of two men.

Four years before the rediscovery of Mendel, what was known of the cell nucleus and of its constituent chromosomes had been critically expounded for the first time by the American cytologist, Edmund Beecher Wilson. We need to consider here only a few crucial points in Wilson's work, discussed in Muller's penetrating study from which quotations will be taken. In his book, *The Cell in Development and Inheritance*, published in 1896, Wilson brought the past into relation with the future.

Four principles were laid down by Wilson as the foundation of the chromosome theory:

First, the exact lengthwise division of the chromosomes at mitosis allows for the equal distribution to the daughter nuclei of specific and different particles arranged in a line or thread; this had been noted by Wilhelm Roux in 1883; the same chromosomes that came out of each mother nucleus went into both daughter nuclei.

Secondly, their material existence in the nucleus between mitoses, assumed although invisible, gives the genetic continuity necessary for the organs of heredity; this had been shown by Boveri in 1891: the same kind and number and arrangement of chromosomes that went into a nucleus at one mitosis always came out of it at the next mitosis.

Thirdly, the fact that the nucleus goes where things are happening shows its governing position in the work of the cell; this had been recognized by Claude Bernard in 1878.

Finally, the equality of the chromosomes of the fusing germ-cells, egg and sperm (an equality which does not apply to their cytoplasm), corresponds to the equality of male and female in heredity.

These arguments led Wilson to accept the primacy of the nucleus in the cell, and hence in heredity and development. They had long been known. But they were still widely disputed or misunderstood. For example, Weismann in his diagram of chromosomes, as we saw, showed the mixing of maternal and paternal parts. Thereby he had failed to grasp the principles of linear arrangement and differentiation of particles in the chromosomes which had been revealed by his own countryman Roux. But, of greater consequence even than this, in Wilson's account for the first time we can see that heredity and development are not involved in antithesis. The confusion of Spencer and of Weismann is dissolved. Heredity and development are equally the results of the activity of the chromosomes. It is merely that one is a long-term, the other a short-term, action.

On this basis Wilson gave his judgement on the working of heredity and development, of nucleus and cytoplasm, and no one has ever expressed the matter better:

In its physiological aspect, therefore, inheritance is the recurrence, in successive generations, of like forms of metabolism; and this is effective through the transmission from generation to generation of a specific substance or idioplasm which we have seen reason to identify with chromatin. . . . If the nucleus be the formative centre of the cell, if nutritive substances be elaborated by, or under the influence of, the nucleus while they are built into the living fabric, then the specific character of the cytoplasm is *determined* by that of the nucleus.

Wilson shows here that comprehensive interest and capacity for long-range inference which has so often been condemned as speculative among his successors in this field. His determinism is explicit. Moreover the determination involved no identity of 'unit-factor' and 'unit-character'. When these naïve notions were in their heyday among Mendelians in 1912 Wilson alone explained the position as we understand it today: ' . . . Every character is produced as a reaction of the germ considered as a whole or unit-system.'

Indeed, at this stage of our history the cell gave a much clearer picture of heredity than did animal or plant breeding.

What held matters up, in Muller's view, was the ignorance of the correspondence of chromosomes in pairs – one of each maternal, the other paternal – and of their crossing-over, when they were paired at meiosis, at points of contact. These had in fact been seen and correctly interpreted by a German cytologist in the shark's egg in 1892; but the speculation was shy, hazardous and unnoticed. However, soon after 1900, Wilson's colleagues saw in grasshoppers the pairing of chromosomes large with large, and small with small, proving a difference of kind between pairs and, at the same time, a likeness of kind, or homology, within pairs (Figure 7).

CROSSING-OVER DISCOVERED

Progress was slow in making the bond between the chromosomes and heredity. The difficulty was two-fold: to discover the right plant or animal to make the experiments with and to discover the right man to make the experiments. It certainly did not seem when Wilson's cautious colleague in Columbia University, Thomas Hunt Morgan, began to breed the fruit fly, *Drosophila ampelophila*, in 1909, that the decisive step had been taken. For it can only be supposed that Morgan's expectation was to limit, or obscure, or perhaps disprove, the Mendelian theory.

Until 1911 Morgan stood out steadfastly denying both the Mendelian laws and the chromosome theory. Then, suddenly, from a fierce opponent of the new view, who objected even to the purity of the germ cells, Morgan became its apostle. From a sceptic about chromosomes who doubted the pre-eminence of a 'single element in the cell', he became a believer.

Morgan was converted by his parthenogenetic aphides (the plant lice of Leeuwenhoeck), by his flies, and perhaps by his assistants, who bred the flies. They found that the pairs of 'factors' in *Drosophila* were not all inherited at random, as Mendel had thought, but were linked in groups. The parental combinations of certain pairs of factors (such as AB and ab) were commoner in the second generation progeny than the new combinations that might be expected (such as *Ab* and *aB*). This situation had been discovered, but not understood, by Bateson in plants. But the Drosophilists went further. They found that the linkage groups corresponded in number with the four chromosomes in the germ cells. This brings us to the second crisis in our history.

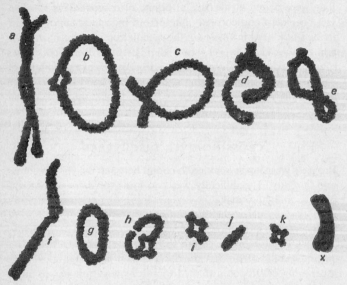

Figure 7

The pairing chromosomes at meiosis in a male grasshopper with 23 chromosomes as drawn in 1902 by W. S. Sutton, a pupil of E. B. Wilson: *a, b, c, e, g, h* probably have two chiasmata each; *d, f, i, j, k* have one chiasma; *x* is the single unpaired sex chromosome of which the female has a pair. The difference between one and two X chromosomes determines sex in the grasshopper.

It happened that two years earlier Frans-Alfons Janssens, a Jesuit professor at the University of Louvain and the third Catholic priest to play a crucial part in genetics, had made an important suggestion. This versatile man, having laboured for many years at the structure of the gills of the acephalous molluscs, had been given the task by his bishop of establishing a school of brewing at Ghent. After appropriate studies at Munich and in the Carlsberg Laboratories, he had set to work himself and he had discovered the nucleus and the fusion of nuclei in yeast, an organism which had only become an organism by virtue of the work of Pasteur fifty years earlier. Returning to Louvain, in 1897, Janssens took up the fundamental question as to what the chromosomes did when the mother cells underwent halving or reduction of chromosome number in forming sperm and eggs. He was impressed with the universal regularities of this behaviour. He was impressed with the direct bearing this problem had on the principles discovered by Mendel.

In the process of reduction, which we now call *meiosis*, there were always the two divisions of the mother cell and its nucleus which gave four daughter cells. This was a principle that applied equally to eggs and sperm and pollen mother cells, equally to men, molluscs and mosses, to flies and to flowering plants. Everyone had these 'tetrads' of four regular cells. Why were they always, as it seemed, necessary? Why not two or three?

To the Abbé Janssens (who knew the microscopic facts, and the plants and animals, better than most botanists or zoologists of his day) there must be some purpose in it:

If four spores are produced and not two, it must be that each of them has something particular about it.
1909

The four cells must always be different; different, that is, in respect of their chromosomes. How did they arise? They came from two divisions which always followed a prolonged pairing of the corresponding chromosomes from mother and father. Each drawn out into a long thread, they coiled round one another, and when they separated the chromosomes seemed to stick together at certain points. Could it be that some exchange occurred between the paired chromosomes? Might the exchange be visibly represented by this sticking?

The separated chromosomes formed cross-like figures to which Janssens gave the name of *chiasma*. At this stage the chromosomes had already split lengthwise into half-threads. Perhaps the chiasma was the result of an exchange between two of the four half-

113

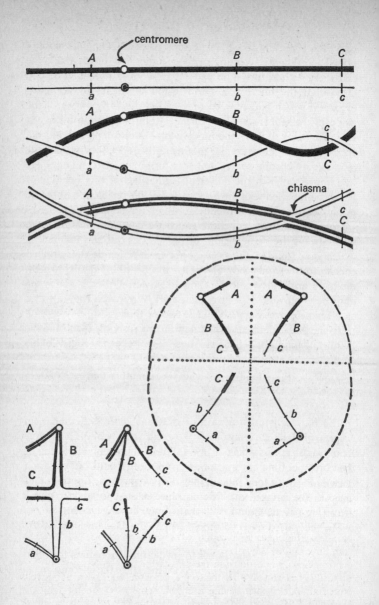

threads, one of which would go into each of the four spore or sperm cells. Each of these cells would then have a different chromosome, or at least a chromosome partly of different origin and ancestry from any in the other three cells. And every individual in every generation would have new kinds of chromosomes from recombining in different places the parts of the parental chromosomes in the germ cells from which it arose. Indeed every individual would be something new, with new chromosomes and new heredity.

Janssens' theory was of course very like Weismann's. But it was one step nearer the facts in both directions – both towards the breeding experiments and towards the chromosome observations. The recombinations were no longer inferred from a general consideration of differences among brothers and sisters but from Mendel's own experiments. The chromosome exchanges were no longer a matter of pure imagination. Both chiasmata and tetrads had been seen: they had been seen in great numbers of plants and animals.

Here then was a theory that would account for recombination between different 'allelomorphic characters' on the same chromosome, of which, Janssens realized, there was already some indication. And it would open the way for 'une plus large application cytologique de la théorie de Mendel'. Indeed it was a theory of the same scope and grandeur as Mendel's own principles. And like them it could be tested by particular experiments.

Like the evolutionists examining heredity Janssens did not much mind how he got his result. He was not at all clear about the structure of his chiasmata. He wanted, at any price, an

Figure 8

Diagram showing the consequences of two chromosomes pairing at meiosis. The chromosomes differ in respect of three genes, A/a, B/b and C/c. They coil round one another, split into halves, their halves cross over, and they separate, the point of crossing-over then appearing as a chiasma. This chiasma holds the two chromosomes together. The bottom three figures show the pair of chromosomes (i) orientated by their centromeres up and down in the axis of the cell ready to pass (ii) to opposite poles so that after the second division (iii) there are four cells with four nuclei each having a chromosome of distinct origin and character ABC, ABc, abC and abc. When the chiasma is between Aa and Bb different combinations will be formed.

exchange, and preferably an exchange between the split halves of the dividing chromosomes. A great deal of dispute and a great deal of confusion therefore arose from his statement. But when it had all been cleared away (twenty years later) it was accepted that after pairing the chromosomes are held together by exchanges of partners amongst their split halves; that these exchanges can be seen as chiasmata; that these chiasmata are the results of breakage and reunion between split chromosomes, i.e. by

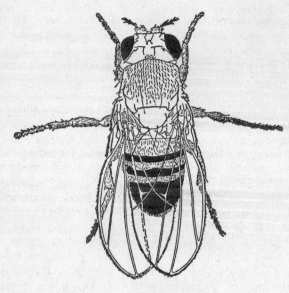

Figure 9

Drosophila: the fly. A grey male: the female is larger in comparable stocks (from Morgan, 1929, Carnegie Pub. 399). × 25.

crossing-over; and that these properties hold for meiosis and germ cell formation in all sexually reproducing plants and animals (Figure 8).

These principles are now, theoretically as well as technically, the focal point of the study of heredity. Why this is so can readily be seen. For, if there were not such exchanges and crossing-over, the whole of each chromosome would behave as a single lump in heredity. Recombination would take place, not between minute parts of chromosomes, genes or whatever we wish to call them, but only between lumps, between whole chromosomes. It is not only that the gene could not have been discovered. It could never even have existed. And instead of the exquisite machinery of adaptation that we see expressed in nature, we should have a crude lumbering steam-roller system that could not have brought evolution to the level of a bacterium – indeed, very far from it, for we now believe that bacteria also enjoy something like this process of crossing-over.

It was in September 1911 that Morgan realized how Janssens' theory explained his experimental results. This was how he halt-ingly and quite obscurely broached the subject:

> If the materials that represent these factors are contained in a linear series, then when the parental pairs (in the heterozygote) conjugate like regions will stand opposed. There is good evidence to support the view that during the strepsinema stage homologous chromosomes twist around each other, but when the chromosomes separate (split) the split is in a single plane, as maintained by Janssens. In consequence, the original materials will, for short distances, be more likely to fall on the same side of the split, while remoter regions will be as likely to fall on the same side as the last, as on the opposite side....
>
> Science, 22 September 1911

Figure 10

Drosophila: the chromosomes from mitosis in a body cell. *Left*, of a female with two x chromosomes. *Right*, of a male with x and y. The small pair are known as the fourth. × 3000, diagrammatic.

In other words the pairing chromosomes could cross-over so that two parental chromosomes of structure *ABCD* and *abcd* would give two new chromosomes in the four products of meiosis of the structure *ABcd* and *abCD*, or, if the position of the crossing-over or chiasma was different, *Abcd* and *aBCD*. Now the point of crossing-over may lie anywhere along the chromosomes between A and B or B and C or C and D. If therefore there are two factor differences between two partner chromosomes, the frequency of crossing-over should be measurable statistically like the segregation itself. It would appear as a distortion of the 9 : 3 : 3 : 1 ratio in an F_2 family.

This frequency of crossing-over should be, in some sense, a measure of the distance along the chromosome between the two pairs of factors, so that, if there are several factor differences in one pair of chromosomes, their order along the length of the chromosomes should be ascertainable. This can be done, and has now been done, in hundreds of species of plants and animals. In the original fruit-fly hundreds of factors or genes have been mapped and each chromosome appears in the map as a row of points, the loci of the separate genes.

MORGANISM

The technical importance of this discovery, the means of mapping a linear order of determinants (quite apart from the theoretical question of a relationship with chiasmata), was of course appreciated by the little group of workers – Sturtevant, Bridges and Muller – who were helping Morgan at the time : appreciated, that is, at its scientific value. But to others, like the present writer, who first heard about it ten years later (but before the European world of biology had absorbed it) the intensity of this historic moment was intensified. This was something to be appreciated above all common scientific values.

Now, fifty years later, when we coolly survey the scene we can see that the achievement was indeed above the common level of science. Suddenly, and at the same time, the living molecule of the chromosome had been shown to be the organ of heredity and had also been laid out on the dissecting table to be mapped by processes of genetic trigonometry for which the instruments had already been designed. The principle of determination now lit up the whole picture and the great schisms of the eighteenth century as well as the admitted ignorance of the nineteenth could be allowed to fade away.

For the first time the gulf which had always sundered body

from egg and likewise mind from matter could be joined by a bridge of experimental method. Separated from its prosaic description by the passage of time the final revelation of the chromosome theory begins to appear as one of the great moments in the history of human achievement.

In view of the historic importance of these connexions between Morgan's experiments and Janssens' theory of chiasmatypy it is all the more remarkable to notice how Morgan himself looked upon them. Did he recognize the focal brilliance of the situation? Not at all. The reference to Janssens just quoted is clearly intended for the smallest circle and it could not have been more hesitant or casual. He gave no indication of the time or place of Janssens' publication. His second acknowledgement seven weeks later in the same periodical referred to the journal but gave no volume. His third acknowledgement in collaboration with E. B. Wilson fifteen years later (1926) gave the volume, but gave it incorrectly and left out the page references which were given for other articles. It is as though Morgan had taken the whole thing on hearsay. In his books on the physical basis of heredity, with even less acknowledgement, Morgan embodied the determinants of Weismann, the genetic continuity of the chromosomes of Boveri, and the pregnant observations of Wilson. All was grist that came to his mill. He seemed to have thought out everything for himself from the very beginning. He had certainly forgotten how he (or was it others?) had reached his conclusion.

The failure to think out the relationship of one's own ideas to those of one's predecessors is not uncommon among discoverers. It may be due to many things. Is it mere vanity? Or is it due to a kind of fear of disturbing too deeply the foundations of one's own beliefs? Apart from his one slip in 1911 Morgan was always sceptical and conservative. He rejected Mendelism for ten years. He rejected the word gene for another twelve. And thereafter he rejected all further innovations as vain and tiresome conjecture. Genetics had reached its culmination.

Yet there is a third possible reason for Morgan's carelessness of antecedents – after 1911. We cannot expect a victorious general in hot pursuit of the defeated enemy to stop and survey the battlefield in order to record the causes of his victory for the benefit of historians. His employers expect a dispatch, but not a whole book. The scientific discoverer at the moment of his discovery is more deeply engaged. He does not always trouble to read the papers he refers to with the same care that he would use if he were merely a novice writing an academic thesis.

TABLE 2

Comparison of the results obtained by Mendel and Morgan from crossing parents which differed in two respects or characters

	Mendel 1865 Factors in Different Chromosomes	Morgan 1911 Factors in Same Chromosome			
Parental Gametes	$AB \times ab$ or $Ab \times aB$	$AB \times ab$ $Ab \times aB$		$AB \times ab$	$Ab \times aB$
F_1: Aa Bb					
Sex of F_1	☿	♀	♀	♂	♂
Gametes AB	25	40	10	50	—
of F_1 Ab	25	10	40	—	50
as % aB	25	10	40	—	50
ab	25	40	10	50	—
Crossing-over between A or a and B or b	*irrelevant*	20%	20%	*none*	*none*

Notes: (i) The proportions of gametes or germ cells produced by the F_1 are revealed by backcrossing to a double recessive individual *aabb* all of whose gametes are *ab*.

(ii) In Mendel's experiment there is no linkage between the pair of factors.

(iii) In Morgan's experiment the two factors are linked There is crossing-over in the female fly but not in the male fly where the association as existing in the parents consequently remains complete.

He is engaged, and deeply engaged, in his pursuit for years.

The consequences of the discoverer's lack of retrospection, whatever its causes, are manifold. They corrupt the manners of lesser men. They give to the history of science a factitious discontinuity. They give an excessive simplicity to the announcement of the discovery itself. And there was a simplicity in Morgan's conclusion that stood in profound opposition to the balanced, sophisticated, and historical, view of Wilson and of the European schools of biology.

The material chromosomes were not at once filled with material genes. At first these were merely factors, loci, Euclidean points, located in a straight line at distances statistically ascertained from the progenies of flies. Later they became particles but even then they were still mechanical agents not unlike their contemporary billiard-ball atoms. They moved in the cell but not as part of it, not as part of a Wilsonian system. Their work, if they had any, was purely formal and their internal changes, their mutations, likewise. The doctrine, as it grew up in Morgan's hands, had no complexity of structure and of course no philosophical implications. Like Mendelism in the hands of Bateson and Johannsen, it was free from unnecessary hypotheses; it had been stripped clean, a necessary hygienic precaution since hypothesis, at least the word, had been discredited by Weismann's mistakes. Morgan's theory therefore merely explained the facts of heredity as they would be revealed by experiments conducted, as he had conducted them, with flies in bottles.

All this was naïve, but, from Morgan's point of view, inevitably so, since the knowledge that was to give life to the gene as an organ of the cell, a determiner of development, did not then exist. The genes were as empty as Mendel's elements and Weismann's ids. In principle the union of chromosome study and experimental breeding had been consummated and proved fertile. In practice they lived in adjoining rooms in the Columbia University building in New York. Yet still the difference in point of view between those who saw the determinants and those who looked at what was determined was as decisive as it had been in the eighteenth century. Such statements as those of Wilson were still meaningless to Morgan. Between the gene and its expression lay an explanatory vacuum.

The contradiction between the particles which did everything, and yet did nothing, disturbed many. Johannsen in 1923 objected to the way Morgan jumped (even though it was a twelve-year jump) from the Mendelian difference to the conclusion of a particular gene. The differences on Johannsen's view – and it was a common view – were only, as it were, in the *skin* of heredity. There was a central impenetrable core of heredity of which the differences alone could tell us nothing. In this core differences and determinants and material particles were happily unknown. There, perhaps, the homunculus still slept an enchanted sleep.

Moreover, might not the skin differences themselves be of many kinds? This second objection was partly just. Morgan and his colleagues had made a large, partly invalid, and, as so often happens, partly unconscious, assumption. Their consideration of the nucleus and the chromosomes entirely justified the argument that heredity, or genotype, depends on chromosomes and, hence, that units of heredity or genes are connected with particles or beads, the visible 'chromomeres' which, strung together in a row, make up a chromosome. And, hence again, units of variation are probably related to units of heredity. This conclusion in turn largely came to be vindicated by the specificity of the changes of each factor or chromosome locus in *Drosophila*. These could mutate from normal to abnormal, and from abnormal back again, not only proving specificity, but also eliminating Bateson's simple idea of Presence and Absence.

The Drosophilists were inferring the existence of units of heredity from the recombination of characters in an F_2. They were also inferring them from the occurrence of sports or mutations in the body. And they were inferring them from the beaded linear structure of the chromosome. Sometimes the results of these inferences agreed and sometimes they disagreed. They had the same trouble that afflicts the physicists who probe the nature of waves and particles. There were naturally some who would argue from these troubles that the gene does not really exist, and even that the study of heredity might therefore be disregarded. As a first step, however, the Drosophilists' assumption was justified. The bibliophile may infer the existence of a man from a book that he has written. The archaeologist may also infer it from digging up his bones. If sometimes one skull has been responsible for two books, or two skulls have to share one book, this does not disprove the theory that human beings write books and that no one else writes them.

The problem, however, was very soon to be clarified. What was not known to Boveri and Wilson, and was not therefore understood by Morgan, was that chromosomes could also vary in other ways than by changes within the genes, by ways therefore no longer characteristic of each gene. There are gains and losses and inversions of whole segments, whole groups of genes.

It is as though the word *chromosome* were to be changed by breakage and rearrangement of letters to give *chromomosome*, or *chrosome*, or *chrosomome* or *chromoso*. This kind of change, going on at one level, while simple gene mutations such as make *cHromosome* or *chrouuosome*, are going on at another level, gives a more complicated basis to variation. Two chromosomes from opposite parents when they meet at meiosis have often been found to be of this relationship:

$$\begin{cases} \text{CHROMOSOME} \\ \text{CHSOmOROMe} \end{cases}$$

Two such chromosomes tie themselves in a knot when they pair. If crossing-over takes place between them, in the middle of the knot, two new chromosomes are formed which usually fail to live, thus:

$$\begin{cases} \text{CHROMmOSHC} \\ \text{EMOSOOROMe} \end{cases}$$

Or, if crossing-over does not take place, then the gene-blocks ROMOS and SOMOR will be held together as unbreakable units in heredity, as new *super-genes*.

All these conditions were soon to be demonstrated directly from the study of the chromosomes at meiosis in plants and animals and in the nucleus of the salivary glands of *Drosophila* itself as shown in Plates 1b, 2 and 3.

Genetic differences can thus be related in many different ways to the chromosomes, the ways we may call broadly intragenic, inter-genic and super-genic: they may be within the gene, between genes and above individual genes. The notion of a gene is no longer Euclidean; it is elastic, organic and evolutionary.

But it has only been by fifty years of experiment and analysis that such complications have been understood and that this abstract relationship has come to fit all the concrete details of variation. Now indeed we know that Johannsen's skin of difference goes as deep into the core as we have the machinery to cut.

Only gradually could the great antitheses between factor and character, between germplasm and soma, between genotype and phenotype, between heredity and environment, between nucleus and cytoplasm, be realized, understood and explained. All these antitheses are different. They have different sources, different uses and (as we shall see) different future developments. But they have one thing in common. They represent the difference between the determiner, self-propagating and enduring, and something elsewhere, something less enduring and perhaps not self-propagating at all – either what is determined or what is subordinate in determination.

When we regard the painful steps by which European biologists retreated in front of the notion of the determinant, fighting all the way, the same kind of battle as was fought in the seventeenth century over mechanics, and in the eighteenth century over phlogiston, and in both centuries over animalcules, we are bound to be struck by the apparently simple unquestioning enthusiasm with which Morgan and those who followed, or led, him embraced the chromosome theory. The Europeans (or at least those who had matured before Morgan came to them) were in fact shocked by this conversion; as one of them, the late Richard Goldschmidt, put it to the writer: so naïve a notion could never have arisen in Europe. Of course the notion was naïve. All new notions are naked and naïve and for that reason perhaps are readily accepted only by the innocence of youth. The history of genetics from 1910 to 1960 has been the process of clothing this naked notion with the garments of sophistication which now enable it – as we may see later – to move in philosophical society without shame or misgiving.

Bateson and Johannsen, and Morgan too, objected to the gene's being exposed, indecently exposed, where everyone could see it. Today we can all see it in photographs – not merely with visible light but with ultra-violet light, with x-ray diffraction photographs and with electron microscope photographs. This

124

sounds crude and materialistic. But the evidence arises from a multiplicity of sources and the use of a multiplicity of techniques which we need not here consider. Let us rather now turn back and take a glance at the beginnings of all these ideas.

THE CHEMICAL CODE

What gave confidence to the Drosophilists in asserting the chromosome theory, as it had done to Weismann, was their knowledge of the wonderful uniformity of character and movement that the chromosomes showed throughout plants and animals. All growth and development depended on mitosis with its regular reproduction of the chromosomes and separation of their halves. All sexual reproduction and Mendelian inheritance depended on meiosis with its regular pairing and separation of the partners. As their work proceeded from one success to another therefore the study of chromosome movement also gained a new impetus. For the chromosomes began to be seen in a double role as the mechanism of heredity and also as the product of evolution.

It was not until twenty years after Morgan had taken Janssens' chiasma hypothesis as his guide that the meaning of the chiasmata became fully clear. They then proved to mean much more than Janssens or Morgan had imagined. For it turned out that, in the ordinary form of meiosis found throughout sexually reproducing plants and animals, chiasmata were not only the result of crossing-over: they were also the means by which partner chromosomes were held together at the first division of meiosis. Where chiasmata failed to be formed the partner chromosomes just fell apart without orientation and were distributed without relation to one another.

Thus crossing-over, which is necessary in heredity for recombining the genes, proved to be necessary in reproduction for separating the chromosomes and halving their numbers. First, by a direct mechanism, it rearranges the genes within the chromosome. And then a few minutes later by another mechanism, working this time through the spindle, it rearranges the chromosomes within the complement.

The exception to this rule could moreover be made to reveal its evolutionary meaning. Recombination of genes is obviously necessary – now and then. But in an organism like a fly which passes through a sexual generation as quickly as once in ten days (and that was why Morgan had chosen it for breeding) a new combination has no chance to declare itself before it may be destroyed. The fly therefore has to reduce recombination. It does this by keeping its chromosome number low: four pairs in *Drosophila* (Figure 10). And in addition it does without crossing-over and chiasma formation in one sex, the male. But it is only in organisms with separate sexes, as well as short life cycles, that such a trick has been attempted. Crossing-over and chiasma formation remain indispensable for meiosis in one sex in all organisms. And in all long-lived organisms they remain in both sexes.

Chiasmata and crossing-over, separation and segregation had to be studied in the chromosomes if the rules of exceptional breeding were to be understood. But beyond them the great mechanical uniformity of the chromosomes at mitosis and meiosis suggested another problem. It implied something deeper, a chemical uniformity in chromosome structure. For example, at the beginning of meiosis the association of chromosome threads always seemed to be specific, particle by particle, gene by gene, in linear sequence, and always limited to pairs of particles, even when there might be three or four chromosomes of a kind in the nucleus. Further, the threads, once they were paired, always proceeded to coil round one another: they developed torsion as soon as they were attached, the torsion which later broke them and led to crossing-over. The evidence of such torsion was, moreover, present in all ordinary mitosis, for the contraction of chromosomes from long threads to short rods was always due to their assuming by internal torsion a coiled, spiral or helical structure. This was not a simple coiling like a spring, or a double coiling like the wire of an electric fire, but a coiling of three or even four superimposed orders. The coiling undid itself in every resting nucleus and started afresh at the beginning of every new mitosis. Apparently it undid itself completely, for the new coiling in the next mitosis could be in the opposite direction, left-handed could and did succeed right-handed coiling completely at random.

These discoveries, combined with the evidence that the chromosomes managed the cell and carried its heredity, made it important to discover what chemical basis the chromosomes had for all this activity and movement. In fact for nearly a hundred years the chemistry of the chromosomes and the nucleus had been under investigation quite independently and without regard to their genetic and microscopical study.

In 1872 a German chemist, Miescher, extracted from salmon sperm two fractions which he described as protein and – since sperm are almost pure nuclei – 'nucleic acid'. Later this same nucleic acid was extracted from other sources rich in nuclei such as pus and the thymus gland of mammals. This true nucleic acid became known as DNA. Another nucleic acid extracted from yeast and known as RNA was characteristic, not of the chromosomes or nuclei, but of the nucleoli and the cytoplasm outside the nucleus. Slowly the structure of these nucleic acids was unravelled, a process now nearly complete.

What is this structure? Chemical analysis split it up into units which were called nucleotides, plates of a standard composition always in the same arrangement:

| Nitrogenous Base | — | Sugar | — | Phosphate |

The sugar, to begin in the middle, is always of the same kind, a different kind in DNA and RNA. It is indeed the sugar of the DNA which makes the chromosomes recognizable when suitably stained. The bases are of four kinds which differ in size and may be usefully labelled in order of size 1, 2, 3, 4. It is these bases which make the chromosomes recognizable even in the living cell by their prodigious absorption of ultra-violet light. But in the chromosomes themselves it is the bases which are the key to genetics for it is they which make the four nucleotides different in form and action and hence make their relative arrangement of crucial importance.

It was indeed at first thought that the arrangement of the nucleotides was like that of so many crystalline structures with the uniform repetition of similar sequences. This mistake was assisted by the belief that the nucleotides were equally frequent in nucleic acid, each being a quarter of the whole bulk in each sample of each nucleus. Perhaps then they were arranged regularly 1, 2, 3, 4, 1, 2, ... and so on. But Chargaff in New York discovered that they were in fact unequal in proportions. 1 was always equal to 4 and 2 always equal to 3, but the proportion $1+4$ to $2+3$ was unequal. For example in man's chromosomes there was 30 per cent each of 1 and of 4, 20 per cent of 2 and 3. Further, this proportion was characteristic of the chromosomes of each species. The order of the nucleotides must therefore itself be characteristic of the chromosomes of each species. And the nucleotides must be in some sense paired, 1 with 4 and 2 with 3, in paired columns of DNA.

A second important chemical discovery, made independently in France and the United States, was to show that not only the quality but the quantity of DNA was characteristic of the chromosomes of each species. Each resting nucleus as it was formed at the end of mitosis had a fixed bulk of DNA in its chromosomes. And during the resting stage this bulk doubled as the chromosomes reproduced to give the double DNA and double chromosomes at the beginning of the next mitosis.

Meanwhile x-ray crystallography was revealing how the nucleotides were put together in DNA. They form potentially endless columns of units. At first they were said to be like a pile of pennies. Then in view of the spiral structure of the chromosomes it was thought they must lie like the steps of a spiral staircase. Now it is believed, following the model of Watson and Crick, that the staircase is right but it is a double staircase. That is to say that there are a pair of steps matched or fitted on opposite sides of the axis. And these pairs are the partners of chemical analysis $1+4$ or $2+3$, partners equal in numbers, unequal in size.

Thus the chemical analysis and the physical model could be reconciled on two assumptions. First the order of the units was fixed in each gene and in each chromosome like the letters in a word, or a sentence or a book. Secondly, the order of the units in a single column of a nucleotide must determine the order in its partner. Thus one column of nucleotides will act as a cast or a mould or a template for its partner column, thus:

$$1:1:3:4:1:2:4..$$
$$4:4:2:1:4:3:1..$$

If the two columns separate in the resting stage and a double column is reconstructed from each in the reproduction of the chromosome, the same double column will be reconstructed.

THE COMING OF GENETICS: II

Moreover the process by which the chromosomes uncoil in the resting stage will make this separation and reconstruction physically possible.

The immense variety of sequences in which four kinds of units can be arranged when there are many millions of them, as there are in a chromosome, seems enough to account for the variety of genetic properties which they have to determine. Great progress has indeed been made in showing how the determination takes place. One probable device is that the genes in the resting nucleus act as templates for RNA and then peel off short segments of RNA which pass into the cytoplasm. Another probable device is that three successive nucleotides of DNA or RNA may specify the character of a protein constituent, an amino-acid, which may be generated in contact with them.

Since the RNA (unlike the DNA) varies in composition in different tissues, this would indicate that the nuclear genes were delegating their work in protein production to deputy genes or cytoplasmic genes. And different genes were acting in this way at different times and in different tissues, a process of which we have evidence in the salivary gland chromosomes of the fly *Drosophila* itself (Plate 1b).

Summing up, the chemical, physical and microscopic study of the chromosomes show that they have a structure capable of combining three very different requirements. First, they can perform complex and accurate and uniform movements which ensure a uniformity in the processes of heredity throughout all organisms. Secondly, they can carry a code capable of determining the immense diversity of heredities in different organisms. And, thirdly, in different tissues, they can do different kinds of work fitted to the needs of different kinds of cells. We may therefore say that the invention of the nucleic acids, RNA and DNA, played a similar part in the evolution of life to that which the invention of speech, writing and printing did in the evolution of human culture. A chromosome complement representing the heredity of an individual is like a book. The whole individual's chromosomes are like one edition of that book. And the whole range of chromosome structure in the world is like the whole range of literature in the world might be after a corresponding period of evolution. But in addition to *informing* it is *determining*.

ATOMIC ANTECEDENTS

The fact that the scientific revolutions in mechanics, chemistry and biology came in succeeding centuries, and were spread over increasing periods of time, may be attributed to the increasing technical and theoretical sophistication necessary to solve the problems of motion, combustion and heredity. It also has to do with their relations with classical science. The achievement of Newton was brought about if not as a continuation, at least as a discontinuation, of the theories of Aristotle. The achievement of Lavoisier was also connected with the views of the Greeks, although more dimly, and into it crept the speculations of the atomists. The achievement of genetics, based on the notion of the living determinant, on the other hand, has no historical connexion with the knowledge or opinions of the ancient world. By the time of Lamarck and Herbert Spencer, Mendel and Weismann, the ancient philosophical views, which might have either inspired or obstructed them, were dead and largely forgotten. The battle was with those current theological superstitions which led Darwin to pass over man's affairs so quietly in 1859 and led Mendel (according to his biographer, Iltis) to demonstrate Mendelism in public by breeding the spiritually neutral pea, having previously picked up the clue in more private experiments with the mouse.

In consequence of this extinction of classical theory no one recognized the ancient antecedents either of Lamarck's theory of the inheritance of acquired characters or of Mendel's notion of material determinants. The nineteenth-century scientist paid no attention to the Greek materialists. But the materialism of nineteenth-century physics, and the gift of microscopic vision, brought back the theory of determinants which the scientists, and later the philosophers, had to discover again for themselves. Small bodies like pollen, sperm, and eggs, even nuclei and nucleoli, could be seen. In 1848 Hofmeister was able to figure the paired chromosomes in the living pollen mother cells of *Tradescantia*. Heredity was obviously carried by such bodies. Small bodies determined the properties of large bodies. From contemporary use of the microscope, not from any remote atomistic theories, arose unconsciously the units of Spencer, the pangenes of Darwin and the ids of Weismann.

Before writing the *Origin* Darwin had balanced in his mind the evidence for blending inheritance and some kind of non-blending. In 1857 he wrote to Huxley (as Fisher pointed out in 1930):

> I have lately been inclined to speculate, very crudely, and indistinctly, that propagation by true fertilization, will turn out to be a sort of mixture, and not true fusion, of two distinct individuals, or rather of innumerable individuals, as each parent has its parents and ancestors. I can understand on no other view the way in which crossed forms go back to so large an extent to ancestral forms.

But in the end Darwin found the idea of non-blending too 'crude and indistinct'. He could neither invent a model nor formulate a rule for it and he therefore plumped for blending inheritance. The idea of particles was bound to be favoured by the new views of the cell. The germplasm in 1892 would seem to owe something to Galton's idea of the stock or stirp. But in exchange Galton must have read Weismann's letter in *Nature*, in 1887, in which he predicted the separation and reduction of the chromosomes in germ-cell formation. We therefore find Galton expressing the most enlightened views in his *Natural Inheritance* in 1889:

> We seem to inherit, bit by bit, this element from one progenitor, that from another ... while the several bits are themselves liable to small change during the process of transmission. Inheritance may therefore be described as largely if not wholly particulate ...
>
> p. 7

Thus Galton holds the balance between Darwin and the unknown Mendel. A character that does not blend in inheritance will reappear 'undiluted' in later generations – 'giving it repeated chances of holding its own in the struggle for existence' (p.14). He prefers, however, not to plunge too far: 'Neither is it requisite to take Weismann's [*sic*] pairs into account ...' (p.193). But he has already taken them into account and foreshadowed the union that was to be achieved only forty years later:

> It is not possible that more than one half of the varieties and number of each of the parental elements, latent or personal, can on the average subsist in the offspring.
>
> p. 187

The same effects made themselves felt in de Vries in the same year:

... specific characters of organisms are composed of very distinct units ... the simple character should be considered as a non-divisible unit ... the so-called elements of the species or elementary characters one thinks of as bound to material carriers. To each character there corresponds a special form of material carrier.... [or again] The visible characters of the organism are determined by the invisible properties of the living material.

Intracellüläre Pangenesis

All these ideas were derived from the microscopic discoveries of the day. They had no connexion with a remote past. The founders of modern genetics might well ignore Aristotle. But that they should notice no analogy, and receive no guidance, from the Greek Atomists is a notable lapse. Perhaps it is the most notable of all lapses in the cultural continuity of the ancient and modern world. Here were they, arguing as to who first thought of natural selection, disputing between continuous and discontinuous variation, questioning the material nature of genetic determinants and inheritance of acquired characters. A whole century they spent in this way. Yet the only possible consistent conclusion had already been reached deductively from materialistic principles by the Greek Atomists whose particulate chemistry had already been accepted. This conclusion had been expounded with the utmost lucidity by the poet Lucretius, whose works were continually being translated and commented upon and subjected to textual exegesis by classical scholars as ignorant of their scientific meaning as the contemporary scientists. Both the literal and the literary translations have, in consequence, lost the sense of the original.

The genetic principles of the Atomists are contained in three passages of *De Rerum Natura*. The first gives the basic notion of genetics:

For, if each organism had not its own genetic particles (*genitalia corpora*), how could we with certainty assign to each its mother?

I. 167–8

This passage asserts the theory of successive determinations as opposed to its ancient alternative of direct inheritance. It contains the gist of all our argument. The *genitalia corpora* of Lucretius are better than the physiological units of Spencer although not quite so good as the genes of Morgan. They are about on a level with the ids of Weismann.

The second passage explains the recombination of genetic particles:

It can happen that children resemble their grandparents and even repeat the characters of more distant progenitors for this reason that parents often have concealed in their bodies many primordia, mixed in different ways, which they derive from the stock, and hand down from generation to generation.

IV. 1218–1222

Here Lucretius infers the recombination of determinants in a way also inferred by Darwin in 1857, and by Spencer in 1863, and demonstrated by Mendel in 1865.

The third passage introduces a materialistic theory of evolution:

For nothing is born in the body in order that we may use it but rather, having been born, it begets a use.

IV. 834–5

The tongue, he adds, existed before speech. In this last passage Lucretius diverges from Spencer, and the later Darwin, in asserting that new characters arise not in response to use but at random with respect to use. They merely acquire a use later. Here we have the repudiation of the inheritance of acquired characters (a popular myth which is otherwise ignored by Lucretius). We have also a clear statement of the idea that adaptations arise before the circumstances to which they are adapted – the modern notion of pre-adaptation, to which we shall return later. And finally we have the insinuation of the idea of natural selection. Lucretius avoids the error, into which Spencer and Darwin fell, of accepting the effects of use and disuse and inventing those pangenes which until Weismann had disposed of them, shelved the serious consideration of heredity. Lucretius therefore brings us right up to the twentieth century. Before the year 1900, we may say, almost all that was believed of the principles of heredity that was not in Lucretius was wrong. Except of course by Mendel.

What was the secret of this extraordinary penetration? It was no accident. The Greek Atomists, whose views Lucretius reported in his splendid verse, shaking off purpose and providence, humours and essences, and the metaphysics which we moderns shook off only with the help of the microscope, cleaving to the hard unpalatable doctrine of determinism and to the evidence of the senses, were compelled to reach the conclusions that they did reach. They had to use matter as the basis for prediction and they had to use particles as a basis for matter. To heredity itself, although impenetrable in its detailed character, they had to give a deterministic, material and particulate basis. And only the technical, the experimental, and the mathematical, resources of the twentieth century could establish this basis in the face of the popularly more plausible alternatives. The failure of these alternatives, mystical, superstitious, and especially teleological, in the last half century opened the way at last for the principles of matter and determinism in biology. The cries and groans of the early Mendelians and anti-Mendelians were the birth pangs of the new way of thinking.

7

The Origin and Breakdown of Life

SPONTANEOUS GENERATION

So far we have been pursuing the causes of heredity, the most fundamental problem of life. But behind heredity, and nearly as deep, there are other questions which it was beyond the wit of man, almost until our own times, to separate from it. These are the questions of how life began and how to tell its chief forms of activity – heredity, development and disease – one from the other. These are questions indeed of which the expert biologist – let alone the generally educated man of today – is often only dimly aware, questions to which he has certainly not dreamt there could be an answer.

The ancients believed, and the jarring sects of philosophers agreed on the point, that life could arise from matter which had no life. Anything warm and wet (or cool and dry as the case might be) would breed new life where none had been before. Life was not, as I hope it now is to the reader, the property whereby individual bodies propagate themselves; it was a capacity for movement, a capacity which was imperfectly developed in vegetable forms. In our older English the distinction was between the quick and the dead. For Aristotle the semen imparted life to the womb, quickening mere matter very much as we imagine an electric shock may cause a movement in dust. Thus, from time to time, frogs might rain down from heaven and, as a matter of course, barnacles would grow on the rotten wood of ships. Three hundred years ago (in 1651) the inquiring mind of William Harvey, who discovered the circulation of the blood, was content to accept the opinions of Aristotle on such a spontaneous generation of life.

A belief in the origin of life from lifeless matter was first assailed by an experiment carried out in Italy in the seventeenth century. A certain Francesco Redi, a physician, had been reading of the death of Patroclus in the *Iliad*. He noticed that Achilles was afraid of leaving his friend's body for fear that flies would come and foul the wounds. Redi (so Guyénot tells us) wondered whether Homer did not understand the matter better than the people of his own day. He resolved to test the idea. He took a snake, some sea fish, some eels from the River Arno, and a slice of veal and put them in four jars, tying up each jar like a jam pot with paper. Four other jars with corresponding specimens he left open. This is what we call a *control* for the experiment. He left the jars for a few days. Then he says:

> The fish and the meat of this second series were filled with worms. On the other hand, in the sealed flasks, I saw not a single worm, even after several months. . . .

And if some sceptical souls objected that the paper kept out the air our experimenter replaced the paper with fine muslin which had the same result. Thus 'worms' do not arise from meat alone. They arise from the eggs that flies lay in the meat. That was what Redi concluded in 1668.

But in biology all things must be proved several times. Hardly had Redi cleared up the problem of worms than a new discovery muddied the water of belief once more. The energetic Leeuwenhoeck, using his simple microscope, with a magnification of perhaps 300 or 400, to look at all things, noble and base, having examined his blood and found little red bodies floating in it, the corpuscles, turned his attention to some putrid rain water. This was in 1675. He found in it, what anyone who enjoys the use of such an instrument may see today, those delightful animalcules which rolled and tumbled and whipped and spun and scurried their way across his lenses' vision. He had discovered the PROTOZOA, little creatures of unimagined simplicity and smallness, some of them little larger indeed than the animalcules in the semen which he was to discover later. A few years later indeed he found even smaller things than the spermatozoa, in size a millionth of the dot on our letter *i*, which must have been bacteria: as many in his mouth, he correctly suggested, as there were men in the United Provinces. Where did they come from?

Buffon, the celebrated French naturalist, nearly a hundred years later offered an explanation. Redi's conclusions might be true of grubs. But the little germs of Leeuwenhoeck must arise spontaneously. Everywhere, Buffon supposed, organic molecules float in the air, a kind of 'universal seed'. These, by absorbing one another, grow to form animalcules and sperm. They stamp one another with an 'interior mould', a template, as they grow to form larger creatures and thus come to give a specific character to the individual and his different tissues. If Buffon had admitted that the organic molecules, the universal seed, and the interior mould, were all aspects of what we call the gene, and were derived from pre-existing genes, his description would be close to our own idea. As it was, his ingenuity drew ridicule upon him. But the theory of the spontaneous origin of life was still very much alive.

The second attack on the problem of where microbes came from was also made in Italy. A hundred years after Redi (in 1765) Spallanzani repeated Redi's experiment. But he used broth instead of dry meat; and he had a microscope to help him to see the new microbes. Spallanzani found that after boiling the broth for an hour no microbes, no animalcules, no life whatever, appeared in his broth. If he boiled it for only half a minute already the large animalcules were killed – the protozoa. Only if he boiled it longer were the small ones, what we call the bacteria, destroyed.

So, Spallanzani concluded, all these animalcules themselves arise, like large animals and plants, from eggs – for he was an ovist – and he called the eggs *germs* as we do today.

INFECTION AND DISEASE

The question of the spontaneous origin of life was bound to be tied up in the end with another and even more practical question: how far is disease due to the interference of one living organism with another? Are such small creatures as, for example, those seen by Leeuwenhoeck under the microscope responsible for disease, and more especially for carrying disease from one victim to another?

Every kind of opinion has been expressed at one time or another on this question. From Pepys (5 May, 1669) we hear Lord Brouncker complained that 'his new lodgings have *infected* him' with gout, 'he never having had any symptoms of it till now'. Today we may still hear the opposite view that lice growing on the head are a sign, not of infection from some other person's head, but merely of the illness or pregnancy of the afflicted host. Again, when Shakespeare refers to 'a mildewed ear blasting his wholesome brother' he clearly sees the principle of infection. Yet when the famous botanist, Professor Lindley, 300 years later was confronted with the potato blight which brought famine to Ireland in 1846 he was prepared to suppose that the mildew was the consequence, and not the cause, of the disease. He continued to believe that the diseases of plants were plainly and directly hereditary. And Darwin felt compelled to accept his view although other botanists, recognizing the constant form of the mildew under the microscope, knew better. But how much more difficult was it to know the cause of consumption or phthisis (to use the nineteenth-century names for tuberculosis) where no microbe could be seen! Naturally consumption was deemed to be hereditary, a genetically determined decline of the human body from which some families suffered more than others.

The introduction of the great pox by Columbus in 1493 (a gift to be shortly repaid with the small pox, measles, tuberculosis and perhaps typhus) provided the Old World with painful evidence of the sequence of events in the transmission of a contagious disease. It was therefore natural that the Pope's physician, Girolamo Fracastoro, who in 1530 introduced the name Syphilis for this disease as the title of a poem in three volumes, should also first consider the means by which infection may be carried. He distinguished between direct contact, indirect contact, and transmission by the air to a distance. And he also made it clear that what was carried was, in his opinion, a self-multiplying particle, a living germ.

It has often been remarked how great discoveries are made more than once at the same time. It is even more often to be remarked that they are made more than once at widely different times. The time when discoveries are made is sometimes inevitable. The time when they are first capable of being noticed and believed is always inevitable. The notion of living infection had to be discovered again and again before it was believed. Against it stood the growing authority of chemistry. When Boyle pointed out the relation between the changes undergone in fermentation and in disease it was natural for him to think of the analogy more in terms of established chemistry than of new-fangled animalcules. And, as

Dubos has pointed out, the possibility that an animalcule can lay low a huge animal, invading, transforming and destroying its tissues was bound to seem fantastic to a mechanically minded man. Here was the same paradox that we find in the work of the chromosomes whose minute particles in the egg come to order and govern the whole empire of the body.

Something more than conjecture was needed to enforce such a paradox on men's minds. The evidence lay scattered about for centuries waiting for an apt inquirer to pick it up. Two great questions remained in doubt as to diseases – whether of plants, animals or man. First, how far were diseases not hereditary but infectious? Secondly, how far were infectious diseases caused by the passage of living creatures such as the microbes that Leeuwen-hoeck had seen under the microscope, or the mildews, or rusts, or smuts, that could be seen on plants with the naked eye?

It is hard for us now to understand how doubtful these questions seemed only a hundred years ago. That gout might be infectious while 'consumption' might be merely hereditary, merely an internally determined physiological breakdown like the sleepiness of a pear, seems upside down. That the potato mildew might be the consequence of the potato's purely internal or chemical sickness, that anthrax bacilli in the blood might be the consequence of death by anthrax, that dead yeast might be the purely chemical cause of fermentation, all these things seem also upside down, much in the same way as the notion that differences between people are due merely to differences in their environment.

The principles of infection and the causes of diseases were better understood in plants than in animals a century ago. Indeed so they still remain today. The boundaries of specialization were, and still are, difficult to surmount. Why should medical investigators concern themselves with the troubles of potatoes or tomatoes, with the physiological disturbances of the vegetable world?

Two things made it possible to put these events in the right order, the order of cause and effect, as they affected both plants and animals. The first was the microscope, which made it possible to know one microbe from another. And the second was Pasteur using the microscope and making experiments with the things he saw through it.

LOUIS PASTEUR

Pasteur, like Darwin, was impelled through fifty years of active inquiry by an unfailing appetite for discovery. But the contrast between the affluent but dyspeptic English country gentleman and vigorous French peasant–artisan was as deep as it could be in every other respect. While Darwin's observations were those of the forms of plants and animals as he saw them and of the experiments that nature had performed with them, Pasteur was concerned with designing and carrying out his own experiments. And since his gifts for experimenting were altogether beyond precedent, his experiments became the focus of the world's interest in his work. While Darwin's work had a central idea and culminated in a single synthesis, Pasteur's work was to appear as a series, a connected series, of analyses. While Darwin had reached his conclusions from the maximum evidence that patience could collect, Pasteur reached them – with no less patience in the end – from the minimum evidence, indeed from what his critics always regarded as insufficient evidence. And while Darwin was liable to be loose in argument, hesitant in conclusion and sceptical in belief, Pasteur was apt to be strict, dogmatic and even fanatical. Darwin, like Mendel, was pained when people disagreed with him; Pasteur, like Huxley, was pleasurably stimulated by it. To the outside world, therefore, Pasteur seemed to be, as Dubos has put it, Darwin and Huxley rolled into one.

It was in 1848 that Pasteur found that yeast and also the common bread mould, *Penicillium*, would break down the artificial or synthetic ammonium tartrate, an optically inactive substance, leaving a residue, chemically unchanged except that it proved to be optically active. What did this mean? Evidently the artificial inactive salt consisted of a mixture of two oppositely active components, otherwise indistinguishable, one turning the plane of vibration of polarized light to the right (and this was what the yeast or the mould consumed), the other (which was untouched) turning light to the left.

From this first conclusion Pasteur argued that, in the chemical laboratory, we were making, without selection or discrimination, a mixture with equal numbers of left and right molecules. But living things, micro-organisms like yeast, were able to discriminate, or were bound to discriminate. They were bound to build up or break down molecules of only one type, rotating light either to left or to right. If this were true, organic substances found to be optically active in solution would always be the result of the action of living organisms, as a rule of micro-organisms. Fermentations, chemical changes such as the leavening of bread, the brewing and the souring of the beer and wine, and the souring of milk, might well all be the result of the intervention of living organisms.

This was a bold conclusion for a young chemist to reach, one, moreover, who had recently been classified as *médiocre* in his *baccalauréat* examination. People had always believed that the 'working' of ferments in organic materials was inherent in the malt, or the grape-juice, or the dough, under the right conditions. They did not look upon yeast as a living organism: it seemed to be purely inorganic. Old cookery books indeed tell the housewife how, with a concoction of hops, flour, potatoes, salt and brown sugar, she can *make* yeast.

There was also a chemical argument. Lavoisier had found how one molecule of sugar would make two molecules of alcohol and two of carbon dioxide:

$$C_6H_{12}O_6 = 2C_2H_5OH + 2CO_2$$

What could be simpler! Naturally, with their newly discovered power of explanation, chemists were not easily persuaded to admit that microbes were necessary to account for the chemical transformations which they understood quite well without any such help. The leaders of chemical thought, Berzelius and Liebig, consequently rejected the idea with indignation. If yeast was a living thing, composed, as Leeuwenhoeck had thought, of globules; and if it was capable, as some botanists pretended, of propagating itself by budding; and if its chemical activity was necessary for fermentation, it could surely be the dead yeast that did the work, just as a chemical catalyst facilitated any purely inorganic reaction without being changed itself.

To answer these objections Pasteur had to show that when the yeast was killed by heat it did not work. He had to show that its spores floated in the air, like Buffon's universal seed; and that like Spallanzani's germs they could be kept out to prevent, or let in to ensure, the fermentation of malt. He had to show that yeast could live in different ways, either breathing and using oxygen with an abundance of air, or obtaining its energy by breaking down sugar when choked by a shortage of air.

All this Pasteur was able to do. Now the experiments of former times could be repeated but repeated with greater refinements of technique and of theory, especially chemical theory. Now, heating could be carried out to more precise temperatures, air and fluids could be filtered. An arsenal of chemical reagents and of elaborate glassware was now at the disposal of the ingenious operator. And, above all, more could be seen by the microscope.

Step by step the extent of Pasteur's generalizations about the activities of microbes was widened. From beer he passed to milk; from yeast, which is a simple fungus, he passed to bacteria; and from fermentation he passed to disease and putrefaction. This widening scope seemed necessary and obvious to some, unnecessary and indeed irregular to others.

Were the particular kinds of bacteria found in animals that had died of particular diseases the cause or the consequence of the disease? The same question had been asked of the potato blight and answered. But for animal diseases it had to be asked again. Pasteur was able to grow anthrax bacilli from a drop of blood in sterile urine as a source of food. Having multiplied them in this way he could pass the bacilli to new cultures again and again. At the end they remained capable of infection. What did the damage could not be the blood, for the blood certainly could not multiply. It must be the bacilli, which could be seen to multiply under the microscope. The evidence of the Scottish surgeon Lister that cleanliness in surgical operations reduced the chances of death from 90 or 80 to 30 or 20 per cent gained support for the view that germs were responsible for the damage. As such experience accumulated, year after year more surgeons learnt to wash their hands and provided an argument as convincing to the public as Pasteur's experiments were to the scientist.

In all Pasteur's work the business had been to prove that what had been thought to be new and spontaneous was indeed permanently living. The old problem of spontaneous generation had therefore been approached, as it were, from behind. Now it happened that, at the very same time that the germ theory was coming into view, the idea of spontaneous generation was being revived by a new impulse. The theory of evolution was beginning to dominate the discussion of life. And evolution implied that life had at some time arisen from the non-living. Might germs not still be arising anew? The ancient myth became confused with the new science. It was perhaps a pardonable error. But it gave the creationists their chance. Compelled to retreat on the issue of man's descent from the ape, they might throw back the charge of superstition at the evolutionists on the issue of spontaneous generation. With a supply of such fuel it is no wonder that the embers of the old controversy burst into flame again.

Pasteur's experience was bound to involve him in this dispute. He was able to show that an infusion made from yeast, sterilized by boiling, remained sterile if protected in a swan-neck flask from further infection. By the official decision of the French Academy in 1862, his demonstration was taken to disprove the possibility of spontaneous generation. Yet in the event the decision proved unfortunate – as final decisions on scientific matters must. The possibilities of survival of micro-organisms could not be defined by any one experiment. When hay-tea was used instead of yeast-tea, the infecting organisms demanded a temperature of 120°C, not 110°C, to destroy them. When infected urine was used, its acidity made boiling fatal to the bacteria; but the addition of alkali to the point of neutrality made it possible for their spores to germinate. Thus it seemed that the alkali brought life to the fluid. All these things depending on the properties of bacteria, with their immense range of living forms, still had to be discovered.

The exclusion of the possibility of spontaneously creating new life can, as we shall see later, only be complete when we know enough about life to be in a position to create it! In principle, of course, and for the needs of the time, Pasteur was right. And in doing these things he did more than vanquish the contemporary theory of the spontaneous generation of life for the third time. He also, and incidentally, laid the foundations of the study of bacteria, and of the modern theory, the germ theory, of infectious disease.

His ideas led to the standard practice of cleanliness, not so much in the home, where it was known already, as in the hospital, where it was less well known. They led to the present-day industries connected with the pasteurization, and in general the preservation, of food. And they led to the understanding of the teeming and fruitful life of the soil.

THE HEREDITY AND EVOLUTION OF MICROBES

The immense effects of Pasteur's discoveries in solving practical problems that were the centre of interest at the time, and in changing the social behaviour of civilized man, have distracted attention from their bearing on the even more fundamental problems that arose later. For Pasteur and his successors showed not only the absence of a spontaneous generation of microbes but also a *specificity* in their generation far exceeding anything that had previously been believed. The properties of reproduction and heredity which the ancients, and not only the ancients but our own grandfathers, had restricted to large plants and animals were now extended to invisible or scarcely visible particles. These microbes were responsible for chemical actions of such simplicity as to be representable in the formulae of molecules known at that time. They were smaller than the animalcules or spermatazoa responsible for the heredity of large animals. Yet they must have a heredity of their own. The study of micro-organisms and their chemistry was to be the third leg in the tripod of genetics.

The beginnings of this development are to be found in the work of Pasteur himself. They were of two kinds. In the first place, with chicken cholera, Pasteur first discovered genetic differences in the susceptibility of the victim : some chickens resisted the disease but continued to carry it and pass it to others, which then died of it. In the second place, also with chicken cholera, he first found a genetic change in the microbe itself. Bottle cultures of chicken cholera could lose their ability to produce disease. They became what was called 'attenuated'. They could remain indefinitely in this changed or mutated form. Later, indeed, it was found that particular treatments would attenuate the strength, or change the specificity, in many species of microbe. They would thus produce mild forms of disease which would protect the animals against a later severe attack by the unaltered microbe. They could therefore be used to inoculate animals, including human beings, against the natural and dangerous infections.

The immediate practical importance of the attenuation and inoculation which Pasteur used for the prevention of anthrax in cattle, and later hydrophobia in man, again distracted attention from their profound genetic meaning. It was easy to assume, and it was generally assumed, that the attenuation was a direct effect—just indeed as fermentation had been supposed to be. We now know, however, from the breeding of bacteria on nutrient materials in bottles that they are frequently changing their genetic character, their capacity to make use of this food or that. We also know that, if their food is changed, new types arise which can make use of the new food better, and they will therefore survive and multiply. Indeed they will replace the original forms. The change is not a direct one. It is due to natural selection, operating exactly as Darwin imagined, but in a microcosm. Two generations had passed, however, before it was proved that genetic change followed by natural selection was the basis of the methods which Pasteur and his successors had used to modify and control micro-organisms.

Genetic variation and natural selection are equally important among the victims of infection. First in crop plants, then in domesticated animals, and lastly even in bacteria, it has been possible to show that every kind of victim varies in its susceptibility, resistance, or immunity, to particular agents of infection. The same principle applies also to agents of destruction, to the poison and drugs which are used for killing pests and for curing their hosts. The proof depends, as J. W. Gowen of Iowa has shown, on rigorous breeding experiments and the use of moderate infections and treatments calculated to reveal genetic differences and not to overwhelm them.

Genetic resistance to disease works, of course, in a more complex way in animals than in plants. In both, crude structure, metabolism, and specific cell-constituents come into play. But in animals the development of immunity during recovery from infection or after inoculation is itself subject to genetic control and hence to genetic variation. This variation may be due to specific proteins related to a specific infection and often generated in youth by the thymus gland. It may also be due to more general cell-properties, such as complement or leucocyte density in the blood, which are likely to affect in the same way many different types of infection.

The evidence as a whole leads to a general law, the most important of all laws in applied genetics:

1. Every species of victim varies genetically in susceptibility to every species of enemy or parasite or infective agent, and

2. Every species of parasite or infective agent varies genetically in its power of attacking every species of victim or potential victim.

Whenever we consider disease therefore, natural selection is of the first importance. And whenever we consider natural selection disease is of the first importance.

In man at first sight the evidence of these things is less clear. The inheritance of disease resistance is concealed by the heterogeneity of his populations. It is also concealed by the uncertainty of infection, itself enhanced by the immunity that infection often gives against a second attack. But when we compare the resistance of Europeans, West Africans and Fuegians to a variety of diseases like yellow fever, tuberculosis and measles, the racial differences, and hence the genetic character of resistance and susceptibility, become manifest. What we know of resistance and of its components, such as hormone production, in all other animals and in plants, and what we know of the individual nature of genetic character, especially as we shall see from twin studies in man, all these things combine to show that resistance to all diseases is individual and genetic in man as elsewhere. And, when medical authorities tell us that a disease is 'highly infectious', what they mean to say is that an unusually large proportion, perhaps ten or twenty per cent, of human beings in their own populations are genetically susceptible to the attacking agent.

Thus we have moved two steps. Tuberculosis is not hereditary. It is caused by a bacillus which was first seen in 1882. But susceptibility to this microbe varies among individuals and races of men; it varies subject to both heredity and environment. For example, Africans are more susceptible than Europeans when living in towns. And Africans living in Europe are more susceptible than Africans living in Africa. Further, the capacity of the bacillus to attack Europeans and Africans likewise varies subject to heredity and perhaps also to environment.

Infectious disease therefore works by a lock-and-key mechanism. It is a mechanism in which both the lock and the key are continually changing, continually evolving. The important steps in its evolution are represented by the epidemics which result from mutations, migrations, hybridizations, and so on: epidemics which so largely determine the course of history for plants, for animals, and for man.

THE EVOLUTION OF DISEASE

The evolution of diseases is rapid in terms of the lives of species of higher organisms. It follows many different patterns. It varies according to the type of microbe, the molecular particle, the larger bacterium or the very large and less rapidly multiplying protozoan. For smaller microbes can mutate more frequently and adapt themselves to altered conditions more rapidly than larger ones. It varies also according to the microbe's dependence on one host like measles or cholera, two like malaria, or three or more like plague or typhus. And it varies, of course, according to the varying densities and opportunities of infection of the possible victim.

Take what is genetically the simplest kind of case, that of a protozoan with only one host whose date of introduction to a large population is exactly known. Syphilis burst upon the European stage suddenly in February 1495 when the French Army entered Naples. It was believed by some contemporary moralists that the disease had been acquired through intercourse of a man with a mare, a monkey, or even an Egyptian mummy. Better informed observers, however, found evidence that it had been brought back from America by Columbus two years earlier: an explanation that we can hardly doubt.

Syphilis at once showed a virulence that marked it out from anything known before, so far as we can discover, either in Europe or America. This is an effect now well recognized when a disease is introduced to a previously uninfected population whether of plants, animals or men. We attribute it to the development of a genetic resistance in the old population which the new population can acquire only by selective survival and selective breeding. We should expect therefore that the virulence of syphilis would gradually decline. Such a decline was in fact noted by Fracastoro in 1546, fifty years after its original appearance. Not only a decline but a radical and progressive change of symptoms indicated that the disease was undergoing evolution.

This evolution of syphilis reveals the adaptive change not only of the victim but also of the parasite itself in relation to its victim. The parasite was becoming less dangerous because it paid it to do so. Syphilis depends on the activity of its victims. Syphilis microbes which kill their victims (unlike anthrax microbes) are in effect committing suicide. Any genetic changes in the parasite which favoured its multiplication without killing its carrier would therefore be advantageously propagated.

All epidemics share the basic genetic character of the syphilis epidemic of 1495. They depend on genetic adaptations of populations of victims and populations of microbes whose dynamics in turn depend on the modes of propagation and mutation on both sides.

The recent history of the rabbit tumour virus, causing what we call myxomatosis, explains the evolution of infectious diseases in a diagrammatic way. This virus causes mild tumours in wild Brazilian rabbits. It was brought into a European rabbit colony in Montevideo in 1896, producing an outbreak of the fatal tumours which are now so well known. The virus was not successfully introduced into wild rabbits until 1950 in Australia, 1952 in France and 1953 in Britain. It rapidly spread in each country, destroying in each season about ninety per cent of the population attacked. The means of infection was not direct contact but by insect 'vectors' carrying the virus from one animal to another, chiefly mosquitoes in Australia and the specific rabbit flea in Europe.

The destruction of the rabbit continued in each country at this fearful rate, season after season, for ten years. But still the rabbit population persisted. By this time the tremendous pressure of natural selection by the disease had worked an evolutionary effect. The rabbit was more resistant to the disease. The virus was less virulent. And even the flea, as Rothschild and others have shown, was beginning to be less effective as a carrier.

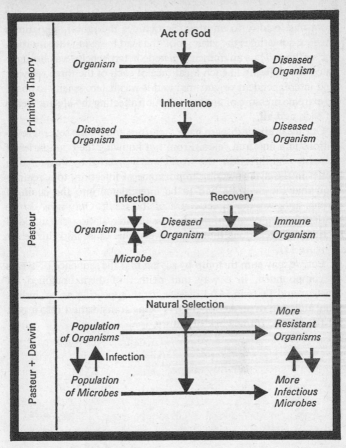

Figure 11

Three stages in the development of the theory of infectious disease.
Each theory contains a part of the truth. The middle stage dominates
the current practice of medicine. The bottom theory dominates the
long-term evolution of men and microbes.

We can however speak more precisely than this. Some rab-
bit stocks had changed in their capacity of developing immunity.
Other rabbit stocks, at least in England, had changed their temper.
They had become less timid and less fully bound to their burrows

where their fleas are passed on. And the strains of virus varied from one locality to another. Sometimes the rabbit, sometimes the flea, sometimes the virus, took the lead in saving the situation for all three. Thus an immense genetic heterogeneity was brought into view differing in each local race of each of the three relevant and interdependent organisms; and it was heterogeneity exposed to extreme pressure of natural selection affecting the life and death of each and all.

Our ideas about disease have therefore undergone several revolutions in a hundred years. From not knowing the boundaries of heredity and infection, the world was converted by Pasteur to a belief in the overpowering importance of infection, to a realization that the microbe had to be intercalated into the chain of events and was the direct cause of the result. Only now do we realize the complexity of this process of intercalation, the world of actions and reactions that lies between this cause and this result (Figure 11).

But we may sum them up by saying that the sequence of events is compounded, in a way that neither of them imagined, of Pasteur and Darwin. And disease, from appearing as an individual affliction or an Act of God, is being transformed into a part of the genetic framework of nature.

8

The Genetic Underworld

PASTEUR'S conclusions about yeast coincided with the first observations of chromosomes in 1848. Thirty years later Koch first proved a particular bacillus to be responsible for a disease, the disease of anthrax, and he did so within a year of the first expression of the chromosome theory of heredity. These coincidences were by no means accidental. To understand minute life required magnifications much higher than those used by Leeuwenhoeck to discover it. The understanding came with an improvement of the microscope, which multiplied magnifying powers effectively several times, chiefly by removing the distortions and colour defects of the earlier lenses, in half a century. The achromatic objective lens of Chevalier in 1825, and the oil-immersion lens of Dolland in 1844 were followed by the Abbe condenser in 1870 and the Zeiss apochromatic lens in 1880.

Like the first invention of microscopes these new lenses opened another new world to our view. It was a world as much enlarged beyond what had been known before as Leeuwenhoeck's world had been. But it needed more elaborate equipment and preparation to make it reveal all its secrets. Stains, beginning with carmine in 1858, came to be used to distinguish one fine structure from another. In 1871 they were first applied to bacteria. And a few years later they revealed the method of lengthwise division of chromosomes. At the same time, therefore, that the numbers of chromosomes were first being counted in cells, the different shapes and sizes of different bacteria, and even of the same bacteria at different times, were also being recorded, and the names of bacilli and streptococci were first being spoken.

The improvements of technique and the widening of vision have culminated in the invention of the electron microscope. This last step brought to light – or at least within reach of photography – yet a third layer of the living world, where magnifications were

151

increased yet another hundredfold and the size of objects that might be seen was correspondingly minutified. This was a world no less instructive, no less astonishing, than the others, the world of the protein molecule. By its size, by the order of its discovery, and in some respects by the part it has to play, we are bound to look upon it as the underworld of genetics.

VIRUSES AND PROTEINS

Early in the study of bacteria it was found that they would grow on plates of a food-jelly, a mixture of gelatine and meat broth. It was also found that cotton wool could be used to keep out air-borne germs and unglazed porcelain filters to separate water-borne germs from the fluids they grew in. Any particle over 0·2 micron (100,000th of an inch) in diameter would be caught by a particular grade of filter. As a consequence of using such filters it was found that an 'infective principle' or 'virus' would some-times pass through. And since, by an unkind chance, this size was just at the limit of discrimination with the microscopes of that time using visible light, these same infective and usually unwholesome or poisonous principles came to be known either as 'filterable' or 'ultra-visible' viruses.

The importance and character of the viruses as distinct from bacteria could only be defined when the bacteria themselves were well understood. What we now know as viruses were often dis-cussed at an earlier time and, when Pasteur separated the active agent or principle of rabies from the fluid in the spine of a mad dog, he considered that some particle was to be held responsible, a particle distinguished from other microbes merely by being smaller and therefore invisible.

Later, when the distinction first came to be made confidently and explicitly, it was made in a plant, ten years after the anthrax bacillus, in 1892. The infection caused blotching of the tobacco leaf and was due to what is now called 'tobacco mosaic' virus. The second virus to be recognized was the agent of foot-and-mouth disease of cattle. For the third or fourth time plants and animals nearly ran a dead heat in one of the great discoveries of genetic biology.

These viruses proved to differ from bacteria not only in the double consequences of their smaller size but also in their inability to propagate themselves from dead nutrient material. They needed a living victim. They needed living cells or something very near to living cells, like white of egg, to grow on. Nevertheless, at first, some – like Ivanovsky who discovered the tobacco mosaic – thought of the viruses as small bacteria. Others favoured an abstract principle, something immaterial and not specific; they would speak of the 'virus', not the 'viruses', of different diseases. The traces of the ancient conflict between particles and principles was still to be seen. Now the climate of thought had changed and principles were at a disadvantage. Even so, the solution of the problem of the nature of plant viruses, when it came, came as a shock in the most sophisticated circles.

It was in 1935 that Stanley in New York, working with the sap of tobacco plants, chemically separated mosaic virus in a nearly pure and crystalline form. From this extract the plants could be reinfected. They could be reinfected after it had been redissolved and recrystallized ten times – always with the same mosaic disease. Later these crystals were shown to be made up, like the genes in the chromosomes, of protein combined with nucleic acid. The nucleic acid was not the DNA of genes and chromosomes but the RNA such as the nucleus produces and sends out into the cell when it is growing.

Later too the crystals of this and other viruses were photographed with the electron microscope to show the regular arrangement of their constituent molecules. And in due course they were photographed even in the sap of the plants that bore them. They proved to be particles of a mere 100 atoms or so across.

The crystalline structure of certain viruses, implying a rigid and uniform pattern of atoms, raised the formidable question as to whether matter in such a mechanically simple form was to be regarded as living. Confronted with this question the long-established ideas of life broke down, just as the long-established ideas of heredity broke down when confronted with the principles of Mendelism, and, as we shall see later, will break down again. We can, however, give a clear answer to the question by dividing up our ideas of life according to the work they do. Genetically, we have to take the long and general view: we have to say that crystalline viruses in general are living because they retain the power of reproducing themselves. Physiologically, we have to take the short and particular view: we have to say that any particular crystalline virus is not living because it is not capable of any living activity without the help of some other and more complex form of life – a chance which may or may not come its way.

A far more important question, however, than this quibble arises from the crystallization of viruses. It is a question the answer to which does not depend merely on the breaking down of ideas. In these viruses we have, as we presumably have also in the genes of the chromosomes, specific, chemically pure, and certainly predictable, determinants of living processes. The situation was envisaged already in 1920 by Muller when he suggested that viruses were naked genes. Both viruses and the genes of the chromosome are genetic particles. Both multiply. Both breed true and work true when introduced into the type of environment that suits them. When introduced into a different kind of environment viruses change their genetic character, as Pasteur found when he was trying to make a weak strain of rabies. They do so, as genes do, by genetic change followed by natural selection in their new environment. The difference between the gene and the virus, the historical difference, is that the gene has arrived in the suitable type of cell by heredity, the virus by infection; and both have been doing so, as a rule, for many generations of heredity or many infections of disease.

Again the virus can propagate itself only together with larger and more genuine organisms – bacteria or plants or animals. Can we suppose that the cells of larger organisms depend for their life and organization on the mutual harmony, the co-ordinated activity and reproduction, of many such particles – each separately incapable of life – of which viruses represent merely a group capable of escaping from the confinement and discipline of the organism? This is a question we can now answer.

PLASMAGENES

The nuclear determinants, the genes and chromosomes whose history we have traced, have given us the explanatory framework for heredity, variation and evolution in plants and animals. It was a framework which, only a few years ago, satisfied most of those who were engaged in building the structure. Nor indeed need we charge them with over-complacency. There were, however, some tenements and outhouses which did not seem to fit, and perhaps never ought to fit, this design. They were concerned with things lying in the part of the cell outside the nucleus, the cytoplasm.

Many questions might be asked about the cytoplasm. Were there genetic particles or determinants in the cytoplasm? Might they be concerned with the origin as well as the activities of viruses? Could they have anything to do with the process of development which Wilson had considered, with the chain of reactions separating the genotype from the phenotype, with the differentiation and self-perpetuation of the tissues of animals? Had the development and transmission of tumours any connexion, any genetic connexion, with this part of the cell? Or, on the other hand, was the nucleus the sole and unconditional custodian of all self-propagating and determining functions in all self-respecting organisms, that is to say in all organisms that had a nucleus?

The answers to some of these questions had been outlined in the early years of Mendelism. There are bodies in the cell outside the nucleus which show a genetic continuity, always arising in nature from previous bodies of the same kind. Some of these, like the spindle-forming particles in animals which organize mitosis and cell division, can be reconstituted from the general cytoplasm if they are lost. But others cannot. Such are notably the particles, visible or invisible, in protozoa which form the whips and bristles, the flagella and cilia with which they swim about, lashing the circumambient fluid. Such also are the organizers of the pigment-forming bodies, or *plastids*, in plants. These bodies arise from self-propagating determinants like the genes of the nucleus, determinants which are known as plasmagenes.

These plasmagenes are too simple to be a law unto themselves. They are members of the cell commonwealth and are subject to its rule and order. But the discipline is less strict than that which the nuclear genes are able to exercise over one another. For the inhabitants of the nucleus have a rigidly co-ordinated reproduction and parade-ground distribution at cell division. Any infringement of nuclear discipline is punished by inexorable laws of growth and movement. Moreover the cytoplasm is bulky and cannot be carried equally in heredity on the two sides. For example, if we cross a white-leaved snapdragon, or *Antirrhinum*, with a green-leaved one, the seedlings take after their mother; they follow the colour of the seed parent, green from green by white, white from white by green; the pollen has nothing to do with the case. In the evening primrose, *Oenothera*, the pollen makes a slight contribution, and these crosses are therefore variegated but with more white if the mother is white. New varieties of variegated *Pelargonium* can be produced by crossing in this way.

The reason for this purely or predominantly maternal transmission is that the male germ cells, the sperm and the pollen grain, travel light. They are not burdened with much cytoplasm. Thus, where the nucleus is in charge there are, by Mendelian law, equal contributions from male and female. But where the nucleus is not in charge the contributions need not be equal. Plasmagenes are therefore detectable by their departures from the laws of heredity according to Mendel and Morgan.

The irregularity of plasmagene inheritance, or the purely maternal inheritance of some particle or character (for here the particle and the character may indeed appear to be one) is our easiest means of recognizing it. There may be much more of it than we realize because most of it keeps near to the nuclear rules most of the time. We already know, however, two important fields of activity that are open to cytoplasmic determinants and closed to the nucleus. They are the fields of differentiation and infection. How do they work?

CELL HEREDITY

It was in 1907 that Ross Harrison at Yale University managed to keep embryo tissues of the chick alive on a food-jelly, or 'nutritive medium', as it is politely called. Later this method was improved by the addition of embryo juices to the jelly. In this way it has been possible to keep tissues alive for over thirty years. They are, it seems, potentially immortal. They still keep the characteristics of the original tissue, the connective tissue or the skin, for example, of an embryo chick.

The same constancy of a tissue is true of tumours, for they can be transplanted from one rabbit to another again and again, year after year. It is also true, of course, in the ordinary growth of the body. There each tissue propagates itself. It was even more obviously true, as Spencer pointed out with telling effect, in the growth of certain regenerated tissues of the animal body. But it is only when the tissues are isolated from one another that the consistency of their properties becomes evidence, inescapable evidence, of an abiding internal difference. These transplanted pieces of tissue or 'tissue cultures' consist, it seems, of cell-lineages and the cell-lineages breed true. They do not breed sexually, of course, since they are organisms only by courtesy of the experimenter. By natural standards they are disintegrated parts. But they breed true, as we may say, vegetatively, like a variety of potato which is propagated from its tubers. Such a variety remains constant, it keeps true to its name as a line, or clone, or breed, of cells whose genetic character or cell heredity is determined by both its nucleus and its cytoplasm. Now the differences between different tissues in the same animal, the same chick, cannot be due to changes in the nucleus, for the chromosomes are visibly the same. They are the same even in the overwhelming detail of the giant multiple chromosomes of the salivary glands and other tissues of the fly (Plate 1b). The differences must therefore be due to changes in the cytoplasm.

Tissue constancy, like the maternal transmission of heredity, demonstrates the existence of genetic particles in the cytoplasm. These particles arise during the development of the higher animals. They arise presumably by the successive actions of the nucleus and the cytoplasm on one another. But it is not only that they arise during development. They must largely determine development. They must determine the differentiation of cells and tissues which is characteristic of development. How this happens is indicated when rule and order break down. In many abnormal types of plants, for example the so-called 'rogues' in peas and tomatoes, we find that, during development, there are differences in the degree to which the determinants of the abnormality are transmitted to the progeny. By this very token we can be sure that the determinants are cytoplasmic.

Again, in piebald animals, the nucleus is stimulated to generate black granules (known as melanophores) which produce pigment in cells of some areas of the skin but not of others: hence the patches. But these melanophores can diffuse into, and indeed infect, adjoining cells which have none. In piebald pigs, the black skin consequently always covers a larger area than the black hair. And occasionally there are animals in which a black patch will spread. Can heredity therefore overlap with infection as well as with development? Of this too there is evidence, evidence which takes us into another field.

CANCER

The perfect animal – among birds, mammals and insects – continues growing to sexual maturity and then ceases growing in all its parts. Apart from the necessary replacement of expendable tissues like skin and mucous membranes, blood and semen, cell-division stops. The perfect animal in this sense, however, is rare or non-existent. After maturity a few cells, from time to time and here and there, are apt to start growing again. Sometimes the result is a lump or wart visible on the skin. Sometimes it is an internal swelling. And sometimes the growth goes on growing indefinitely. It becomes a tumour or ulcer.

The Greek physician and medical philosopher, Galen, writing in the Rome of Marcus Aurelius, made the first definite classification of growths or tumours. And unusually sound and clear it was, even for him. They were, he said, of three kinds: those which *accorded* with nature, like the swelling of a girl's breasts at puberty; those which *exceeded* nature like the callusing of a broken bone when it heals; and those which *conflicted* with nature. These last, he said, might be harmless tumours of localized but often unlimited growth, which he called benign, or they might be tumours of unlocalized growth and therefore dangerous to life which he called *malignant*. It is these to which the name of cancer is usually given today.

As to the origin of malignant tumours, also, Galen expressed an opinion, although a less fruitful one. Were they not evidently due, he asked, to an unhealthy storing up of *black bile* in the tissues? Descartes proposed the lymph and after Pasteur the bacteria were frequently offered the leading role in cancer formation. The first serious step in understanding tumours, however (like so much else in our story), had to be made with the microscope.

Any tumour begins with the character of the tissue from whose cells it arises. The first people to look at tumours under the microscope, soon after 1840, were much impressed by these tissue and cell characteristics, which enabled them to classify what they saw. The medical terms that are still used today such as *sarcoma* (from connective tissue) and *carcinoma* (from skin) arose in this way. These tissue characters, however, do not suffice to tell us what the tumour will do. What is most important is its rate of cell-division. Its speed of growth may increase. If it does so it is then likely to lose its tissue character which it has reached by differentiation. It becomes de-differentiated or, as it were, embryonic. And, finally, its cells may acquire a sinister capacity for floating round the body. They may migrate in the body fluids and, being held up in their migration, they may form colony tumours which quickly prove fatal to the animal in which they have arisen.

These properties of cancer for the last hundred years have been the object of the most varied and profound inquiries. A baffling inconsistency seemed for a long time to be the most consistent feature of the results. On the one hand, Maud Slye in Chicago by 1922 had bred mice and examined, *post mortem*, 200,000 of them. In some of her lines no mice died of spontaneous cancer for thirty generations, mated brother-to-sister; in others every one died, and even died of a type of cancer characteristic in time, place and action of the particular breeding line. Thereby the importance of the heredity factor, the genetic component, in determining cancer was proved; and, in spite of many pronouncements to the contrary, there has been no reason to doubt the universal validity of the proof.

On the other hand, in 1930, Kennaway and a little band of colleagues in London showed that it was a hydrocarbon, a specific chemical agent, which induced cancer on the skin of a man or a mouse to which certain tar products were applied. With a patience equal to that of Madame Curie in isolating radium, and of equal merit, they extracted two ounces of the dangerous substance from two tons of pitch. Thereby a direct chemical causation was demonstrated.

Most remarkable of all, Peyton Rous in New York as early as 1911 with birds, and others later with rabbits and mice, had extracted filterable agents from the tumour cells which could be injected into healthy animals to produce cancer, nearly always a similar kind of cancer. Such agents were found to be constant, self-propagating and ultra-microscopic. They were also found to be nucleo-proteins. In other words they had the properties of naturally infectious viruses. It is not surprising, therefore, that they came to be referred to by the name of virus. But some of them were known to have arisen spontaneously in the animal where they were found. These agents were not naturally infectious. To call them viruses was indeed an unlucky extension of that convenient little word, and it was destined to deceive or confuse a whole generation of medical investigators.

In this welter of conflicting evidence how could anyone get to the root of the matter? In the end, success has only been possible by the use of all resources including those of genetic method, which tells us what self-propagating particles are, where they can arise, and how they go to work.

In the light of this new knowledge we can see that the enduring character of transplanted tumours is on the same footing as the enduring character of tissue culture. It depends on the permanence of cell heredity and arises, therefore, directly and specifically from the cytoplasm. The fact that some extracts of tumours are naturally infectious, others only artificially infectious in the laboratory, and others again incapable of being transferred from one animal to another except in whole cells, is what we might expect of self-propagating particles in the cell. These particles may be of many sizes and qualities. The fact that some of them may have been labelled 'virus', and others not, gives us no key to the position. What does give us the key is that chemical agents may produce the malignant particles from healthy particles in a healthy cell. This change in cell-heredity we are justified in calling a mutation, a mutation not in a nuclear gene but in an otherwise innocuous unnoticeable plasmagene, possibly a permanent plasmagene or possibly a plasmagene characteristic of a particular tissue, a plasmagene produced by the nucleus in the course of development and differentiation.

The results of this mutation, of course, depend on the types of cell and of plasmagene that may be affected. These in turn will depend on the species, and on the tissue, and on the determining conditions of age and health and treatment. From this variety of circumstances arises the vast and terrifying variety of tumour formation in animals. Every tumour is a law unto itself. In every case it would seem as though the docile and subservient protoplasm of the cell had taken over the reins of government from the normally dominant nucleus. In consequence one disobedient cell has escaped from the coordinated discipline of the tissue and of the organism as a whole.

Here it is that the study of tumours, so necessary for their cure, has proved instructive for the understanding of life in general. For it so happens that we possess a means of picking out the disobedient cells from the good cells by the device of treating tumours with what are called 'ionizing radiations'. X-rays and the gamma-radiation from radio-active substances are most commonly used. Not many months after its isolation in 1899, as described by Oberling in his admirable study of the subject, radium was being used in Paris to treat cancer. Two French cancer investigators, Bergonié and Tribondeau, soon discovered, in 1904, the important principle that cells which were undergoing the most rapid multiplication, that is the most frequent cell-division or mitosis, were those most seriously damaged and most often killed by radiation.

This principle of selective killing has been amply verified by those who have studied these effects on plants and animals in the intervening years. When cells enter mitosis after they have been X-rayed, their chromosomes are thrown free into the cytoplasm where they arrange themselves for separation. They are then seen to have been broken. The fragments, the broken ends, are unable to move. The daughter nuclei that are formed are therefore short of various needful bits and the daughter cells quickly die. If, on the other hand, cells whose nuclei are full of broken chromosomes do not divide, the nuclei can carry on and seem to be no jot the worse. In any case the amount of breakage in less active cells is much less. X-rays therefore – provided the dose is suitably adjusted – pick out cancer cells for destruction, leaving the ordinary working but non-multiplying cells not undamaged, it is true, but effectively undamaged. And the most malignant cancer cells are the most quickly destroyed.

This principle is of the greatest consequence in the X-ray treatment of cancer. The plasmagenes, which are responsible for the mischief, are beyond our control because they are the very life of the cells, and of good and bad cells equally. We have to get round them by killing the whole cell, which we do through its higher seat of government, the nucleus, rendered vulnerable as it is by the essential cancerous property of combined nuclear and cell division.

Thus the cause of cancer and its cure – so far as it is accessible to early treatment – are bound up with the understanding of cells, nuclei, and chromosomes, and of genes and plasmagenes, with the microscope as a means of observing them, and with the new weapons which physical science has put into our hands for controlling them. It is the ultimate genetic particles in their several categories which are responsible for the most fundamental disorder, as well as order, in the animal body.

SMOKING AND LUNG CANCER

Quite another method of approach to the problem of cancer comes from studying the connexion between the incidence of different types of cancer and the occupations, climates and races of the victims. Such a connexion has been noticed for nearly 200 years. In 1775 Sir Percival Potts noticed the high incidence of cancer of the scrotum in chimney sweeps and it was this connexion which Kennaway traced to its chemical cause. The fact that skin cancer is many times more common among whites in the southern than in the northern parts of both the United States and the Soviet Union suggests that damage from sunlight makes the difference. And when we find that there is no such difference among coloured people the argument is clinched: the genetic and the environmental variables combine to reveal the effective reaction.

Other cases reveal other reactions. When we find that half the cancer among Bantu populations in Africa is liver cancer, far more than in Europe, we attribute the difference to under-feeding or wrong feeding among African children. But when we find that a heavy incidence of stomach cancer in Japan is still shown by Japanese in the U.S.A. we infer that the genetic variable is predominating. This view is strengthened when we find that stomach cancer is correlated in Britain with the A blood group: people with this blood group are more susceptible than are those with B or O.

Experiments with mice have shown the enormous differences in susceptibility that may arise between strains which have been selected in opposite directions. But even without any prior selection at all, strains exist which differ in their reaction to treatment by new cancer-producing agents. Thus the injection of a 10 per cent solution of urethane induces lung tumours in mice. But strains differ in their susceptibility, showing from as low as 23 to as high as 48 per cent of individuals affected.

These kinds of experience and experimental evidence may now be summarized in practical terms. The heterogeneous populations of human societies contain a proportion of individuals who by their genetic characters are destined to develop cancer under any circumstances in which they can survive. They also contain a small proportion who are subjected to conditions under which any one of any genetic character would be bound to develop cancer. Between the two are the vast bulk of us who are in a position to choose conditions which are likely to favour or disfavour the development of cancer.

Look now at what has happened to the population of Britain in respect of one particular choice. Cigarettes yield small amounts of cancer-producing hydrocarbons which are absorbed by the lungs when the smoke is inhaled. The practice of smoking cigarettes increased in Britain and in the U.S.A. among men after 1890 and among women after 1920.

It became obvious during the 1940s that lung cancer was rapidly increasing as a cause of death in men both in Britain and in the U.S.A. By 1950, careful statistical studies showed that this effect was connected with a corresponding increase in cigarette smoking during the previous sixty years. Since then the same connexion has become evident in women corresponding to the later growth of the cigarette-smoking habit. Over the same period other forms of cancer and other diseases of the lung, notably tuberculosis, have been diminishing.

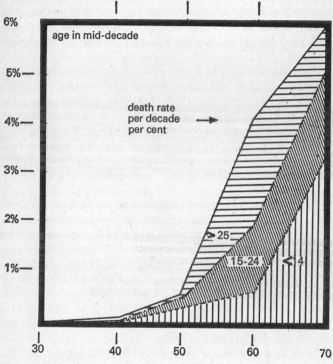

Figure 12

Proportions of deaths due to lung cancer among British medical practitioners in the period 1951–8 following different daily consumptions of cigarettes arranged in three classes (after Platt *et al.* 1962).

This connexion is not only true of the population at large. It is even true of individuals: those who smoke most are the ones who most often die of lung cancer (Figure 12).

Why, we may now ask, do some people smoke cigarettes, others pipes, some heavily, some lightly and others not at all? Studies of twins, whose interpretation we shall touch on later, make it likely that these differences of behaviour also have a genetic component. The late Sir Ronald Fisher supposed that, through this component, susceptibility, or addiction, to smoking had a connexion with susceptibility to its effects in promoting lung cancer. But this suggestion, in itself fantastic, is neatly knocked out by reference to the Seventh Day Adventists in California. This religious sect provides us with a critical test; for they forbid smoking, but, just like other people, they suffer from cancer in general. Only two members of this sect were discovered to have developed lung cancer, and they proved to have been converts. They were converted late in life and had been cigarette smokers before conversion.

Thus smoking cigarettes has the effect of producing lung cancer only in high doses, only after prolonged addiction, and only on a proportion of the addicts. This proportion is probably not more than fifteen per cent in the highest class examined. In the United States, probably because cigarettes are cheaper there and are not therefore smoked to the bitter end, this proportion is slightly lower. Many people found the idea of causation confusing in these circumstances. This kind of 'causation' is however what we expect on the basis of our knowledge of the genetics of variable populations on the one hand and of the interaction of heredity and environment on the other.

DAMAGE BY RADIATION

At the same time that it was discovered that X-rays and other ionizing radiations could cure cancer it was also discovered that they could cause it – and indeed cause other damage which they cannot cure. Now that ionizing radiations are brought to bear on us from so many sources – medical treatment, military experiment and industrial production – it is therefore worth our while to see what damage they do and how they do it.

Ionizing radiations strike us in four sensitive areas: the skin, which they strike directly; the lungs, which they reach from particles breathed in with the air; the bones, which they attack through the radioactive isotope of strontium absorbed in food; and the blood-forming cells, which suffer directly on account of their immense rate of multiplication. In all these tissues radiation generates two classes of change. The first arises in the cytoplasm. It is a cancerous change. The effect is hastened if the exposure is repeated or if other kinds of damage, or irritant, or poison, affect the same tissue. But usually it occurs after a long delay, many months in a mouse and many years in a man. The blood cancer, which we call leukaemia, is of the kind which may be transmitted as a provirus from one mouse to another. The change indeed in all cases is presumably a change in a plasmagene or system of plasmagenes. In this respect it is contrasted with the second class of potentially hereditary radiation effects.

The second class of change concerns the nucleus, or rather the chromosomes contained in the nucleus. Radiation breaks the chromosomes into fragments which may be lost at the following mitosis. Or they may rejoin in new arrangements. And it also changes the finer structure of the genes themselves, thus leading to mutations. The loss of pieces of chromosomes is usually fatal to the cells which have lost them, while the mutations of genes have effects of all degrees of severity from this fatality to what is negligible.

Thus the effects of radiation on the chromosomes fall in a graded series from what is slight and potentially helpful to what is ultimately disastrous or even, if mitosis occurs, immediately disastrous; And the heavier the dose the more frequent is the disastrous type of change likely to be.

The disastrous effect follows mitosis. One of the effects of radiation in the normal healthy body, just as in the diseased body, is therefore to pick out the cells which are dividing most rapidly. First and foremost they pick out the precursor cells of the red blood corpuscles, especially in the bone marrow. These being destroyed, the corpuscles, which come to the end of their natural life in the blood after about four weeks, cannot be replaced. The victim therefore collapses after a few weeks from the delayed effect of this extinction.

Other important cells damaged by irradiation are, in the females, the eggs and their precursor cells in the ovaries, and, in the males, the sperm and their precursor cells in the testes. This effect has been widely discussed, since mutations in sperm or eggs which later are fertilized might produce dangerous hereditary effects in the progeny. Indeed, this is the standard method of producing mutations for genetic studies in experimental animals. The Japanese populations which have been subjected to atomic radiation have, however, failed to show any of the effects on the surviving children of irradiated people which had been feared.

The reasons for this absence of hereditary damage in man are of several kinds. First, the most heavily damaged cells are destroyed, or their descendants are destroyed, by the breakage of the chromosomes. They are removed, just as irradiated tumour cells are removed, before or in sperm-formation by a process of natural selection. Secondly, the less heavily damaged cells with dominant gene mutations enter into sperm and eggs but kill the embryos which result from their fertilization. This effect was in fact shown in the Hiroshima population by an increase both in stillbirths and in infantile mortality. Thirdly, the least damaged cells, those with recessive mutations, can reveal their damage only through marriage between common descendants of the damaged individual. How often they do this can be controlled by way of cousin marriage and of inbreeding generally. Meanwhile they merely add to the total of genetic variation within the community: whether we judge that to be for better or for worse depends on what we want from human breeding.

GENETIC PARTICLES

We have now sorted out some of the self-propagating or genetic particles. An important group of them lie in plant and animal cells, in the cytoplasm outside the nucleus, and near or beyond the limit of microscopic visibility. They have such important effects that we may call them determinants. They prove to be of two kinds. On the one hand there are certain determinants which are responsible for differences in structure, the possession of cell bristles, or pigment-forming particles, or even the correct development of whole plants. These are cooperative particles and they are transmitted through the egg in *heredity*. On the other hand there are determinants responsible for a variety of diseases, which work, as it were, in opposition to the cells on which they depend. These are antagonistic particles and they are transmitted by the air, or by some third party, in the way of *infection*.

To the one kind of particle the name plasmagene has been given; the other has become known as a virus. The distinction between the two types of particle is of manifest practical convenience. There is, however, a likeness. Both types of particle consist, like the genes on the chromosomes, of protein united with nucleic acid. Their ultimate common basis is therefore difficult to ignore. It has come to dominate the question in the following way.

A new grouping among those determinants according to their origin or behaviour has begun to be noticed. Some, which have arisen by heredity or are transmissible by heredity, are also transmissible by infection. They are a motley crowd. They appear spontaneously in plants and in animals. In bacteria, they have very special properties and are known as bacteriophages. Their modes of transmission are so various that it was some time before the absurdity – one might almost say the impertinence – of their existence was recognized or admitted (Figure 13).

One little group consists of occasional plant 'viruses' which cannot be, or at least have not been, transmitted in nature but appear either spontaneously or from injecting the sap, or grafting a stem, of one species of plant on to another. It is as though a nucleo-protein of one species has found its way into the tissue of the other.

Another little group consists of certain viruses which arise suddenly and as a rule spontaneously in normal healthy bacteria or insects but which infect and destroy their neighbours when the first victims break up.

A third group consists of those particles, again known as viruses, extracted from the spontaneous chicken tumours already referred to, which are not infectious in nature but can be transmitted with a syringe in the laboratory. Certain mouse tumours and leukaemias fall in this category when the transfer is made to new-born mice before the antibody-forming system has been built up.

A fourth group consists of microscopic and ultramicroscopic determinants, in protozoa or in flies, which are inherited like plasmagenes, strictly according to the laws of heredity by maternal descent and are certainly therefore not infectious in nature, but again are capable of infection in the test-tube by human interference. One of these, found in *Drosophila*, increases its susceptibility to atmospheric carbon dioxide.

In a fifth group a nuclear gene apparently puts something into the cytoplasm which slowly generates a dangerous new type or new modification of a genetic particle. After some years the whole organism is destroyed. This is true of the 'scrapie' disease in sheep and also of the 'yellows' in strawberries. The agent is not naturally infectious but scrapie can be transmitted by injections.

This twilight world of potential viruses, or *proviruses* as they may be called, particles which are neither one thing or the other, are often trivial, immediately and in themselves. But in their implications they are a sign and a portent. They reveal one of the regular habits of genetic particles, that of changing their way of life: which indeed is their own way of undergoing evolution. In some cases we do not know which way they are changing, whether the plasmagene is moving over to infection or the virus moving back into heredity. In other cases, like the cancer-determining proviruses, the direction is obvious. They have moved away from their normal law-abiding duties in development and have come to adopt a piratical life. And they have done so very often under experimental conditions. Having been produced by the action of nuclear genes to give the normal character of skin or muscle, they have run away from their duty and become the malignant self-propagators underlying the growth of a tumour.

These freaks of nature, or freaks of experiment, show us that the same kinds of genetic particles which are important in heredity and in normal development, and also in cancer development, provide the basis of virus infection. Experiment and the microscope have taken us down to the root of the basic distinctions of life – and to the nucleic acids and proteins underlying them.

They have finally enabled us to see where the sinister army of viruses springs from. Their particles are of a wide range of size. Some are a fifth of a micron in diameter (less than 1/100,000th of an inch); but others are only 1/10,000th of this size. No doubt the larger ones, like the giant virus of smallpox, have a long ancestry of evolving viruses behind them. But the smaller ones may be recent. They may have escaped from the legitimate and respectable life of cell nucleo-proteins, by transplantation from one plant to another or by the transformation of genetic change, which we call mutation, only yesterday. Indeed, may not the same viruses, such as those of poliomyelitis or foot-and-mouth disease, arise again and again in this way spontaneously? We do not know. Certainly in bacteria new phages arise frequently and even play a part in the exchange of genes parallel to that of sexual reproduction itself.

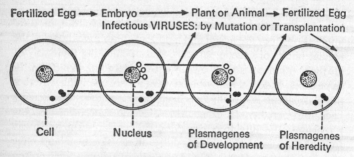

Figure 13

Diagram showing in a simple way how the main classes of genetic particle are transmitted by heredity and infection, and related in evolution. The nucleus stands apart, dominating the cell, the organism and the course of evolution. Plasmagenes of heredity are independent of the nucleus in heredity but subject to it largely in development. Plasmagenes of development are produced by the nucleus during development, but not usually carried over to the next generation. Simple viruses and proviruses can probably arise from either of these types of plasmagene.

Thus the wheel has turned full circle. The pursuit of the seemingly endless superstition of the spontaneous origin of life has in the end revealed something which is unexpected and is not a mere mare's nest. But of course it is still not the spontaneous origin of life. Very often, on the contrary, it proves to be the spontaneous breakdown of life.

WHAT IS A DETERMINANT?

What have the different determinants, nuclear genes, plasma-genes, and viruses to do with one another? We now need some answer to this question. The differences between them are, it seems, incidental to the organization of groups of different particles and to the mechanics of their propagation and distribution. The three classes are not ultimately distinct. The notion of determinism, which has never troubled the student of disease, is thus brought into the field of disease indirectly from analogy with the genetics of Mendel and Morgan.

In the virus, the distinction between the ideas of germplasm and soma, or of genotype and phenotype, scarcely obtrudes itself. Yet the importance of these ideas becomes obvious when we consider that biological determinism is now shown to depend on two properties of the determinants or genetic particles which make up the germplasm or the genotype. These are the properties of self-propagation and specific action. By *self-propagation* a single particle, gene, plasmagene or virus, gives rise to two identical ones. By *specific action* it produces a constant product in reaction with any given surroundings, and the product may be composed of genetic or non-genetic particles.

If we look back over the history of the recognition of determinants we see that they are of two kinds – according to yet another distinction: there are those that stay attached to their products and those whose effects and products are delayed and remote. Attached determinants have never presented us with any difficulty. The particle which merely seems to propagate itself, and takes effect by contact, does not arouse suspicion. This was true of the bacteria so long as they seemed to have no structure. It was also true of viruses so long as they were invisible. It was true of the visible plastids of plants, which appeared to be determinants and determined rolled into one. It was equally true of the cytoplasmic determinants so long as they and their products remained invisible. What of the viruses which appear spontaneously in the cell nuclei of insects? The nuclei are then found to grow a shell. But even here no one would have any difficulty in seeing that the genotype determined the phenotype.

The difficulty arose first in the higher organisms. There, a largely inaccessible and unintelligible process of development and differentiation lay between a minute and apparently structureless germ cell and a large and elaborate adult organism. The problem of heredity lay in the mystery of development. The determinant in the germ cell was separated in space and time from its product; and its effects were complex and cyclical. Now, however, the study of the cell has reduced all these relationships to common terms.

In the chromosomes we can see special genes to which their products remain attached, either momentarily or as storage material in the nucleus. These are always compound genes formed by a repetition side by side which gives rows of identical units. They organize various visible activities in the cell. These are the groups of 'centromere' genes, the 'nucleolar organizers' and the blocks of 'heterochromatin'. We can, on the other hand, see ordinary so-called 'euchromatic' genes whose products seem to diffuse rapidly into the cytoplasm.

In the cytoplasm the same distinction appears. Especially in unicellular plants and animals, we can recognize determining particles responsible for cilia, flagella or eye spots, the 'centrosomes' generating the crystalline fibres of the spindle in the dividing cells, and the plasmagenes forming the plastids which manufacture the green pigment of plants. All these remain attached to their products. But others, like the plasmagenes which endow the fly *Drosophila* with resistance to carbon dioxide poisoning and the black pigment determinants in the guinea-pig, diffuse from cell to cell.

And finally it has recently been discovered that special conditions lead to the change from one of these great categories to the other, causing the detachment of the normally attached products of centromeres and nucleolar organizers.

We thus have stages in the separation of the determinant and its product. This separation is fundamental for biological theory. The whole business of differentiation must indeed be bound up with different degrees of diffusibility of just these products of gene action which, interacting secondarily with one another and with other genes, produce an orderly succession of distinct activities of similar and different genes – one gene in its time playing many successive parts.

The solution of these problems that we have now reached is bound to have something in common with the theories developed to explain them in the eighteenth and nineteenth centuries. The preformation and the epigenesis are both there. But it is not the unwanted genes which empty themselves into the cytoplasm, as Weismann thought, leaving the important ones behind to do the work. Rather, they all remain in the nucleus, the important ones emptying not themselves but something perhaps like themselves, the products of their activity, into the cytoplasm.

The general determinism which we witness in heredity and development is thus compounded of countless component processes each separately determined. These separate processes being in sequence as well as in parallel could not smooth out one another's irregularities even if they had any. We know from the study of differences determined in the nucleus that they can only magnify them. The absence of the minutest particle in the nucleus leads to a gross deformity in the animal. And the earlier any irregularity occurs the more disastrous it is to the developing organism. Yet we know that even the breakdown of order, even the contradiction of regularity, in tumour formation, is itself subject to genetic determination. The long-term consequences of this determination, magnified beyond measure, are revealed to us by the processes of evolution which we can now examine.

PART THREE

CHANCE AND CHANGE

Evolution does not arise from a principle of progress or improve-ment inherent in life. It arises from the occurrence of changes in heredity due to chance. They affect only one's descendants, among whom natural selection converts what was a chance into a near-certainty. The organizing as well as the suppressing of change are themselves subject to heredity. And where change is suppressed evolution is brought to a standstill.

When we put these processes into their proper order we find that evolution is a matter of first creating and then exploiting uncertainty.

9

The Sources of Uncertainty

GENES and chromosomes, genetic particles and the general concourse of determinants, are by definition deterministic in their action. Their use, their *raison d'être*, is to provide a basis of certainty, a predictable component in heredity and in life. Now that we have allowed for this predicted action, now that we have taken to pieces the main themes in the study of life, we can discuss the residue of uncertainty which we find left over.

Variation, the occurrence of unexpected hereditary changes, is the first obvious uncertainty in life. We divide it into two parts. There is *discontinuous* change, which is directly traceable to individual changes in determinants, changes which we call mutations. And there is *continuous* change, or quantitative variation with a continuous range of differences, which is not so traceable. Recombination, the field of operation of Mendelian ratios, is the second great field of uncertainty with its components of crossing over, segregation and fertilization.

Selection and evolution are the means by which variations are sorted out and give rise to changes in whole populations and species of organisms. They are another field of study in which the operations of heredity seem to be affected if not governed by uncertainty. Yet another field is development, where we may encounter, for example, unexpected differences between the two sides of one animal.

Now we have reached a point where we can ask ourselves how far these uncertainties require a modification of the deterministic hypothesis that the founders of genetics were working on. We can see that Mendel and Darwin, Weismann and Johannsen, and even Bateson and Morgan too, were going on the assumption that a uniform and undeviating relationship of cause and effect governed all the properties of life. We can follow in detail how they pressed home this assumption in face of technical difficulties and sometimes of theoretical misunderstanding. And we can test and try, over the whole range of living things, the deterministic framework which they put together by their handiwork. Does one and the same principle of determinism govern the working of mutation and recombination and selection? Does it govern equally the survival of organisms and the movements of chromosomes and genes in the cell? Or is chance, as some say, the ultimate rule of heredity and of life in general? These are questions we can now try to answer.

RECOMBINATION

The first task of genetics was to show how far Mendel's principles worked. They work, we now know, wherever sexual reproduction works. They work for all differences arising in the nucleus. Indeed, we found that all differences for which they did not work could be put outside the nucleus. When this had been done the next business was to discover the absolute mechanism in individuals. Such an absolute mechanism, as Mendel had imagined, must underlie the statistical rule he had found from surveying and counting groups of individuals.

In his experimental families Mendel had found among individuals of three types in a second generation from a cross, a ratio that was close enough to 1 : 2 : 1. He had assumed, clearly and explicitly assumed, that this ratio arose from the random recombination of equal numbers of germ cells of two alternative types. If the grandparents had contributed the elements A and a to the parents, to give the combination Aa which would again give A and a in equal numbers of germ cells, they would indeed yield three classes of offspring. They would fuse in pairs in the proportions 1 AA : 2 Aa : 1 aa. Mendel made this inference from the statistical rule in 1864. But it was not until threescore years had passed that it was confirmed by individual observation. In a sense, of course, it was confirmed by the segregation of chromosomes at meiosis which gradually became clear at the turn of the century. But the full inference was only confirmed when it was seen that two of the four cells in the tetrad produced at meiosis were of one kind in respect of size, shape or mating properties, and the other two of another kind. This was shown in mosses, in algae, in fungi, and in the embryo-sac mother cells of evening primroses (*Oenothera*), all in Germany, and all at about the same time between 1919 and 1924.

Here there was no longer any need for a statistical generalization. Here there was no longer any approximation to a ratio, any uncertain assumption of cause and effect. Here at last was the direct determination that Mendel had assumed. The assumption had been taken for granted, and had been indirectly verified and multifariously expanded, ever since the discovery of *Drosophila's* linkage groups in 1911; for so long indeed that no one noticed when it was first directly verified or, as we may almost say, proved to be true.

Recently this discovery has been elaborated and refined in a most striking way. In many fungi meiosis gives rise to a row of four cells, the reproductive haploid spores, thus :

O————————→OO————————————→OOOO
(first division)   (second division)

By crossing different strains hybrids are produced, *Aa*, whose gene difference controls pigment formation in the spores: *A* is black, *a* is colourless. Now if the separation of the two alleles occurs at the first division the four spores should appear thus :

AAaa or aaAA

But if the separation occurs at the second division the spores should appear as :

AaAa or AaaA or aAaA or aAAa

Reference to Figure 7 will show that centromeres should always follow the first pattern. Further, the frequency of the second pattern for any gene should depend on the frequency of crossing-over between that gene and the centromere. It has in fact proved possible to find the different proportions of the two patterns. And these proportions are characteristic of each gene difference. They therefore mark the position of a gene on the chromosome, just as the frequency of recombination did in Morgan's original experiments, but by quite a different kind of inference.

In all these situations it was now clear that two cells were of one kind and two of the other. But it was not clear why a particular two should be of one kind. Indeed in the intervening years the problem had broadened beyond measure. The chromosomes had been shown to be the bearers of Mendel's elements. Their pairing and other movements could be seen. Their recombinations, when the partners were of different sizes, could be watched. Their failure of pairing or of recombination, if it so happened, could also be recorded in individual cells.

Now the question arises: Why should all the thousands of genes in the chromosomes of parents undergo crossing-over, segregation, and reunion by fertilization, with apparently utter randomness, to give in new particular groupings the genetic outfit of each particular individual of the next generation? These processes, so far as they are described, are still for the most part described only statistically. Can it be that, like segregation itself, they are to be regarded as the steps in inevitably determined sequences of events?

CROSSING-OVER

Take the first of the series, crossing-over. Many millions of plants and animals have been bred and classified in order to show the properties of crossing-over between pairs of genes on the same chromosome. When this crossing-over has taken place at meiosis in individuals which are hybrid with respect to two genes in the same chromosome pair (e.g. *AB* and *ab*), its frequency can be inferred from the proportions of recombinations of the two (*Ab* and *aB*) in the progeny. Moreover, as we have learnt, any crossing-over becomes visible immediately afterwards, where the chromosomes are large, as a chiasma in the cell undergoing meiosis. We can therefore trace the process back to within a few minutes of its origin. And in demonstrating this, some millions of chiasmata have been observed and recorded for number and position.

All these results, like Mendel's, are statistical. The chromosomes are too small and too delicate to be individually handled in experiment. It is an assumption that the chiasmata arise in the chromosomes as a result of the excessive torsion that follows their pairing as thin undivided threads. It is an assumption that this strain is released by their breakage when the threads divide. Such deterministic assumptions, however, have encouraged us to find out how the position of a chromosome in the nucleus, its length and shape and internal structure, can influence the time and sequence of its pairing with a partner from the opposite parent; to discover how these conditions in turn influence the amount of relative twisting that the partners develop or are likely to develop, and the frequency with which they in fact cross over.

By formulating and testing deterministic hypotheses and by an alternation of individual and statistical observations an apparently undeterministic, and still quite uncertain, process has, in the opinion of the observers, taken its place in a chain of causation. Like countless other assumptions by which we convert statistical generalizations into statements of cause and effect, the assumptions embodied in a torsion theory of crossing-over are justified at the moment of their conception by the past success of determinism. Afterwards they add to that success by suggesting experimental tests and predicting the results. The working hypothesis is indeed the hypothesis without which we cannot work. And it is the assumption of a deterministic relationship which can be tested.

The results of these studies have been to show that crossing-over is so adjusted, indeed so determined (for we cannot avoid the word), that it does not take place in the same positions in any two mother cells of the same organism. Or rather, the number of combinations of position is so great – probably varying between 10^{20} and 10^{200} for different species – that the chance of repetition can be ignored. Multiplying these are of course the chances of recombination of 2 or 200 whole chromosomes, maternal and paternal, arising by reduction at meiosis in the spore, egg, or sperm, mother cell. And further, the chances of recombination by reunion of different sperms and eggs at fertilization are equivalent to a squaring of all these chances.

All these chances are determined by physical conditions at a lower level. They are chances of relative position in the nucleus or in the cell, differences of conditions readily observable but quite accidental or irrelevant to the biological differences, the differences between alternative genes, which are being recombined. By comparison and experiment, however, each of these chances can be shown to operate on a deterministic basis. In special circumstances it can be brought under exact predictable control. For example the control of crossing-over and chiasma formation is revealed by its characteristically localized distribution in many plants and animals. It may be near the ends of the chromosomes or far away from them. When species differing in this respect are crossed, the distribution of chiasmata is confused in the F_2, owing to segregation in the F_1. The control is therefore genetic and Mendelian: it must lie within the chromosomes themselves. And we must suppose that it is applied to the advantage of the species.

Recombination, likewise, can be suspended by the adoption of parthenogenesis in plants or animals – of the kind found by Leeuwenhoeck. Recombination ceases and hence, apart from dominant mutations, variation disappears. Selection, artificial or natural, can have no effect. Evolutionary change then comes to a standstill and the species is brought to a dead end. Thus the evolutionary mill ceases to grind when the uncertainties of recombination are polished away.

The position now seems to be as follows. The mass of the mother cells produced in a lifetime by each one of us, 10^6 by a female, 10^{11}, 10^{12} or 10^{13} by a male, are all utterly alike. By a succession of deterministically controlled uncertainties, eggs and sperm are produced in their vast numbers by these mother cells and no two are alike. Hence the offspring of the same parents, no less than of different parents, are all different: all determinedly distinct individuals. That so much determination should be organized to express the results of uncertainty or that so much uncertainty should be organized at the very beginnings of determination as a kind of engine of diversification is the outstanding paradox of genetics. Its meaning we must explore further to discover.

MUTATION

The second great field for uncertainty in biology is mutation – that is, historically. If we were building up the subject from the bottom, of course, mutation would come before its own recombinations: without mutation, recombination by sexual reproduction would be merely an ornamental exercise in microscopical mechanics. Since we had to begin by taking the subject apart, however, mutation comes second.

In the beginning, mutation, the original occurrence of genetic change, caught men's attention when it was extreme and outrageous. Nothing short of a monster or a sport seemed to need an explanation. The explanation that Aristotle was able to supply was that such things arose from Occult Causes, an explanation which satisfied all the ancients and probably satisfies most moderns. To men of the renaissance the elegant expression of *lusus naturae* filled the same gap in understanding. Darwin's views on the problem provide a welcome change: they represent a slight but uncertain advance.

To Darwin the important changes that occurred in heredity were not freaks and sports. They were changes so slight as to give the appearance of continuous variation, like the differences in height and weight of human beings. He could not find out how these variations arose. He could not even prove that they were inherited. He rejected the view that 'variation was a necessary contingent on reproduction'. But, as we have seen, he hedged in giving his opinion as to whether it was contingent upon external conditions as popular belief supposed.

Weismann was more explicit and precise. Summing up his views he considered that:

variation is always the effect of external influences. ... Were it possible for growth to take place under absolutely constant external influences, variation would not occur.

The Germplasm, 1892

But, since this is impossible, all growth is connected with smaller or greater deviations from the inherited developmental tendency:

When these deviations affect only the soma, they give rise to temporary non-hereditary variations; but when they occur in the germplasm, they are transmitted to the next generation and cause corresponding *hereditary variation in the body*.

No one knows what 'constant external influences' might be, so that this statement is practically meaningless to us. But it is evidently intended to express a direct relationship of cause and effect between variation in the environment and in heredity. In this respect it is very like the Lamarckian theory. Indeed this view of Weismann – with which he concludes his great anti-Lamarckian work – is distinguished from Lamarck's view only in two respects: first, by the assumption, clearly stated, that changes in the body, unlike changes in everything else in its environment, have no effect on the germplasm; secondly, by the presumption, by no means clearly stated, that the induced change in the germplasm does not correspond in its effects on later generations with any individual change in the body in which it occurred. It therefore has no special chance of being adaptively useful. This, however, is the vital distinction and it enables us to come back fairly close to Weismann in the end, although by a different path.

The Mendelians, by experimenting with distinct and separable units of change, mutations, arrived at quite a different conclusion from Weismann. Today we should agree that mutations occur in the body, outside the germ track, and that these are not hereditary. We should also agree that they occur as well in the cells of the germ track, potential ancestors of germ cells, and that these are potentially heritable. A brown streak in a blue eye (or one wholly brown eye, occurring perhaps in one man in a thousand), a red streak in a yellow apple, or a white streak in a green leaf, are all due to mutations, changes in nuclear genes or plasmagenes, of the tissues affected. But unless the changes happen to have taken place in cells which are ancestral to germ cells they will not be inherited. Now the ordinary range of external conditions affects the frequency with which mutations take place, either in body cells or in germ line cells, only slightly and only when the frequency is high. Such mutations are what we call spontaneous. That is to say, the determining conditions, no doubt largely internal to the organism, are unidentifiable.

Above all, the mutations that occur have no relation in kind or frequency with the use they may have to the creature in which they occur. Darker moths have always been appearing in every species and in every generation. And being more exposed to the eyes of predatory birds than their paler brethren they have been wiped out. But when 150 years ago the chimneys of industrial England began to belch forth their prosperous smoke and cover the leafage of our woodlands with a waterproof coat of tarry black it was the paler moths that were seen and swallowed more readily. And parish by parish, district by district, the darker kind, the 'melanic variety', began to displace the older type. The black gene began to drive out its Mendelian allelomorph from the population. Within a century an evolutionary change had taken place and species were transformed from one uniform kind to another mixed kind better adapted to the new mixed way of life in a semi-industrial community. As the experiments of Kettlewell have shown, this is the result of natural selection.

Natural selection then provides the motive power of change. But the units of change, the mutations, that are subject to selection arise independently of the conditions to which they will provide the means of adaptation; and indeed independently of any identifiable external conditions. The mutations, the actual changes, not the living results of change, are of course very rare. They would seem to be utterly unpredictable, utterly unrelated to causal circumstances, examples of indeterminacy *par excellence*. Yet step by step the deterministic principle has forced its way in. How has it done so?

The resolution of the uncertainty of mutation as a deterministic process we owe to the work of one of the founders of American genetics, Hermann Muller. His method, like Mendel's, was statistical. It consisted in recording the precise frequencies of particular mutations, gene by gene and fly by fly, in the laboratory fly (which by now had changed its name to *Drosophila melanogaster*). He began with the spontaneous or natural frequencies. He then varied conditions and treatments. And he soon showed that by giving the spermatozoa of his flies a dose of a few hundreds of Röntgen units of X-rays he could increase many times the numbers of mutations (with white eyes, or crumpled wings, or lacking in bristles) of which he found evidence in their second-generation progeny.

That was in 1927. Later Muller found that each gene had a characteristic frequency of induced mutation. With a given dose of X-rays a given proportion of the progeny showed a changed character. The frequency depended, it was to be assumed, on the chemical structure of the gene and on the capacity of the radiation used in releasing free ions in the proximity of the gene: that is, in the cell nucleus. Soon, other types of ionizing radiation were tried – gamma-rays, neutrons, ultra-violet light. Still later, in 1942, chemical agents such as mustard gas were found to induce mutations, in a characteristic way of their own, by Charlotte Auerbach in Edinburgh.

Side by side with these increasingly discriminating experiments, changes were seen in the chromosomes under the microscope at the next cell division after treatment, and also in the progeny. Chromosomes could be shown to have been broken by the treatment. Having been broken, the fragments could join up in new ways to give inversions and interchanges of segments, such as are actually found in nature. The chromosomes could even be broken at particular places, depending on the chemical structure and physical surroundings of their different parts at different stages of development.

Thus it became evident that the mutation of a gene and the breakage of a chromosome – which was sometimes connected with it and sometimes independent – were determined like chemical reactions. But since the genes and chromosomes are inside the cell, and indeed inside its nucleus, the determination of their changes cannot be controlled as they might be controlled in a test-tube. We cannot therefore exclude the possibility that the residual unexplored uncertainty of mutation arises from an ultimate sub-atomic physical uncertainty. But any investigator of mutation who made this assumption would of course have to resign himself to a life of contemplation rather than experiment. For those who do not assume it, on the other hand, the chase gets hotter, and the deterministic assumption becomes more explicit. The results may be summed up by saying that, in one lifetime and in one inquiry, we have witnessed the same kind of transformation as we witnessed in regard to disease, the transformation of an Act of God into an effect of ionization.

The property of instability shown by organic molecules in face of temperature changes, powerful chemical reagents, and ionizing radiations, is a thing given and inescapable to life. The problem of trying to escape from it will itself provide an interesting chapter in the future of genetics. It will then be of interest to elaborate the theme that the stability of genes and chromosomes need not extend to the full range of conditions over which life is possible. And, since instability in moderation is useful, we are not surprised to find it greater under marginal or unusual or extravagent conditions. Now the action of these abnormal external conditions is of course uncertain with respect to the laws of living matter under normal conditions: there is no connexion between the kind of external conditions and the kind of mutation. But there is no detectable indeterminacy within the chain of biological events that follows the mutation. And there is no evidence for assuming it beyond that chain. It is merely that outside lower-level physical events interfere with the inside certainty in the working of the living system. We shall soon be examining the evidence as to whether, or how far, living systems attempt to escape from the hazards imposed upon them by the vagaries of lower-level existence.

THE BATTLE OVER BIOMETRY

Plants and animals in the same family always vary in size and other quantitative respects. Whole populations show a continuous range of variation in respect to measurable differences. Darwin held that these differences were hereditary in part and were the basis of selection and evolution. Others, like de Vries, have held that they were due to effects of the different conditions to which, in the best controlled experiments, brothers and sisters are inevitably subject: and that their selection, like those differences within Johannsen's pure lines, was therefore without consequence. Both parties realized that they were uncertain and (at that time) beyond technical control.

In these circumstances two methods of proceeding offered themselves as alternatives. The first we owe to the statistical studies of Francis Galton. By the measurement of groups of comparable individuals or structures, Galton discovered that the frequencies falling into different classes could be arranged or distributed so as to show properties of great interest. In heights, for example, men in England could be shown to be most numerous at 5 feet 8 inches (it would be more today) and less numerous in higher and lower classes. These frequencies could be plotted on a graph to show the 'frequency distribution', as Galton called it, as a curve. The mode, or peak, or point of highest frequency, was then usually not far above or below the average, or arithmetic mean, frequency (Figures 14 and 24). Such 'normal' curves had long been known to astronomers in studying the errors of measurements where departure from the mean is due to 'a multitude of accidents'. But Galton found that the normal curve was characteristic of the variation in almost every measurable property of living organisms. This curve had its own mathematical characteristics. For example, the curve could be described in terms of its mean and its degree of spread, its coefficient of variation, or its 'variance'. Its steepness or flatness was a measure of the amount of variation in the population and the number and importance of independent causes of variation (whether hereditary or environmental).

For all these statistical purposes a sample of a population would suffice to give a picture of the whole if it was selected without bias or, as we say, at random. Moreover, the variation of two independently variable characters like height and weight could be compared and shown pictorially in a table. And the comparison could be given a precise mathematical value, a coefficient of correlation, expressing the relationship. In the same way a correlation could be discovered between the properties of different classes of individuals. A correlation between men and their wives in height would prove the existence of what is known as *assortative mating*. A correlation between lengths of arm and leg would prove a regularity in development. And a correlation between parents and offspring, or between brothers or sisters, would prove the effectiveness of heredity.

Thus the multitude of accidents revealed by the normal curve of variation were divisible between heredity and environment. And the data used to compile the curve could be used to extract some knowledge of these two components. Moreover, the principle itself that the variation of individuals in all ordinary cases falls into a normal curve enables us (as we shall see later) to infer its existence, and use it to understand situations where direct measurement has not been possible.

These discoveries of method now enable us to handle many problems of heredity. They also furnish us with powerful instruments for the study of the growth and working of individuals, of races, and of societies. But when they were first applied at the beginning of the century, they failed to add very much to popular ideas on the subject.

It was Galton himself who first introduced these notions into heredity and he did so in relation particularly to the inheritance of height, intelligence and susceptibility to disease in man. Finally, in 1897, they led him to a theory of heredity. He suggested that the inheritance of each individual was half determined by his two parents, a quarter by his two grandparents, and so on, diminishing with the remoteness of the ancestor and compounded of all ancestors. This 'Law of Ancestral Inheritance', as it came to be called, could of course be tested only with measurable differences. A wary observer might have noticed that it fails to account for differences between brothers; yet in merely quantitative respects it was often not very wide of the mark.

Bateson, at this time, was in the throes of collecting evidence of changes by jumps for his *Materials for the Study of Variation*. He had no use for frequency distributions, normal curves, and an utterly, or at least minutely, subdivisible heredity. But when the possibilities of Galton's mathematical inventions became clear in his *Natural Inheritance* in 1889, they quickly seized on the imagination of others among the younger English Darwinians. This generation had believed in the natural selection of continuous variations as a dogma. But they had felt that affirmation and reiteration were not enough. They wanted to prove it. Galton's irrefragable logic showed them how. It gave them a method and a programme. The moving spirits were Raphael Weldon, a Cambridge zoologist, and that versatile and pugnacious statistician, Karl Pearson, then enagaged on writing *The Grammar of Science*. The combination was a powerful one. Weldon taught Pearson biology, Pearson taught Weldon mathematics.

Their point of view, the point of view of biometry, as they called it, was expressed by Weldon in these words:

The questions raised by the Darwinian hypothesis are purely statistical, and the statistical method is the only one at present obvious by which that hypothesis can be experimentally checked (1895).

And for Pearson evolution had taken place:

by continuous selection of the favourable variation from the [statistical] distribution of the offspring round the ancestrally fixed type, each selection modifying *pro rata* that type (1906).

What these statements meant was indicated by a paper published in 1898 with the attractive title: *Attempt to Measure the Death-rate due to the Selective Destruction of* Carcinus moenas *with respect to a Particular Dimension.*

Weldon here showed that crabs of some shapes suffered from sewage in Plymouth Harbour more than others. But his evidence was disputed by some, and his method by others, so that a dispute was soon engaged. The biometers, like the Pythagoreans of old, brightened by the inner light of their belief in numbers, in *pure* statistics, were at war with the unbelievers. The Royal Society Committee on Evolution, from which the money for conducting and publishing the experiments had to be extracted, became a bear-garden. By 1900 the faithful few had been ousted by their opponents. They had to found a journal of their own, *Biometrika*, to fight the matter out.

It was at this critical moment that Mendelism broke cover. Its claims were at once taken up and urged (as we have seen) by Bateson, the most vigorous critic of continuous variation, of Darwinian selection, and of the whole method and assumptions of biometry. So vigorously had Bateson already, before the rediscovery, asserted his belief in impure statistics, statistics resting on particular experiments, especially on the crossing of known parents, that, when it was rediscovered, Mendelism almost appeared as his own invention.

Battle was at once joined between the two camps. And for six years, while one side pointed out the pitfalls of biometry, the other exposed the snares of Mendelism. While Weldon bred moths, mice and poppies, Bateson bred poultry, rabbits and sweet-peas. Both were zoologists but both studied botany assiduously. When the periodical *Nature* – and of course *Biometrika* – refused to publish Bateson's views on Mendelism, and incidentally on Weldon, the controversy, so well described nearly fifty years later by Punnett, may be said to have reached its climax.

Weldon died in 1906 and with him died the biometrical attack on heredity. The struggle had brought colour into the scientific tableau but its consequences were bad. The biometers had overshot their mark. But they had recognized the importance of continuous variation. And, when they went, continuous variation fell into disregard and disrepute. Of their work, only their measurements and surveys of intelligence remained of permanent value to the student of psychology and education.

Had Weldon lived there might well have been a compromise. And not only a compromise but an understanding of the underlying determination of heredity in the cell which both sides in the English controversy had failed to understand. Biometry, as conceived by Weldon and Pearson, succumbed because a Mendelian analysis was necessary first. There was work for the biometrician to do. But he tried to do it while refusing to make the distinction between an F_1 and an F_2, or between a homozygote AA and a heterozygote Aa; and his failure painfully revealed the inevitability of Mendel.

How grave was the biometer's misunderstanding will be realized when we recall that it still constitutes the main popular stumbling-block to the understanding of genetics and of the first principles of life. The geneticist says that the individual owes his inborn character to heredity. Popular opinion assumes that all brothers and sisters, having the same parents, have the same heredity. Differences between brothers and sisters are then due to an uncertainty in the action of heredity or perhaps merely to the effect of environment. Again, to the geneticist, individual characters are hereditary if they are genetically determined. Popular opinion holds that they are hereditary only if they have been seen in ancestors or offspring. Genetics has shown therefore that genetic determination is far stronger in the individual than any popular idea of heredity could conceive – and, further, that the uncertainty in resemblance of parent and offspring is not due to any lack of determination, or of control of the development, of the individual. It arises from the characteristics, necessary and indeed adaptive characteristics, of sexual recombination.

Mendelian theory began by making these distinctions, and, having done so, could then sort out the effects of heredity and environment. The classical case and the simple case we have already seen. It was that of Johannsen where the hereditary variable was eliminated. The variation should therefore have been due to the environment. And it was proved to be due to the environment. We must take our genetics *with* mathematics, said Johannsen, not *as* mathematics.

But when hereditary differences were not eliminated could they be held responsible for continuous variation? Might numerous small gene-differences between individuals in a population, blending in effect with differences in the environment, lead to the normal curve of variation?

CONTINUOUS VARIATION

In theory, Mendelism could solve the problem of quantitative uncertainty in heredity: one just assumes that many genes exist in two alternative forms which segregate and act with slightly different effect. But in practice a great deal more work had to be done. It was easy to say that a great number of genes, each of small effect, were governing the size of an organ or the number of organs. But how to prove it? It was easy to maintain the opposite and to say that big fluctuations were due to heredity, the small ones, the 'fluctuations', to the environment. The value of the components remained beyond analysis. How were they to be reached?

Since external conditions affect our growth every one of us might be an inch shorter or an inch taller under different conditions. Yet there might very well be a hundred genes segregating in one human family and each only making a difference of a fraction of an inch. How could their effects be separated from those of external conditions?

This problem engaged the attention of Mendelian geneticists from the beginning. But it was only possible with later refinements to get to the root of the matter.

Between 1918 and 1926 R. A. Fisher developed, for purposes of agricultural research at Rothamsted, the statistical and analytical methods which give rigour and efficiency to modern experimental work. By their breeding-work with wheat, maize and other plants, East in America and Nilsson Ehle in Sweden had shown that the continuous variation revealed by Darwinian studies were compatible with the Mendelian inheritance of many small differences; Fisher showed that they required such inheritance. For an experimental proof the methods of Fisher needed to be tried on *Drosophila* with its rapid breeding and its mapped chromosomes. With this equipment, Kenneth Mather, of the John Innes Institution at Merton, was able to demonstrate the action of systems of genes which are unrecognizable as individuals. He could show how such variations can be referred accurately to their external and internal causes.

Mather's experiment is most easily understood by comparison

with Johannsen's. They both practised selection on inbred and apparently true-breeding stocks. Flies could not be self-fertilized but they were mated brother-to-sister. They both selected for increase and decrease in a measured character – bean weight or bristle number. Both continued their selection for many years. But while Johannsen was studying six generations Mather could breed 260. While Johannsen could weigh thousands of beans, Mather (and his collaborators) could count millions of bristles. And with a constant heredity the variation is enormously greater in the size of beans on plants than in the numbers of bristles on flies. Moreover, the huge families of the fly made it possible to discover genetic changes by the statistical properties of a family composed of individuals varying in the number of bristles.

The consequence of all these advantages was that the constancy found in the beans broke down in the flies (Figure 14). Selection began to take effect. After twenty-five generations flies with more bristles appeared; heritable variation had evidently occurred; some of it could be traced to mutations and some of it to the effects of crossing-over within groups of linked genes. A 'polygenic' system of many small and supplementary genes controlling minute variations of quantity was exposed and could be tested by breeding. The genes could be recorded for linkage and even for dominance; they could be assigned to particular chromosomes and predicted as to their future behaviour with deterministic confidence.

Thus Mather had shown that the genetic components of continuous variation are genes whose actions were individually beyond identification – blurred by environmental effects. Nevertheless he had assumed (and the assumption had led him to discover precise evidence in its favour) that individual genes of precise locations, actions, and properties of mutation, determine these effects and thus provide the materials for evolutionary changes in size, proportion, the timing of development, and other quantitative changes.

It is a paradox worth pausing to admire that the statistical study of groups has thus again been used (as it was by Mendel) to reveal individual actions. Again they were actions that were otherwise invisible. The statistical method has been used, of course, under the impulse of confident deterministic assumptions. By its

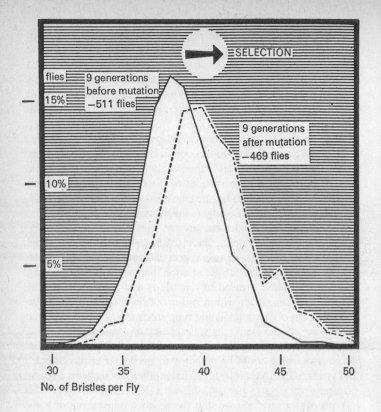

Figure 14

The result of selection for increase in a variable character, the number of belly bristles in the fly *Drosophila melanogaster*, which had been bred by brother–sister mating for 78 generations before selection. An increase in average number came after 27 generations, and the two curves (which agree with Normal Curves of Error) show the range of variation in bristles among the families bred during the nine generations before and after the presumed genetic change or mutation. Note that the mutation can be detected only from the statistical properties of the group and not from the properties of particular flies. Unpublished data used by Mather and Wigan (1941, *Proc. Roy. Soc.* B, **131**, Table 2) arranged by G. M. Haskell.

success it has established the validity of these assumptions, and in doing so, of course, it has established the partition of variation between heredity (or genotype) and environment. Weldon had dreamt of a whole range of behaviour between 'simple Mendelism' and 'blended inheritance'. After forty years the compromise conclusion was reached – without, however, a compromise of principle.

Finally, we observe that the uncertainty of continuous variation does indeed arise from a 'multitude of accidents'. The hereditary part of these accidents consists in the mutation and recombination – which cannot be separated by their effects – of innumerable small genes, the polygenes. The uncertainty of quantitative variation therefore arises from the same two causes as that of all variation with an ordinary Mendelian basis.

Understanding how quantitative or continuous variation is inherited has been a technical business. Its practical consequences, however, are easy to grasp. The early Mendelian was so anxious to prove that what was hereditary was always Mendelian that he willingly threw overboard quantitative and continuous differences, the part of his cargo which he could not manage, the part which he thought might well shift in a gale and cause the whole ship to founder. He was prepared to say that such differences were mere fluctuations due to the effects of the environment. He was prepared to restrict the field of heredity to what he could analyse. What was *not* Mendelian was *not* hereditary. He was apt to disregard or put in a different department any evidence requiring the use of statistical methods.

From the trials and struggles of the early Mendelians there thus arose a choking of their own science. Questions of human genetics which could not be referred to Mendelian genes he preferred to dismiss. A theory of heredity was therefore built up on the principle of restricting the scope and power of heredity. The whole balance of the subject was shifted. The worst effects of this attitude arose in the study of man and by extension in the social sciences: matters we shall discuss in relation to the second part of the work of Galton.

These errors are now slowly subsiding. Now we can see that all the properties of organisms must be rigorously resolved into their genetic and environmental components. We need no longer trouble in every case to resolve the genetic component itself into individual genes. Indeed, we do much better, in a non-experimental animal living in highly heterogenous cross-breeding groups like man, to speak merely of the genotype as a whole. For in such groups the Mendelian situation cannot arise. 'Characters' in the Mendelian sense, as found in a self-fertilized pea, cannot exist. On the contrary every difference of character depends on many differences between genotypes quite apart from the uncontrolled influence of differences in the environment.

Thus the Mendelian crisis is over. The necessity of expressing variation in terms of experimentally workable units is now of the past. The achievements of that method are now embodied in the structure of our thought. But our thought about heredity in a state of nature is no longer bound by the needs of experiment and analysis. It corresponds, or at least it seems to correspond, with the complexity of nature itself.

UNCERTAINTY FROM OUTSIDE

Summing up, we now see our wonderfully constant and unvarying systems established by vegetative or mitotic heredity, unvarying even in regard to the genes controlling minute and continuous variation in size and shape of organs and organisms. And into these systems we see mutation and sexual recombination introducing uncertainty. This uncertainty arises from the accidents imposed on living matter by the external inorganic world or by the complexity of its own organization and behaviour, as, for example, in the arrangement of pairing chromosomes in the nucleus.

This uncertainty does not seem to arise from any inherent or ultimate indeterminacy. But in order to be sure of this we must ask certain further questions. Can it by any special means be abolished? Has it perhaps been introduced and maintained because it is advantageous? We can next attempt to answer these questions.

10

The Exploitation of Uncertainty

SELECTION OR DRIFT?

UNCERTAINTY invades the working of living systems in mutation and sexual reproduction by the interference of physical and
mechanical accidents. Accidents befall individual cells and
nuclei, chromosomes and genes, owing to a lack of control, or
an imperfect control, over the complexity of their own organization or over the fluctuations of the outside world. What happens
to this uncertainty has to be considered in relation not only to the
cell and the individual and their lives, but also in relation to larger
units and longer periods of time. It concerns the processes of
selection and evolution which appear when we look at populations
and species, and indeed life as a whole.

The consequence of regular self-propagation modified by occasional change is that a new principle begins to operate. The
changed genetic particle will nearly always be better or worse than
its mother particle, or its sisters or cousins. It will be better or
worse in the vital business of self-propagation or specific action,
better in itself or better as part of the whole system of cell,
organism, or species. It will therefore be subject to selection. It
will compete for survival with its alternatives: that is to say, its
sisters and cousins, all of whom will be multiplying like itself, if
they have the chance. And, by its selection, the particle itself, the
cell, or the organism, or even the species to which it belongs, will
maintain or increase its fitness to live and multiply, its adaptation
to the conditions of its life. This is the Darwin-and-Wallace
doctrine of natural selection, which reappears not merely un-
tarnished but considerably brightened and sharpened by passing
through the furnace of our modern genetics.

We now have to ask ourselves what happens to the uncertainty
brought in from lower levels by mutation and recombination. Is it
preserved in evolution by the consequences of selection? Or is it
suppressed?

197

Evolution takes place as a result of changes in the genetic character of a group of interbreeding organisms from one generation to
another. The genetic character can be measured as a frequency of
a sample of representative genes in the group, which is always a
mixture. The estimate of any change it may undergo is then a
statistical one. The change itself is determined by the combination of three agencies: mutation, selection, and sampling variation, the sampling being the sampling of nature and not of an
experimenter. All of them are uncertain since they are due to
other-level agencies beyond our reach. A particular white rabbit
will die when a particular grizzly brown or agouti rabbit will survive on account either of expected or unexpected circumstances.
One gene mutates when its partner does not, subject to the laws of
atomic behaviour. But surely, it will be argued, sampling variation must be regarded as not merely uncertain but genuinely
undetermined? Let us see how it works.

Every population may be represented as consisting of pairs of
mating or mateable individuals. In a population that is stable in
regard to numbers, each fertile pair will beget on the average two
fertile offspring. Each of these will have a random half of the
chromosomes of each of its two parents. Hence for every parent
in the population one half of its chromosomes will be passed on
once to the next generation, one quarter of the chromosomes will
be lost, and one quarter will be passed on twice. They will be lost
or doubled by chance. In the ratio 'chromosomes' are understood to be the whole complement which has usually been split up
by crossing-over into parts of chromosomes. The chance represented by this ratio is a *pure* chance, so far as the population and
the individuals were concerned, prior to the occurrence of selection. The processes of heredity have been adapted, very neatly
adapted, to secure that the chromosomes shall recombine with one
another by a pure chance, although, as we have seen, every step in
this biologically 'chance' process is determined at a lower mechanical level.

Now the Mendelian ratio of Chromosome Propagation, as we
may call it, is true of the products of meiosis and even, in animals,
of the newly fertilized eggs. Like all perfect Mendelian ratios this
one is unimpaired and unimproved by selection: the merits of
individual chromosomes or genes have no influence on it. It

provides them with an irregularity, such as heat motion gives to uniform molecules, irrelevant to their individual merit.

The only departure from this 1:2:1 ratio in nature will thus depend on sampling error (an error which, let us remember, is uncertain with respect to the genotype of the fertilized egg but not undetermined by the mechanics of its cellular antecedents). How will such chance changes affect the course of evolution? Possibly, if the population is very small it may carry gene variations that are selectively neutral or even potentially disadvantageous and different small populations will carry different potential disadvantages. If such populations are very small and very heterogeneous (owing to past or present mutation) the pressure of variation, the supply of uncertainty, may be beyond the capacity of the recombination and selection system to sort and sift and keep under control: there might be what Sewell Wright in Chicago called a 'drift' under pressure of the error of natural sampling.

Experiments have often failed to discover evidence that drift, uncontrolled by selection, occurs in nature in regard to identifiable single genes. They have failed to reveal populations, effective mating-groups, small enough to be expected to show drift. Uncertainty at other levels has provided scope for the determined action of selection: change has become adaptive as soon as it could be expected.

To discover whether the origin of the same beneficial change in different ways in two parts of a species is due to chance or to adaptive advantage is not, however, a simple matter. We may surmise (and it is a question to which we shall return) that the frequencies of mutation and crossing-over, the number of chromosomes, and the mechanisms of meiosis and of outbreeding, are adapted to reduce the uncertainty of selection. For uncertainty of selection is waste of life. But can the leakage of uncertainty be absolutely excluded?

The question as to whether advantage determines all selective change raises in turn another question. Is there always an unconditional advantage or disadvantage in one gene over its alternative that might be selected?

The answer is twofold. In regard to the *internal* relations of organisms, genes, that is single units of exchange, are not practical alternatives in sexual populations: genes, super-genes and the invisible polygenes are all being recombined. Their recombinations are such as to avoid as effectively as possible the occurrence of unconditional advantages or disadvantages or even neutrality. Above all, the variation of polygenes provides a cushion against the shocks of grosser mutations.

In regard to the *external* relations of organisms the effect of the uncertainty of recombination is no less profound. For the recombination of genes means also a recombination of environments with which individuals come into contact. A variety of places, times, and durations of life, arise as alternative conditions of survival and reproduction. There may even be a choice of environments. Such a choice may be, as we shall see later, most effective in causing the cleavage of a species. How then can we speak of selective advantages or disadvantages of single units of recombination derived from test-tube experiments? Drift is something which acts on one part of the system of variation to be compensated for by the reactions of all the other parts.

Drift will have the greatest effect through an agent of variation which begins by being adverse and only later becomes beneficial : namely, chromosome rearrangement. Structural change in the chromosomes, as we call it, often has no physiological effect on the organism in which it arises. Inversions of a piece of chromosome, for example, have no importance except in relation to the corresponding piece which has not been inverted in a possible partner-chromosome. It then has the effect of preventing crossing-over or, if it fails in this, of causing sterility.

Hybrid sterility, on this view, will sometimes take its origin from drift : the chance divergence of two parts of a population living in different places will eventually create a barrier to crossing and the origin of two new species from one ancestral group. From this process selective control has been removed, sometimes owing to its being neutral at the time of its origin; and sometimes owing to geographical isolation at this time : that is, through mere absence of mixing until it is too late to avert the evolutionary change; and sometimes again owing to the advantages of polymorphism or hybridity. The most important of evolutionary agents would thus seem to operate subject to a biological uncertainty, a spurious indeterminacy.

The role of chance is quite opposed for the *parts* and the *whole*.

The separate parts – genes, and arrangements of genes, and the beginnings of super-genes – out of which different small mating groups construct their genotypes, may come to differ by chance. But the whole combinations will be internally selected by a deterministic and non-random process. Selection determines the whole balance in each race but not all the differences out of which different balances are constructed in small separated populations.

A second circumstance of drift may be said to arise among cytoplasmic particles. Such particles, as we have seen, depend for their survival on adaptation to one of two avenues of success. They may successfully cooperate with the nucleus in whose company they are inherited. Or they may multiply without regard to the nucleus, thereby increasing their chances of transmission by infection. These two evolutionary paths are, as we might expect, mutually exclusive. No particle for long can attempt to run with the hare of heredity and hunt with the hounds of infection. And the point of divergence for a single particle may well be determined by uncertainty at other levels.

In the difference of opinion as to whether drift occurs, the twin principles of evolution – the supply of uncertainty and its suppression by a deterministic process of selection – come into collision. The result is to show that the one exploits the other. It is now clear that other-level conditions whose determination is irrelevant to the problem on hand, by their interference, are continually introducing uncertainty into evolutionary processes. The importance of uncertainty increases, as Schrödinger has pointed out, when the unit becomes smaller. And it also increases when its action is delayed. Neutral changes, preserved by their neutrality, may become of momentous importance by later finding the right, the effective, combination. The decisive steps in evolution may thus arise by drift. These products of lower-level uncertainty, once they have been introduced into the system, however, are passed through a series of selective sieves, generation after generation, any one of which may catch them and turn them to use in constructing a profitable deterministic pattern. To use the phrase of Lucretius, they beget a use (*procreant usum*). A few of them leak through yielding a residue of genuine uncertainty, which for a shorter or longer time may remain unexploited.

Turn this the other way round and you see something else. The fraction of uncertain changes which are turned to profit are a measure of the success of the genetic system. This fraction will vary. Genetic recombination is adapted to expose variability most efficiently to natural selection. But it can be adapted to do so only in mating groups of the size found in the ancestors of a particular group. When a group contracts rapidly, as often happens in nature, the adaptation will not keep pace with the change. It is then especially that natural selection will fail to keep drift under control.

In considering the broadest of biological problems – not in a system artificially isolated for experimental or theoretical simplification – we are thus continually brought up against the interference of determination at one level with determination at another level. There is an uncertainty relationship. The many-level organization, with the interference between levels which it entails, introduces an effectively new principle characteristic of biology. This principle limits the simple statement that living organisms obey the same laws as non-living matter. The outstanding example of the inter-level reactions of living systems, however, still awaits us. It is found in the evolution of heredity itself.

THE EVOLUTION OF HEREDITY

Heredity, Selection and Evolution are systems at three levels of increasing complexity. Their components operate deterministically but uncertainly at each level. We have seen that there is an interference of lower with higher levels, more so than in physical systems. There is, however, also an interference of higher with lower levels. These forms of interference are often now known as feed-back mechanisms. They are peculiarly biological and deserve careful scrutiny.

Natural selection can discriminate only between particles, cells, or organisms which differ in heredity; that is, between self-propagating units which differ in what they propagate and in what they determine. It favours those units which leave the more numerous posterity. Now this is an advantage which may inhere merely in the individual concerned or partly in the properties of its posterity. The principle that the properties of an individual may be selected not for themselves but because one of them favours the fertility or other properties of its children, or grand-children, puzzled Darwin. He could not understand the selection, for example, of a suitable sex-ratio. He found that an equality of the numbers of the sexes seemed to be favoured in most species. Yet such an equality could be due only to certain properties of the *previous* generation. Thus he writes:

> In no case, as far as we can see, would an inherited tendency to pro-duce both sexes in equal numbers or to produce one sex in excess, be a direct advantage or disadvantage to certain individuals more than to others ... and therefore a tendency of this kind could not be gained through natural selection. Nevertheless there are certain animals (for instance, fishes and cirripedes) in which two or more males appear to be necessary for the fertilization of the female; and the males accordingly largely preponderate, but it is by no means obvious how this male-producing tendency could have been acquired. I formerly thought that when a tendency to produce the two sexes in equal numbers was an advantage to the species it would follow from natural selection, but I now see that the whole problem is so intricate that it is safer to leave its solution for the future.
>
> *The Descent of Man*, 2nd ed., 1878, ch. 8

Darwin's difficulty is removed when we realize that what is being selected is not only the organism but its genetic system as well; the capacity it has of begetting, when mated within its ac-customed group, equal numbers of the two sexes. Is this capacity itself hereditary and separable from other capacities in heredity by Mendelian recombination? We know now that it is. The sexes are determined by alternative sex chromosomes which pass into sister germ cells. The survival and consequent frequency of the sex chromosomes in the germ cells can be modified by particular genes which they or other chromosomes carry. Thus the chromo-somes, although they control heredity, are themselves subject to it. They are in the same position as Members of Parliament who are subject as individuals to the laws they enact as a body. The chromosomes are subject as individuals to control by the heredity or the genotype which they constitute and operate as a nucleus.

These principles of antecedent, ancestral, or racial selection, and of the genotypic control of the chromosomes, have operated to favour improvements, or rather successive adaptations, which, as we saw, are required by the system of heredity itself. Chromosomes can be made larger or smaller. Their properties of pairing and their frequencies of mutation and crossing-over are genetically controlled and are genetically variable. They can be selected, and they obviously have been selected, for we find related species differing by as much as a thousand times in the size of their chromosomes. We also find them differing many times in the frequencies of crossing-over among their chromosomes. We even find them differing entirely in the ratio of the sexes. In some species there is equality while in their near relatives the males are, as Leeuwenhoeck discovered, largely or entirely suppressed, leaving the indispensable female sex to multiply unassisted for a season or for an age.

It is not difficult to survey the various kinds of reproductive and hereditary systems found among plants and animals. And when we do so we find that they may be arranged in evolutionary sequences. These sequences themselves make sense if we suppose that all the changes responsible for them – with which we are separately familiar in experiment – have been favoured by their advantages, not to the plants and animals in which they began, but to their posterity, a posterity which extends from their immediate offspring to their remotest descendants and so takes us right back to the origins of sexual reproduction itself.

One of the simple evolutionary changes that we can put our fingers on with most confidence is that by which sexual reproduction is suddenly stopped and replaced by parthenogenesis. It has happened certainly thousands of times, probably millions of times, in the course of evolution that a fertilized egg develops through a failure of mitosis with double the usual chromosome complement. It is 4x instead of 2x. This is well known in earthworms and weevils, in ferns and dandelions. The new polyploid plant or animal is often able to reproduce without sexual fertilization, that is by parthenogenesis. It then establishes a new race.

This new race has no meiosis, no crossing-over, no segregation, no reduction of chromosome number. Under cover of the appearance of egg production and ordinary development it is in effect asexual. It has abolished all the uncertainties of sexual recombination. It has replaced them by the certainties of ordinary vegetative development. A new race of organisms is produced, uniform and invariable. It is usually but not always shortlived.

From this evolutionary process we learn that the uncertainties of sexual recombination are not inherent in animal and plant propagation. They arise from processes which have survived natural selection, processes which are retained for their adaptive value. When they break down we learn beyond question what they have been doing. They have been promoting variation. They have been guaranteeing not survival in the present but adaptability in the future.

Effects of selection on the processes of heredity and conversely of heredity on the processes of selection, delayed by their interlocking, lead to involved cycles of evolutionary change, and to discontinuities, themselves of many kinds, which interrupt this change and give rise to species, also of many kinds. The whole scheme is more complex than any that was understood by Darwin – or the Darwinians. What remains true, and far more effective than Darwin imagined, is the pattern he envisaged, operating by way of natural selection. Here, with the interference in heredity from the higher level of evolution, there is yet another of the sieves for catching uncertainty and fitting it into a profitable and determined pattern.

Further, we notice that selection favours not only one gene at the expense of another, but also one cell or one individual, one structure or one habit, one race or one species, at the expense of another. The materials for natural selection are all the propagable differentials of living organisms both separately and in all their combinations and interactions in varying environments freely chosen or externally enforced. From its action on these, by deterministic processes, adaptation and evolution result.

The machinery of sexual reproduction depends for its importance, as Weismann pointed out, on genetic recombination. We may now say that this recombination depends for its importance on the uncertainty introduced into biological systems from a lower physical level, inside and outside the cell. This uncertainty, magnified by all the processes of the multiplication of chromosomes, and of their pairing, crossing-over and segregation, enables natural selection to act on populations of organisms so that they respond deterministically to changes in their environment: that is, to changes outside the individual organism and of too large an amplitude in time, space and materials for the individual to register, or even to perceive.

We can also look upon the process of the evolution of heredity from yet another point of view. The marvellous organization of the genes in chromosomes, and of the chromosomes in nuclei, and the precisely identical propagation of genes, chromosomes and nuclei, by mitosis, have been made possible by the fact that all relative imperfections are eliminated by the death of the result. Thus the whole business of crossing-over and recombination, superimposed upon mutation, is a means of *exploiting* uncertainty by using it as the basis of deterministic biological change, of rapid and efficient adaptation of an unlimited lineage of sexually reproducing individuals. But underneath this system is another. This is a system which has been evolved as a means of stablization, a means of *abolishing* uncertainty in the development of the individual. How this system works we may now consider.

DEVELOPMENT

The problem of determination and uncertainty in development is entirely different from that in variation, recombination and selection. Indeed the difference provides an instructive contrast, an experimental test, the experiment being the largest that nature has been good enough to arrange for us.

What is remarkable about development, and what the eighteenth century refused to believe, is that an egg should develop into a whole plant or animal; an egg consisting of jelly or protoplasm and showing little or no recognizable structure, indeed no large structure, as we now know, beyond a nucleus containing invisible chromosomes.

Still more remarkable is it when we reflect that the whole mature organism, which is determined within the egg, is determined to develop not merely into something that will work, and bearing the general character of its species, but into something bearing a character defined down to the remotest detail or aberration that may appear only fifty, sixty, or seventy years later. No inorganic machine is thus remotely comparable in its precision with the invisible apparatus of the egg. Whatever uncertainties it suffers from must be, it would seem, of a very trivial nature. How does it do it?

The appearance of the egg is deceptive. The newly laid egg of a fly or a moth has of course only a single nucleus. Yet sixteen hours after it is laid its heart is beginning to throb. How can this come about? The cytoplasm of the egg is mapped out in regard to how it will react with the nuclei which will be spread through it

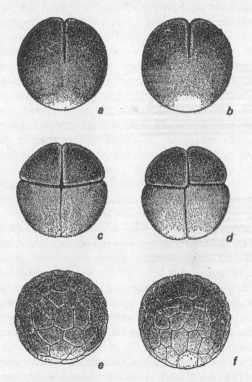

Figure 15

Surface views of the two sides of a fertilized frog's egg during the early mitoses or 'cleavages' which divide it up into cells. The top two stages correspond with the inside view shown in Figure 3. Note that the division is not the same on the two sides, even in the size of the cells (from Morgan, 1934, after Brachet).

by mitosis when development begins. It has a pattern, an invisible pattern. Each part is determined as to what structure of the grub or larva or embryo it will grow into. This can be proved (as Geigy and Lüscher in Switzerland found in 1941) by burning one spot on the egg with ultra-violet light and leaving the rest undamaged: a leg, or an eye, alone is prevented from developing. A few hours later even the specific determinants for the wings of the adult fly or moth, which will emerge from the pupa only after the metamorphosis of the larva, are themselves already sorted out.

In the unfertilized egg, it would thus seem, the plasmagenes of development have already been secreted by the egg nucleus. And the cytoplasm has, as it were, set into a mosaic of determinants. It is a mosaic whose parts will react in hundreds, perhaps thousands, of specifically different ways with a constantly self-propagated nucleus. As the egg develops, this stereotyped nucleus (and there are ultimately 600,000,000,000,000 of them in our bodies) doubling by mitosis every ten minutes will be multiplied and sent round to each part of the egg. They will be sent round somewhat like a circular letter posted by a candidate for election to his constituents, each of whom will react to it in his own way (Figure 15).

The diversity of cells in one body is of course quite a different kind of thing from the diversity of human beings in a community. The cells fall into classes. The cells of different tissues, bone, muscle, nerve and skin are different. But cells of the same tissue can to a great extent replace one another. This we can tell by transplanting tissues from one part of the body to another.

The development of two embryos from one egg, which we shall be discussing later, shows that our picture of the egg mapped out as a presumptive plan of the future individual is not sufficient, not at least for the higher animals. Indeed, experiments with the eggs of frogs (which are more accessible and convenient for chopping up than our own) have shown that the developing egg is organized in the same sense as it will be later when it has grown up. That is to say, its parts interact, influencing one another. The lines of determination do not simply diverge. They are entwined; they anastomose. The different processes are not solitary and independent. They cooperate. The effective chemical reagents, the

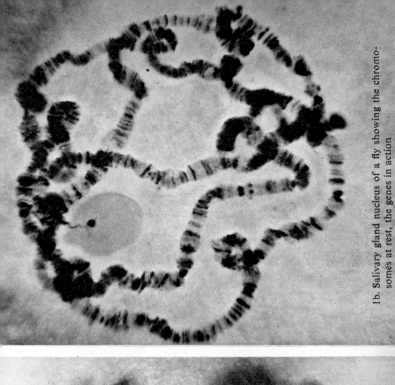

1b. Salivary gland nucleus of a fly showing the chromosomes at rest, the genes in action

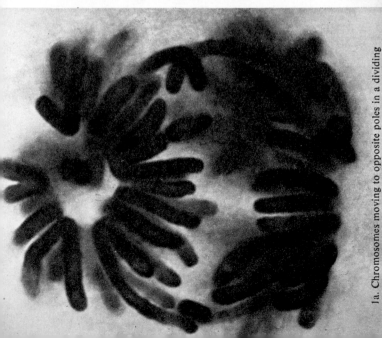

1a. Chromosomes moving to opposite poles in a dividing cell from the blood of a newt

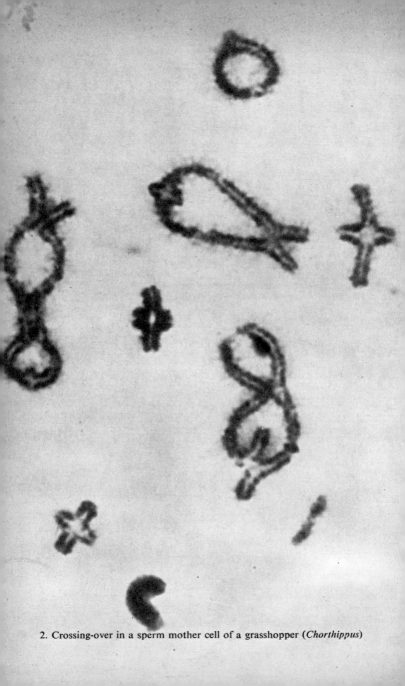

2. Crossing-over in a sperm mother cell of a grasshopper (*Chorthippus*)

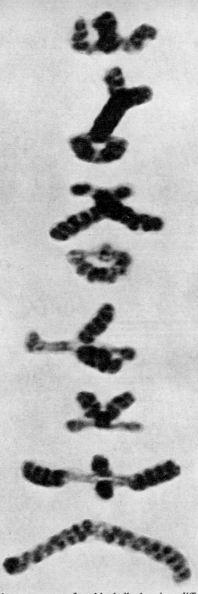

3. The paired chromosomes of a bluebell showing different places of crossing-over

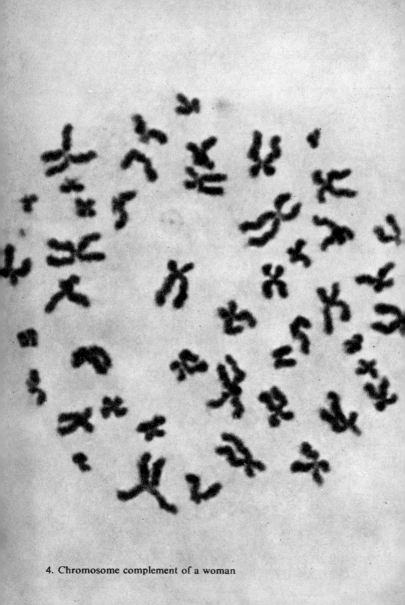

4. Chromosome complement of a woman

specifically responsible molecules, are not held within the cells in which they arise; they diffuse from cell to cell and from tissue to tissue. Thus organization depends on a determined localization and also on a determined breakdown of a localization.

For the moment, just within the limits of this isolated field of thought and experiment, how utterly unimportant the nucleus of the egg looks! But let the experimenter slip, let the single spot containing the nucleus of the fertilized egg be burnt, and the full responsibility of the nucleus soon becomes evident. The egg will come to nothing. It will, in a few hours, cease to live.

The long-standing determination is in the hands of the nucleus. This can be shown very well in crosses between species. The egg cytoplasm with its pattern of plasmagenes has been laid down by the nucleus of the mother species. The embryo nuclei on the other hand are hybrids or mixtures containing the chromosomes of two species. The beginning of development is therefore like that of the mother species, but soon it switches over to a mixed character. And, if the two parent species are widely different, the disharmony becomes too great, development comes to a standstill and the embryo dies. Thus, evidently, in the egg the maternal nucleus has laid down in advance the determinants with which its successor will, after fertilization, have to deal in producing the differentiation on which the character of the new individual will depend.

In this way the great eighteenth-century squabble between pre-formation and epigenesis has been resolved by genetics.

How do we now picture the process of development? A differentiated and asymmetrical structure of the animal or plant egg – itself derived from the structure of the organ on which it develops – leads indirectly to a differentiation of cytoplasm among the different cells, or spheres of nuclear action, into which the egg segments itself by nuclear division. In different types of cells different genes in the nucleus are stimulated to produce and pass into the cell different proteins, which react later (the delay being inherent in diffusion and also in self-propagation) with other genes.

The reactions of nucleus and cytoplasm are successive or synchronous, competitive or cooperative. They produce various cycles of activities in the nucleus characteristic of the cells of different tissues, cycles which are visible in the expansions and contractions of the genes in the polytene chromosomes. These cycles determine differentiation – a diversification of shape and work among cells, and within cells, both in space and in time – to which the variety of plant and animal forms owe their origin.

Each form in its maturity derives itself ultimately from the differentiation between the nucleus and the cytoplasm of the egg, and between the genes within the nucleus. The character of the cytoplasm in the egg has itself, of course, been determined by the genes during its growth, but, owing to the delay in interaction, it is the genes of the mother which have been effective. There is an endless chain of reactions overlapping from one life-cycle to the next.

To the working of such an endless chain system indeterminacy would be fatal. The assumption of indeterminacy would have been fatal to its discovery. Uncertainty, on the other hand, there certainly is; but now the uncertainty is error, error no longer encouraged, but limited and controlled.

One of the most interesting instances of uncertainty or spurious indeterminacy, since it is found in each one of us as well as all around us, is that arising from the lack of symmetry or likeness between the two sides of the animal egg. The two sides of a human being are never exact mirror images. Part of the asymmetry such as that which puts the heart on the left-hand side and also that which makes most of us right-handed, is neither an error nor an uncertainty; it is adaptive and therefore a determined developmental effect. But part of it may well be uncertain in the sense that it arises from an accidental asymmetry of the egg. Our two hands are never quite alike. But they ought to be. Here is an uncertainty which, beyond a slight degree, must become seriously disadvantageous. It is therefore an uncertainty which (unlike those of sexual recombination) the constitution of heredity, and the processes of development determined by it, must be nicely adapted to avoid. It must also be responsible for a part, although, as we shall see, not all, of the differences which are found at birth between one-egg twins.

Now reflection will show that these uncertainties imply not the least dilution of the principle of determinacy in heredity. No system of development and reproduction is conceivable by which an absolutely symmetrical egg could be produced. The very materials of heredity in the chromosomes of the egg nucleus are incapable of absolute symmetry, for their continual and random reconstruction is, as we have seen, the material of evolutionary change. And an ovary producing many eggs cannot easily be symmetrical with respect to each in turn. The asymmetry of development is therefore an example of uncertainty arising from the randomness and asymmetry of evolutionary change and individual development and not from any absence of uniformity in cause and effect.

When we follow all the physical events which make up the processes of heredity, reproduction and development, we accordingly find no need to suppose that any step in the sequence is in a physical sense *undetermined*. But here and there we find the interference in genetic processes of actions which are *irrelevant* to the process on hand or incompletely controllable, and therefore uncertain.

In the special field of mutation and recombination these uncertainties are not suppressed but kept within limits and exploited. In the field of reproduction and development, on the other hand, the uncertainties are suppressed as completely as the chemical and physical conditions allow.

THE SHIFTING EDGE OF DISCOVERY

In this long argument and sequence of discovery, an appearance of indeterminacy has no part except at the end of each sequence. Always at the end we come to an unexplained margin, an ultimate or peripheral uncertainty. But the process by which we get there, the process which gives us the means of making verifiable predictions over the area already covered, is one of assuming and proving, or disproving, the determined relationships that are implied by the name Genetics. This process has met with serious hitches, such as the sixty years' delay in transferring Mendelism from a statistical to an individual basis of ascertainment. But biologists are naturally unlikely to abandon it now at the moment of its fruition.

In the understanding of this sequence of discovery, genetics differs from other sciences only in its greater complexity. The chief difficulty is the use made by genetic systems of devices for creating and exploiting uncertainty which, it now appears, is the basis of organic evolution. The process of this creation or exploitation is deterministic. If we mistake it for the operation of indeterminacy (which we can do only in ignorance of the modes of suppressing uncertainty) we miss the point of the evolutionary mechanism.

In the past the point, it now seems, always has been missed. It has become a commonplace of polite philosophy to say that the first principle of heredity is *chance*. We now see that the first principle is *certainty*. Chance comes second, and certainty comes in again in the third place.

Another aspect of the problem is seen in relation to scientific method. If we were to assume a true or final indeterminacy the statistical description of an occurrence would bring all inquiry to an end. We should be in an even worse position than if we assumed an entelechy, a final design or purpose whose intermediate processes might still be inquired into. The analogy is instructive in the present instance for it so happens that the first to suggest with any argument the relationship of crossing-over and chiasmata, as we saw, was Janssens. His view was that the occurrence of meiosis in all sexual plants and animals would have no purpose unless these products were genetically different. Morgan, who (as he told the present writer) regarded Janssens' argument of purpose with ironical amusement, was nevertheless richly rewarded for adopting his conclusion.

A similar assumption of purpose underlies the fruitful idea of Winge. This most versatile experimenter in 1916 suggested that polyploids arose by doubling of the chromosome numbers in sterile hybrid diploids in order that each chromosome should have an identical mate with which to pair. If indeed this view had been accepted in its integrity no further progress could have been made. But both Janssens' and Winge's views were, as a matter of course, stripped of any implications of purpose they may have contained and examined merely as generalizations of cause and effect, to be tested by the control of cause and effect, by the processes of experiment.

Statistical methods of generalization do not imply that we regard the units of behaviour as activated undeterminedly. They merely mean that the units which matter are (for the time being) too small, or too complex, or too inaccessible, to be observed or handled as individuals at the significant stage of their history. Gas molecules are too small to be experimented with individually: hence the kinetic theory of gases is statistical. The germ cells and the chromosomes in them, which connect one generation of plant and animal with another, are too delicate to be handled one at a time: hence the Mendelian laws are statistical; or rather they were statistical and still are partly so. But the advance of genetics has depended on showing that the uncertainty contained in statistical statements arises from determined processes acting at lower and lower levels – ultimately non-biological levels – and capable of being used deterministically in evolution and also in experiment.

We can now perhaps make the distinction between indeterminacy and uncertainty, as we have been using these notions, quite clear.

Indeterminacy is the situation in which we cannot predict the future of a system on the basis of all the *relevant* physical data. It is the situation in which we can no longer suppose that

> ... the first Morning of Creation wrote
> What the last Dawn of Reckoning shall read.

It is a situation which is sometimes supposed to occur but (in spite of the radium atom) can never be proved to occur.

Uncertainty, on the other hand, is the situation in which we cannot predict the future of a system on the basis of all the *accessible* physical data. This is a situation which arises with the discovery of every new level of observation or analysis. It disappears with the discovery of a technique which allows us to penetrate to a still lower level.

INTERLUDE

After considering these weighty matters we deserve a lighter interlude. The moral solution of genetic problems, the theory of the inheritance of acquired characters, has long been food for laughter. But it is so much easier to understand and so much more satisfying to believe than the analytic and experimental solution that it continues to be generally held. There is, however, a demand nowadays for 'scientific' evidence for all kinds of belief. This evidence is produced in an abundance and accepted with a faith which are here shown to constitute a world movement. The movement is intellectually negligible and it has recently become fraudulent, but its traditional continuity assures us that all branches of human thought will have to reckon with it.

11

The Evergreen Superstition

THE RESURRECTION OF LAMARCK

DOWN the ages we have seen a cleavage always separating two theories of heredity. The first was the old theory, the direct or vitalistic theory, that the parent in his whole character at the time of begetting was represented in the offspring. Each generation was supposed to be somehow condensed into a seed or an egg from which it expanded into the next generation. The offspring therefore bore the marks inflicted by nature on the person of the parent. Acquired characters were inherited. This theory, as we have seen, was adopted or even taken for granted by the early Hebrews, by Theophrastus, by Buffon, by Lamarck, and by Darwin and Spencer.

The second theory, the new theory, the *indirect* theory, was more difficult. It was represented in the notion of the *genitalia corpora* of Lucretius. It was expressed in the repudiation of the inheritance of acquired characters. It assumed that something which was passed down from generation to generation determined the character of the body but was itself uninfluenced in its character by what happened to the body. This theory was espoused for the first time in an unequivocal form by Weismann. It was obviously supported by the chromosome theory as it took shape in the hands of the German and American cytologists. And it fitted the new teachings of Mendelism like a glove. Indeed every improvement in the design and interpretation of experiments made the direct theory more difficult and the indirect theory more convincing.

At the beginning of our century the ancient cleavage between the two theories of heredity thus became, for the first time, a cardinal issue in the study of life. On the one hand, where the impact of genetics and cell study were felt, a change was taking place. The old idea that personal adaptations to the environment, the peculiarities forced upon us by lucky or unlucky circumstances, or by an ameliorative purpose in the Creator, or by the power of the will were inherited was giving way. The new notion of hard particles, microscopically visible and mathematically predictable, incorrigibly deterministic and resistant to the interference of any divine purpose apart from that reflected in natural selection, was taking its place.

Where the impact of genetic experiments was not felt, however, older views held their ground. Physiologists still liked to think that heredity was under the influence of development. Museum naturalists still liked to explain evolution, as revealed by the chronological order of fossil specimens, by the direct action of the environment and without recourse to formulae or microscopes. Bacteriologists too were confronted by the most confusing plasticity in their materials which left them wondering whether to doubt the safety of their cultures from contamination. And in the wide world, of course, the educated man, the scholar and the economist, the psychologist and the jurist, the historian, the social scientist, and the liberal or optimistic philosopher, universally, and sometimes enthusiastically, believed in the inheritance of acquired characters. There was therefore a great public demand for a reply to the uncompromising doctrine of genetics.

This unusual tension in the world of ideas led to a strange response, an intellectual undercurrent which, arising at the same time as the rediscovery of Mendelism, soon ran powerfully in human affairs. It had many beginnings, obscure or notorious, in Western Europe, in the United States and in Russia.

One beginning was in 1904 when a plausible young zoologist found his way into the Biological Research Institute in Vienna. His name was Paul Kammerer. He showed himself to be expert in breeding and rearing all kinds of frogs and toads, lizards and salamanders. He discovered that remarkable changes of behaviour could be brought about in these animals by changes in their conditions of life. With these changes went transformations of structure. Salamanders against a darker background, like chameleons but more slowly, would themselves turn darker. The changes were sometimes of a kind that distinguished different species under wild conditions.

What if these changes were inherited? That was the question

that Kammerer asked himself. Soon he began to make breeding-experiments. Induced colour changes behaved as Mendelian factor differences; or so he believed. When he published his results they were disputed. Confidently he went on with new experiments on new animals. Soon the eerie croak of the midwife toad was heard in his laboratory. In ordinary frogs and toads, which mate in the water, the male embraces the slippery female with the help of horny pads on his thumbs. But the midwife toad mates on dry land. He takes hold of the strings of eggs as the female squirts them out and then wraps them round his legs, carefully fertilizing them as he does so, and keeping them there until they hatch. He has no thumb pads.

These toads Kammerer persuaded to mate in the water in the ordinary way, merely by keeping them warmer. The males then, he said, developed the pads found in male toads and frogs of the water-mating species. Nay more: the change increased from generation to generation (*Nature*, **112**, 237-8, 1923).

Kammerer's experiments were keenly debated from his first publication of the results in 1909. Attempts were made to repeat them but no one succeeded. Discrepancies were found in his statements and then he would slightly shift his ground. From time to time he published new results and made new claims. When toads fell under suspicion lizards took their place. The debate between those favouring the inheritance of acquired characters and those disputing it became hotter. When political peace came in 1919 the academic war was resumed. At length, in 1923, Professor Kammerer was invited to England. He brought with him as evidence a solitary male toad preserved in a bottle. This animal he exhibited at meetings in Cambridge and at the Linnean Society in London. Kammerer stated his point of view on the effects of changed environment which he illustrated by an analogy:

A new piece of clothing irritates, but this irritation diminishes the longer the clothing is worn, and it ultimately disappears. Likewise there is a morphological irritation from each part of the body and this diminishes in the same way. When there have been recurrent changes the irritation is stronger. Under suitable conditions of duration and intensity the irritation penetrates to the germplasm. [Notice the use of

Weismann's elusive term.] There it renders permanent a potentiality for repetition of the actual change which brought it into play.

Nature, **111**, 738

What is this doctrine? It is Lamarck's theory with the will dropped out. It is the neo-Lamarckian theory. Unlike Lamarck's giraffe, Kammerer's frog does not desire to stretch his neck, perhaps because he has no neck or perhaps because he has no desire. For desire does not govern even his mating-pads. His dominant passion is one of irritation. He refuses to be a victim of circumstances. He responds to the challenge of adversity by growing what is needed.

At the meeting of the Linnean Society there was certainly much irritation. Passions were roused. Kammerer exhibited his specimen. An embryologist, Professor MacBride, a stout little Irishman with a shrill voice, and like his compatriot, G. B. Shaw, a pugnacious Lamarckian, sponsored and defended the visiting lecturer. Bateson disputed both the evidence and the argument. He doubted whether either Kammerer or MacBride knew how toads used their thumbs when they embraced. He compared Kammerer's illustrations with 'spirit photographs'. He suggested that the induced mating-pad was merely a patch of pigment and he hinted that Kammerer had attempted to 'correct nature': in other words, had faked his results. More was said which did not appear in the columns of *Nature* (**111**, 739).

After this discussion Kammerer was a lost man – that is, in the western world. The discussion, however, had not passed unnoticed in Soviet Russia. It was not usual in that country to mention the name of Lamarck officially, partly perhaps because Marx never mentioned it. But as long ago as 1906, J. V. Stalin had pointed out the 'Neo-Lamarckian theory is taking the place of neo-Darwinian theory'. If true, this was a good thing because the neo-Lamarckian theory demonstrates a point in Marxist doctrine; it 'shows how quantitative changes give rise to qualitative ones'.

Whether on this account or for directly political reasons, the belated discovery of evidence for the neo-Lamarckian theory was much appreciated in Soviet Russia. In 1925 the Russian physiologist, Pavlov, himself claimed to have shown that mice, whose parents had been trained to answer bells, themselves learnt to answer bells more quickly, thus proving an inheritance of acquired characters. But Pavlov was no fraud. He was not even interested in pleasing the government, and he withdrew the claim when he found it was a mistake. Kammerer, however, had stuck to his guns. In 1925 Kammerer was accordingly invited by Lunacharsky, Soviet Commissar for Public Instruction, to become head of a laboratory of the Soviet Academy of Sciences which would be built for him in Moscow.

Kammerer prepared to leave for Russia, but, before he left, a member of the staff of the American Museum of Natural History, Dr G. K. Noble, obtained permission from the Vienna Institute to examine microscopically the mating-pad of Kammerer's now famous toad. On 7 August 1926, he published the result in the London periodical, *Nature*. He had failed to find any horny growth on the foot. But he had found a deposit of something injected under the skin. This deposit had the recognizable properties of Indian ink. Five weeks later Kammerer wrote a letter bequeathing his collections to the Soviet Academy of Sciences. And, going out to the country near by, to the Hochschneeberg, he shot himself.

For Kammerer and his reputation this tragedy was the end. For the world in general, however, it proved to be only the prologue of a larger catastrophe.

THE SCENE MOVES TO MOSCOW

Lunacharsky was an accomplished playwright and one of the intellectual generation of Bolsheviks. His scruples, however, were those of the politician rather than of the scientist. Thwarted of his immediate object, he proceeded to the same goal in an indirect way. He wrote, produced, and (with his wife) appeared in, a film dealing with the problem of the inheritance of acquired characters. It was entitled *Salamandra*. It described the heroic life and tragic persecution of a man whose achievements were modelled on those of Kammerer. It revealed the Soviet Government's attempts to save him from his capitalist persecutors which were (in the film) successful. This film as described by Goldschmidt was being shown generally in the Soviet Union in 1929. It marks the beginning of the adoption of the Lamarckian theory, without the name, as the official doctrine of the Soviet Government.

The process of adoption was spread over twenty years. During this time, its antithesis, the accepted theory of genetics resting on chromosome studies and experimental breeding, was step by step repudiated. In place of it a new science, a revived Lamarckism, was established. This revival did not attempt to trace its ancestry (as we have done) to the views of Aristotle or St Augustine or even, at first, to Buffon or Lamarck. It claimed to be a revolutionary novelty, the exclusive invention of a new Soviet biology delivering its authority from inside Russia. It was inspired by the observations and opinions of a Russian amateur plant-breeder, Ivan Michurin (1860–1935), who did his chief work under the Tsarist regime, before the Revolution of 1917. Michurin was breeding fruit near Moscow at the same time that Kammerer was raising frogs at Vienna and they arrived at just the same kinds of conclusions. What did Michurin claim to have done?

Michurin found that his results in breeding fruit were different from those of Mendel in breeding peas. The apples did not show sharp differences or simple ratios in their progeny. The reason for this is well known. Peas are self-fertilized, apples are cross-fertilized. Indeed, most fruit trees are self-sterile. They can be bred only by cross-fertilization of two different varieties. And they are themselves always, therefore, the result of such cross-fertilization. They are complex hybrids, and, like human beings, they are therefore not capable of reproducing the Mendelian situation. Writing in 1916 Michurin would have known this if he had read scientific journals. In his ignorance he writes quite mildly. Mendel's law, he says, is not applicable to 'perennial fruit trees', nor to 'animal hybrids', nor to 'kitchen garden crops'. Not even to peas, presumably! Michurin's description of what he regards as breeding-experiments is often unclear and often at variance with the corresponding experiments carried out in western countries at the same time.

Apart from breeding, however, Michurin made experiments of another kind. He claimed that pear seedlings which would not fruit for twenty years can be made to fruit in nine years by grafting scions of good old varieties round the base of the seedling's stem at seven years. The old variety teaches the young seedling how to flower; hence he gave it the name of Mentor. But we find that pear seedlings fruit at times varying, when they are bred from the same parents, from eight to fifteen years (Crane: *Heredity*, **3**, 254, 1949), so that Michurin's result would happen without any grafting every now and then if he just picked a lucky seedling. And he does not say how often it happened.

From this beginning Michurin proceeds to claim that in three instances he was able to use the mentor method of teaching the young plants how to improve the quality, colour and flavour of their fruits. And finally, returning from practice to theory, he concludes:

It is quite apparent that the method can be used to effect various other changes in the properties and characters of hybrid varieties, such as the increase of fertility, attainment of larger sized fruits, etc.

Before the discovery of the sexual meaning of pollination in plants the distinction between crossing two plants and grafting them was bound to be obscure. Indeed, all philosophers who discussed the matter, from Theophrastus to Francis Bacon, believed that, in grafting, the stock changed the breeding properties, that is the genetic character, of the scion. Even Darwin, as we saw, could not be sure of the difference between 'sexual reproduction' and 'budding' or vegetative reproduction. Thus the act of grafting, they thought, produced a hybrid. How indeed could they think otherwise? The matter could not be cleared up finally until the Mendelian theory was related to what was seen of reproduction under the microscope and modern genetics was brought forth.

The principles of grafting, however, have long been understood by practical gardeners. The budding and grafting of scions of superior fruit-trees on inferior stocks, as a means of multiplying the better kinds, has been practised in the western world for over 2,000 years. The use of grafting was described by Theophrastus and by Virgil (*Georgics* II). Chaucer's host took it for granted that 'Of feble trees ther comen wrecched impes.' Nowadays scions of good old varieties of all kinds of fruit-trees are, every year, in their millions, grafted on young and inferior seedlings. Every year, in western countries, millions of scions of the veteran rose varieties are grafted on to callow stocks of last year's dog-rose seedlings. Yet no one has ever found an improvement of the

223

kind Michurin claims in the stock. Indeed, the absence of such an improvement is constantly remarked on when stocks accidentally replace scions and shoot from the base in neglected orchards and rose gardens. No educated gardener in the world could therefore accept Michurin's theories.

A particular type of experiment throws light on the genetic consequences of grafting: namely, the production of so-called graft hybrids. The most famous graft hybrid arose in 1825. A French nurseryman, M. Adam, had grafted a twig of the little purple broom on a stock of the common yellow laburnum. To his surprise a shoot grew out of the join between stock and scion which was neither one thing nor the other. Its flowers were neither yellow nor purple but a mere muddy colour. This new plant has been propagated ever since. M. Adam thought it was a hybrid, a graft hybrid, and called it *Cytisus Adami*. It is, we find, a monster to which we give the name of a *chimera*, that mixture of lion and serpent with which our ancestors used to terrify one another.

The chimera is sterile but it is not a hybrid. It reveals its nature from time to time by throwing out a shoot of pure broom or pure laburnum. A skin of broom, as microscopic study shows, has grown over a core of laburnum. They have grown next to one another for over a hundred years. Yet out of this intimate mixture, cell-to-cell and year after year, the original forms regularly emerge pure, undamaged, and also unimproved. Anyone can see it who cares to grow the plant in his garden.

Scores of other such graft hybrids or chimeras have been made in the last fifty years, especially between medlars and hawthorns and between tomatoes and black nightshades. Some of them have proved fertile. Their seedlings have then always shown the same absence of true combination, the same emergence of the original types without any contamination, as in *Cytisus Adami*. The environment, even in the shape of the immediately surrounding cells, does not touch, or tamper with, heredity.

The distinction between the graft hybrid, or vegetative hybrid, and the true sexual hybrid derived from a single fertilized egg is thus indisputable. It depends upon the fact that in the vegetative hybrid the cells and nuclei of the two species keep apart while in the sexual hybrid the cells and nuclei fuse. The distinction is not only indisputable, it is quite indispensable for the understanding of life. Indeed, it stands on just the same fundamental footing as the distinction between a mixture and a compound. If one does not accept or understand these distinctions, the one in biology, and the other in chemistry, one need not expect to get any further with one's investigations.

The idea that treatment can alter the individual plant or animal, especially in relation to hybridization, is a recurrence of a very old species of the Lamarckian genus of superstitions. For example, Aristotle (*Hist. Animal*, 6, 23) states that crossing the horse and the ass is only possible if the ass, male or female, has been suckled by a mare. This idea is quite untrue, but it is the idea of the Michurin mentor. The ass is made more like a horse by absorbing into its blood a mare's milk. In the same way a poor seedling is made more like a good variety by having the sap of that variety introduced by grafting into its own sap.

In Michurin's opinion the environment can be used to change the genetic character of plants. The most effective form in which it can act is the mentor in grafting. The vegetative union of the mentor with the stock was (he supposed) just as complete as that of the germ cells, egg and sperm, in seed formation. The most important effect that could be produced by mentors was to make hybrids between species become fertile which had always been sterile before – hybrids which still remain sterile outside Russia. These claims were at first astonishing. They became less so when we discovered that Michurin's hybrids were always like the mother plant. Moreover, in making hybrids, Michurin recommended using the pollen of several species at once. He believed, as Darwin but not Mendel believed, that more than one pollen grain might in some way influence the formation of one seed. But, if hybrids can be entirely maternal, even one foreign pollen grain would seem to have been superfluous. Michurin's maternal hybrids are not, of course, hybrids at all. They are to be seen growing as curiosities in experimental gardens of Finland, England and the United States. But nowhere have they been found, outside Russia, to be of any practical value.

The loose observations and enthusiastic advice of Michurin have been discredited, both in particulars and in generalities, wherever they were capable of being tested. And the use of chromosome numbers with their known laws of action and transmission makes possible tests that Michurin would not have dreamt of. In Soviet Russia, however, the political implications of his work, like those of Kammerer's, were not overlooked. When he died in 1935 his town of Kozlov was renamed after him, Michurinsk, and 'thousands of small laboratories' (so we are told) were founded to develop his work under the title of Michurinism.

THE RISE AND FALL OF LYSENKO

Michurin bequeathed to his government a biological theory which fitted their political needs. His bequest was not left unclaimed. An apostle of Michurinism quickly arose: one, moreover, who was willing to preach to the Gentiles. The mantle of Michurin descended on Trofim Lysenko, an ambitious young Ukrainian agriculturist who, disbelieving in orthodox genetics, claimed to be able to alter heredity by various kinds of treatment. Lysenko took over Michurin's doctrines and began to work them up. He began with his own theories of 'vernalizing' wheat seeds. These having proved unsuccessful in their advertised purpose of improving wheat crops, he adopted Michurin's method of 'mentoring' fruit trees. He then infused both with the language of physiology, explaining genetic behaviour as due to processes of digestion and assimilation. Going a step further, he introduced greater popular interest by ascribing the imaginary merits of mixed population to a selective fertilization, or a choice of mate by the egg cell, which he recommended as a 'love marriage'.

Lysenko's efforts were rewarded when he was appointed President of the Lenin Academy of Agricultural Sciences in 1940 in succession to the Mendelian geneticist, Nikolai Vavilov, who died in 1942. In 1943, Lysenko, supported by an alliance with the favoured school of Michurin, put together his new theories in a booklet entitled *Heredity and its Variability*, translated by Professor Th. Dobzhansky.

The foundation of the new science is Michurin's doctrine raised, as it were, to a higher power by Lysenko:

Vegetative hybrids do not differ in principle from those obtained sexually. Any character can be transmitted from one breed to another through grafting as well as sexually.

p. 34

To account for the marvellous possibilities of grafting, as imagined by Michurin, extraordinary properties have to be ascribed to the non-living or plastic materials in plants:

The scion and the stock cannot exchange either the chromosomes of the cell nuclei or the cytoplasm. And yet the hereditary properties can be transmitted from the stock to the scion and vice versa. Hence, the *plastic substances elaborated in the scion and in the stock possess the properties of the breed,* i.e. the heredity.

p. 32

The fusion between Lysenko's ordinary Lamarckism and the specialized Lamarckism of Michurin's mentors is accomplished or acknowledged by the simple assertion of their similarity in the supreme name of science:

To science, vegetative hybrids are a kind of an intermediate step, a transition, from changing the heredity of plant organisms through crossing, to changing it through the influence of living conditions.

p. 38

Some of the properties of the new heredity are very difficult to follow:

But all the molecules and cells of the organism arise from the zygote [*the fertilized egg*] *by means of reproducing their unlikes rather than their likes, i.e. through differentiation and development.*

p. 8

Others, equally in italics, are all too simple:

The heredity is, as it were, the essence of the conditions of the external environment assimilated by the plant organisms in a series of preceding generations.

p. 65

In this series of revelations the name of Lamarck is not used by Lysenko: his name is mentioned only five years later. But Lysenko's theory is in the authentic Lamarckian succession following Kammerer and MacBride and the less articulate Michurin. The environment, at least the Soviet environment, is supreme. This environment changes heredity to suit it. Now, therefore, the environment can be used, and should be used by good breeders, to change the species. And how does the environment work? Its operation is easy for anyone to understand. No tedious hours of midnight study are needed. It works through the metabolism. It propagates itself by the ordinary activities of the body. It digests the genotype. It assimilates the chromosomes. It converts conditions into particles. It winds up the spring of life and sometimes overwinds it. It presides over hybridization. It tortures the old, but for the young it arranges love marriages. And in the end it *becomes* heredity.

After five years of argument on these lines Lysenko was ready to confront the unhappy remnant of those in his own country who still stood by western genetics. On 31 July 1948, he presented his views to the Lenin Academy of Agricultural Sciences. On this occasion he added a few new theories and one new fact, viz. that he had been able by two, three or four years of autumn sowing to convert the macaroni wheat, *Triticum durum*, with twenty-eight chromosomes into the bread wheat, *T. vulgare*, with forty-two chromosomes. 'The conversion of one species into another', he says, 'takes place in one leap.' Apparently this surprises Lysenko for he puts the statement in italics. It need not surprise us, however. In the west when new species arise suddenly (as has happened many times in the last fifty years) they are *new* species, not existing ones that have previously been grown in the same field.

At the end of his address Academician Lysenko reported that the Central Committee of the Communist Party of the U.S.S.R. had approved what he had said. A month later, on 26 August, the Praesidium of the Soviet Academy of Sciences took the necessary step of bringing to an end the teaching of genetics, and of dissolving the institutes and removing the personnel concerned with research in genetics, in the Soviet Union.

Since this time the achievements of Soviet plant and animal breeding have not been brought to the notice of the outside world.

AN EXCURSION ON FRAUD

The problem of scientific fraud is large and intricate. On account of its recent growth, it is larger and more intricate than most of us, scientists or otherwise, realize. Faking the results of experiments seems to be an easy habit to drop into for those who have little aptitude, but great confidence, in such work. Nature often deceives such investigators. And when they discover that they have been deceived the weaker sort will try to get their own back. This they, or their assistants, can easily do by 'correcting nature', as Bateson put it.

The experiments of Kammerer were probably not faked by Kammerer himself. Those of Michurin and Lysenko, which like Kammerer's prove the Lamarckian argument, were at first not faked at all. At first their errors were largely due to accidents in handling and in interpretation. Such accidents are made easy by the experimenters' ignorance of the standard methods of conducting experiments, their ignorance of the results obtained by other people from experiments, and their overpowering desire to reach a conclusion which they are certain is the right conclusion, the morally right conclusion, and therefore the only conclusion that any honest man can reach.

This brings us to the crux of the whole matter. Ancient philosophers and prophets, as we saw, did not always distinguish between biology and morals. In practice they could not therefore distinguish between inductive and deductive reasoning. In matters affecting human life, it is now becoming clear that the development of modern scientific method and its predominance over moral judgement were both needed before these distinctions could be established and recognized.

When scientific method comes into conflict with a confident and dogmatic morality, like that of Marxism in a Marxist state, it loses its authority. Marxism says that it is not enough to understand nature: we must also change it. A theory of life which does not promise the manifest power to change it must therefore be wrong. A theory which does give this power must be right. What should be so, must be so.

In this moral climate men know at the beginning of the inquiry where they will arrive at the end. The journey therefore need only be made on paper. The flow of reasoning turns in a deductive direction. The inductive method of science is drowned in dreams and visions. Expectation is confused with observation. Past and future gradually merge into an apocalyptic unity. The charlatan and, usually, the layman are unaware of the revolution. And, for those who might be aware of it, an extensive reading of certain philosophers – it does not matter whether it is Marx or

Bergson – will deprive them of the means of understanding.

There remains, however, with all Lamarckian theorists an inward yearning for the old-fashioned experimental demonstration. Experiments are therefore usually quoted. We then find that three precautions are necessary to make the Lamarckian conclusion inevitable and the experiment successful. They are taken by Lysenko, just as they have usually been taken by any one, east or west, who was expecting to prove the Lamarckian theory right. First, the experimenter begins with plants or animals of a mixed stock, of mixed origin: he can then discard those lines which fail to show the response he wants. Secondly, he tries his abnormal conditions on a batch of his mixed stock without trying normal conditions on a similar batch to compare the effect. That is without what we call an experimental control. Thirdly, he keeps no records of the numbers of plants or animals treated or bred and of course applies no statistical tests to their sufficiency. Lysenko, immune from scientific criticism, followed this method explicitly by ridiculing all statistical tests whatever.

When the deterrents of scientific criticism are withdrawn the careerist becomes a charlatan overnight. Naturally where ignorance suffices fraud is superfluous. But inevitably ignorance in the master begets fraud in the servant. And, under the new regime, fraud and ignorance have marched shoulder to shoulder in expounding the results of Michurin's and Lysenko's work to the public.

The study of scientific fraud teaches us four valuable lessons:

(i) No observation and no experiment is of any value unless it is described in such a way that others can repeat it.

(ii) Arguments and conclusions lose value when they fail to take into account the relevant observations previously described in this way.

(iii) It is difficult to obey these rules and they will always be forgotten if they are not enforced by an alert, critical and free public opinion.

(iv) Those who do not obey these rules are making themselves accessories in fraud and, if they profit by it, are in danger of becoming principals in the kind of corruption whose history we have now told.

PART FOUR

MAN AND WOMAN

The new understanding of genetic determinism enables us to see all human problems in a new light. The twin method puts the theories of health, education and crime on an experimental basis. Our knowledge of genetic recombination explains the relations of race, class and mating. The principle of choice of environment simplifies our understanding of society. The separation of sex determination into the two steps of chromosomes and hormones clarifies the behaviour and variation of the sexes, the functions of marriage and celibacy, and the basis of sexual irregularity. The whole genetic analysis reveals the gravity of the crisis in human population.

12

The Human Problem

THE idea of studying human society as a scientific problem came to a head at the time of Malthus, but it was not until the time of Darwin and Huxley that the theory could be put into practice.

It was in 1863 that Thomas Henry Huxley published his essays on *Man's Place in Nature*. He pointed out that the gorilla was much more like a man than it was like one of the smaller monkeys. This strange animal, which had only been introduced to Europeans in 1598, was therefore, it seemed, closely related to ourselves. The idea, familiar to Africa, came as a shock to Europe. No one had been shocked when Linnaeus in his *Systema Naturae* in 1758 had classified the mammals and had put man with the monkeys as a Primate. This seemed to Linnaeus and to everyone else a purely academic matter. And, when Lord Monboddo, a Scottish judge, drew the obvious conclusion that men had once walked on all fours, to the literary intellectuals of the day it seemed merely a laughing matter. With Huxley's book, on the other hand, coming after the *Origin of Species*, the question for the first time had to be taken seriously.

The new, or apparently new, doctrine aroused opposition among both scientists and laymen. But when the dust had settled it was clear that new opportunities had been created for the study of man by treating him for the first time as an animal, decended from animals and sharing with animals all physical and mental properties which he had possessed as a species until only a few thousand generations ago.

It was on the basis of this understanding that the infant social sciences took shape. In a hundred ways the evolutionary model seemed to fit. It turned a dead description into a living inquiry whether the subject was religion or law, economics or culture. Unfortunately, in this field just as in general biology, the theory of evolution came too soon. What did it rest on? The public and the philosophers (for philosophers in those days concerned themselves with biology) did not understand the genetic evidence, or the lack of it. But they understood the record of the fossils. They saw the long procession of improvements in shells and in bones which extended over 500,000,000 years and culminated in man himself. Evolution, they said, is progress. And the march of commerce and industry in Victorian times showed that this same principle governed human affairs no less than those of the universe in general.

The exponents of this point of view were many. But the one whose word was taken by students of human society was Herbert Spencer. Having expounded the *Principles of Biology*, he brought forth his second great work, the *Principles of Sociology*. It was from Spencer therefore that social scientists learnt their Darwinism. They did not notice that Darwin never used Spencer's favourite word, Evolution. They did not know that Darwin had said of Spencer: 'If he had trained himself to observe more . . . he would have been a wonderful man.' But Spencer was not made to observe. His opinions were not based on the evidence of heredity, variation and selection. They were based on belief in evolution and progress. The means did not matter much. But acquired characters were certainly inherited and with their help all races and classes of men were uniformly moving forward towards that millennium of culture which liberal thinkers then, and even still today, could see before them.

These views were not held by Darwin or Huxley, but they gradually took hold of the social sciences. In the hands of its pioneer, Edward Tylor, anthropology, the study of man, was all of one piece. It also attempted to be of one piece with biology as a whole. The biological interpretation of man was the charter of the new science. It flourished in the belief that it had at last escaped from the man-centred world of the Middle Ages. But its escape was short-lived. Spencer's stylized ideas of evolution did not work when applied to the detailed complexity of human life. The intellectual transformations, the cycles of advance and decay, the diversity of cultures which characterize human history, had little in common with Spencer's doctrine of progress.

The social scientist was disappointed by the failure of the

formula of progress, but not, perhaps, correctly disappointed. He had formerly been, as he imagined, in touch with fundamental science. He still imagines that he is in touch and that nothing fundamental has changed today, one hundred years after Spencer wrote on evolution. He has satisfied himself that evolution does not work in Spencer's way. Hence, he is inclined to feel, the whole idea of the biological interpretation of man can be repudiated. Evolution and natural selection can be thrown overboard. Time and history can be forgotten. And, while the physical differences between human races are obvious for all to see, such mental differences as they seemed to possess can be put down to accidents of the environment, to cultural contacts, to acquired habits, to 'invention' and 'discovery', indeed to anything in the world that seems to have no biological or genetic foundation. The social scientist has thus come to take his stand on the view that groups of human beings differ in culture which has been handed down to them through the luck of education. People of different cultures do not differ, according to him, in genetic character. The culture is a high or low one quite evidently through the effects of climate, or of differences in natural resources, or the chances of communication. Innate capacity to absorb a culture, to profit by the discoveries of religion or the inventions of science does not, he feels sure, differ from one people to another. It is not men's natures that make them different, he argues, but their habits. And for these God or the devil is responsible, never the chromosomes or the genes.

The social scientist will, we must suppose, agree that *species* differ in their innate mental capacities. He will also presumably agree that *individuals* differ. But he will not agree that *races* differ, because, he says, individuals vary over a wide range within each race. This is indeed true of advanced races. There are imbeciles in every race. And they are even more frequent in the most advanced races where they are given special facilities for multiplying. But when we compare different groups of people by Galton's method, the statistical method, we see that each group shows a normal curve of variation in respect of each measurable character. Different groups differ like the two curves of flies before and after selection in our graph (Figure 14). But this again is of no use to the social scientist because he has not realized that during the last fifty years such statistical expressions have come to be taken as evidence of genetic determination.

The biological interpretation of man has, in this way, come to be surrendered. In place of the breadth of Tylor's survey we now find the view of a specialist. He shuts his eyes to the diversity of human races and individuals recognized by Darwin, Huxley, Galton and even Tylor, and its genetic determination. Having abandoned fundamental study, he dreams of 'the fundamental uniformity of the human mind' as 'a basic premiss of modern anthropology'. He will not allow that Darwin's natural selection has anything to do with man. Instead he embraces the notion of 'universal biological needs' among which he discovers 'the need for reproduction that underlies the institution of the family'.

Stripped of the evolutionary theory, the experimental evidence and the materialistic arguments of modern biology, social scientists have to return to the ancient formulae. Some invoke blind chance or divine interference. Others prefer the design of Aristotle or the harmony of Leibniz. In these ways, of course, they can explain everything. They can even suppose that their explanations are original and this in turn adds to their plausibility. They do not remember that Lamarck's giraffe also had needs; they too were 'universal biological needs'. Nor do they know that Lysenko's wheat plants are insatiable in this respect.

In flying from biology, the social scientist may take refuge in many comfortable thoughts. He may embrace the notion that he is interested in human beings as persons, as wholes, as integrated entities. Do not, he begs, take us apart. We are men: we have souls: do not touch the sacred personality of man. Is this a sound piece of advice? Chemistry has no doubts about the integrity of molecules. But chemistry, as opposed to alchemy, is founded on pulling molecules to pieces. Physics has no doubts of the importance of the notion of energy. But its progress has depended on distinguishing between it and its various components. Biology – above all, genetics – will always recognize a meaning in the individual; but it has no hesitation in breaking up the individual's body into cells or his heredity into genes. To repudiate analysis is therefore only an excuse for avoiding the study of cause and effect and submitting one's theories to the test of experiment. By giving sanctity to the human person the anthropologist is thus repudiating the scientific study of man.

The historian is today (with rare exceptions) as innocent of all other branches of inquiry as is the social scientist. And the results are wonderfully parallel. Toynbee, in his *Study of History*, has expressed the view that the greatness of nations is not due to any permanent genetic or racial quality that distinguishes one from another – if indeed there are any such qualities. Rather, in Toynbee's opinion, given after a strenuous inquiry, achievement arises from the *challenge* of the environment. The reaction to difficulties stimulates people to great efforts from which great civilizations are born. The Dutch were challenged by having so little land to try to take some more from the sea. The English were challenged by having invaded so small an island, with so bad a climate. Hence we had to set about to conquer three or four empires; we had to carry out a scientific and an industrial revolution; we had to breed and bring up an unnecessarily large number of poets; we had to develop our own idiom in landscape gardening, in political institutions and in domestic and ecclesiastical architecture. An agreeable idea! But was it not the challenge of the environment which stimulated Lamarck's giraffe to grow his neck so long? And did not Lysenko's wheat change to rye in response to the same provocation?

These mistakes are now evident and their remedy also. After twenty years of Mendelism the Mendelian had to go back sixty years to pick up again the threads of Darwinian theory. After thirty years he had to go back again and pick up the threads of the cell theory, many of which had been lost. The result of this return to beginnings has been the rebirth we have attempted to describe. We have discovered the proper places of evolutionary and cell theory in scientific thought. Both of these theories are rough generalizations, refutations of the errors of the creation of species and of the operations of humours and essences. Neither of them, we now see, is a principle from which detailed deductions can be made. The valid principles have to be developed when the new methods of inquiry have yielded analytical results. The valid principles are those of genetic determination. It remains for all those on the social outskirts of biology to retrace their steps in the same way, to go back to Malthus, Darwin, Mendel and Galton, and to make use of the new genetics in interpreting the results.

13

Man: The Individual

FROM the earliest times man has disputed with his cattle and his crops the pride of place whenever heredity has been discussed by philosophers. The complexity of his behaviour and the difficulties of breeding him experimentally and of studying him at a comfortable distance have been compensated by the minuteness with which all his varying properties, capacities and disorders, whether of body or mind, have been recorded and discussed – in prose and verse – by the keenest observers for a hundred generations. These records of observation could not lead to the discovery of the laws of heredity. But might they not display the operations of these laws when they eventually came to be discovered? In part this is what has happened. But something else has also happened which makes the history of the subject doubly instructive. It is that, in nailing down, one by one, the minute workings of genetic laws, recent investigators have often lost sight of the broad views which were visible a hundred or even fifty years ago. We saw the small things better before we were dazzled by the big things!

In 1859 Darwin had admitted that the laws of inheritance were quite unknown. But in 1868 he was explaining with a wealth of corroborative detail how they worked in man. He gives his survey of heredity in man, not in the *Descent of Man*, but tucked away in the middle of his *Variation in Plants and Animals under Domestication.*

Some writers [Darwin remarks, referring to Mr Buckle, the Toynbee of his age, who had recently published 'his grand work on "Civilization"'] who have not attended to natural history, have attempted to show that the force of inheritance has been much exaggerated. The breeders of animals would smile at such simplicity; and if they condescended to make any answer, might ask what would be the chance of winning a prize if two inferior animals were paired together.

239

Darwin is as much impressed as Aristotle by the triviality as well as the profundity of inheritance. He uses the same examples, 'Gait, gestures and voice are all inherited.' The slightest mannerism of a man, may reappear in his posthumous children. The inheritance of talent has been conclusively dealt with by Mr Galton but, he adds:

Everyone knows how often insanity runs in families.... Striking instances have been recorded of epilepsy, consumption, asthma, stone in the bladder, cancer, profuse bleeding from the slightest injuries, of the mother not giving milk and of bad parturition, being inherited.

He then deals in some detail with the inheritance of peculiarities and defects of the human eye which even then had been intensively studied by experts.

Darwin uses the horse to fill the gaps where man is wanting. He quotes Youatt, the great authority, as saying 'there is scarce a malady to which the horse is subject which is not hereditary'. Further, the temperamental vices of 'crib-biting, jibbing, and ill-temper, are all plainly hereditary'. On the side of virtue, he points out, heredity is equally strong, for no race-horse outside England had ever made a name unless descended from the English thoroughbred – a generalization which is likely to be true as long as horse-racing continues.

The property of having extra fingers or toes like the Giant of Gath recorded in 1 Chronicles (xx. 6) greatly interests Darwin. He does not recall that in the eighteenth century this 'polydactyly' had caused much discussion. Being so conspicuous a defect, it was noticed to run in families, the classical case being that of one Gratio Kalleia. To the confusion of ovists and spermists alike, it was then seen to be transmitted through both sons and daughters. The preformationists were therefore faced with one of their most awkward problems. But what concerned Darwin was merely the irregularity of its inheritance. We know that the irregularity is merely due to variable expression, in this case variable dominance in an otherwise heterogeneous population, of the Mendelian gene chiefly concerned with the effect.

Many other common consequences of Mendelian inheritance, such as the segregation of Mendelian recessives, puzzled Darwin:

It is a singular fact that, although several deaf-mutes often occur in the same family, and though their cousins and other relations are often in the same condition, yet their parents are very rarely deaf-mutes.

In his ignorance of Mendel's principles these observations confused Darwin's ideas of heredity enough (as we have seen) to allow him to admit the inheritance of the effects of injuries, mutilations, and use and disuse. Apart from this error, however, he had a clear view of the force of heredity. He merely did not know how to use the evidence for a crucial argument. In this task his younger cousin, Galton, succeeded.

GALTON

Francis Galton was born in the same year as Mendel. The deepest interests of both of them were probably in the use of statistical methods for scientific discovery. Both of them began by trying them on the weather. Galton was more successful. Having produced some of the first weather maps, he discovered anticyclones. Both of them, Mendel before, Galton after, reading the *Origin of Species*, turned to the study of the great unsolved problem underlying the Origin, that of heredity. But the methods they developed were radically opposed. In fact, they were the two mutually exclusive methods equally bound to underlie the unborn science of genetics.

The field of Galton's work was no doubt influenced by his early travels, which like Darwin's and Huxley's had taken him among primitive peoples. He turned therefore to the study of heredity in man. By a second coincidence he brought out his first book on the subject, *Hereditary Genius*, only a couple of years after Karl Marx produced the first volume of *Das Kapital*. This was a memorable convergence of events, for the two books were both concerned with improving mankind and their fundamental message lies in their alternative interpretations of the evolution of human society, the one depending on the internal element of heredity, the other on the external element of environment – to be exact, the social environment.

Neither book was fully valued at the time. *Hereditary Genius* could not be understood without the help of modern genetics. Its importance was not, however, entirely missed. 'I do not think

I ever in all my life read anything more interesting or original',
wrote Darwin when he read Galton's book. Its novelty was
double. It introduced statistical method into the study of heredity. And it also introduced genetic method into the study of
history. Six years later Galton discovered the method which was
destined to establish his principles: the device of comparing the
properties of twins:

Their history [he writes in introducing the subject in a popular article
in 1875] affords a means of distinguishing between the effects of tendencies received at birth and of those that were imposed by the circumstances of their after lives, in other words between the effects of nature
and of nurture.

This fundamental discovery Galton made, as he points out
later in his *Inquiries into Human Faculty* (1883), with the expectation, not of revealing fundamental principles of life, but merely
of solving certain social problems:

In solution of the question whether a continual improvement in
education might not compensate for a stationary or even retrograde
condition of natural gifts, I made inquiry into the life history of twins,
which resulted in proving the vastly preponderating effects of nature
over nurture . . . the very foundation and outcome of the human mind
is dependent on race . . .

p. 216

For a long time, of course, people had known that human
twins might be very alike. In 1868 Darwin had quoted a striking
case:

Two girls, born as twins, and in all respects extremely alike had their
little fingers on both hands crooked; and in both children the second
bicuspid tooth in the upper jaw, of the second dentition, was misplaced.
. . . Neither the parents nor any other member of the family had exhibited any similar peculiarity . . . the idea of accident was at once excluded.

How were such things to be explained? This is Darwin's conclusion:

The less close similarity of the successive children of the same family
in comparison with human twins which often resemble each other in
external appearance, mental disposition, and constitution, in so extraordinary a manner, apparently proves that the state of the parents at
the exact period of conception, or the nature of the subsequent em-

bryonic development, has a direct and powerful influence on the character of the offspring.

We must remember that the embryo in the womb has no direct blood connexion with the mother and most human twins have no blood connexion with one another. All that we have in Darwin's suggestion is, therefore, the influence of the old theory of heredity which he formally introduced under the name of pangenesis at the end of his book.

Galton, however, was able to put things on quite a different footing. Twins, he explains, are due to two kinds of event:

... the one corresponding to the offspring of animals that usually bear more than one at a birth, each of the progeny being derived from a separate ovum, while the other event is due to the development of two germinal spots [i.e. nuclei] in the same ovum. In the latter case they are enveloped in the same membrane, and all such twins are found invariably to be of the same sex.

Galton's hypothesis of the two kinds of twins (the truth of which no one now doubts) might seem to deal with a trivial incident, a mere vagary, of reproduction. Yet it has proved to be one of the foundations of genetics. Before we pursue its consequences let us therefore pause to note the circumstances of its origin and birth.

The twin hypothesis is the first recognition of the genetic connexion between the mature individual and the single egg – apart, of course, from the conclusion in Mendel's unknown paper twelve years earlier. Two-egg twins may be of the same sex, like Esau and Jacob, or of opposite sexes, like Apollo and Diana, but in either case they are just as different as ordinary brothers and sisters. One-egg twins, on the other hand, have the same heredity, or as nearly the same as two individuals can have. And they are always of the same sex. Thus the similarities of twins are not due to the 'condition of the parents' at the critical moment but to something in the egg: it is simply that the nuclei, and the chromosomes they contain, are the same in the cells of two one-egg twins.

Galton's willingness to consider single cells as the bearers of heredity represents the advance made on Darwin by a younger generation. It shows the impact of the use of the microscope and the study of the cell. Galton's discovery was made in the same year, 1875, that the fusion of two nuclei in fertilization was first understood by Oscar Hertwig in Germany.

Galton was thus the first man to apply the new cell discoveries to a fundamental problem of genetics.

THE NATURE OF TWINS

We now know that in man, and in cattle, and even in flowering plants with twin seeds, Galton's distinction between one-egg and two-egg twins applies whenever twins are brought forth. In man, three out of a thousand births are of one-egg twins equally in Europe and in Japan. The two-egg twins vary very much in frequency. They are only a third as frequent in Japan; but in Europe they are three times as frequent as the one-eggs owing to an increase of frequency with the age of the mother. Hence out of a million or so twins in Britain, at the present day, probably a quarter of a million, the population of a county, are members of one-egg pairs.

Galton assumed that one-egg twins had the same heredity. They are therefore often described as identical. Such a name, however, as Galton discovered, went too far. Among thirty-five pairs of presumed one-egg twins that he inquired about, he found several pairs who showed some divergence in later life. In these cases he remarks that, to his surprise, 'the parents ascribed such dissimilarity as there was, wholly or almost wholly to some form of illness'.

Clearly, if one of a pair is subjected to the chance of infection to which the other is not, a factor will be introduced into the situation modifying the determination of character by heredity. But there are other causes of dissimilarity of one-egg twins which, unknown to Galton, come into play before birth.

In the first place, what causes twins? The problem seems a simple one but in fact it conceals many obscure subtleties. The mother evidently determines the possibility of two-egg twins by releasing two eggs at once. The father, however (or fathers, for two different fathers may fertilize them), help to decide by their fertility whether each can survive in competition with the other. As for one-egg twins, again, it would seem that the mother's character must decide how the egg behaves during its early mitoses. But in fact the father seems to have some influence.

Consider now how splitting happens. One-egg twins arise here and there among most animals and plants as well. Indeed, in some armadillos and in conifers, the formation of one-egg multiplets is the regular means of reproduction. But, with ourselves, where it is not the regular way, the process by which the egg splits into two or four or eight is itself not regular. It is irregular in the time of the occurrence and in the evenness of the result.

The hazards of origin among one-egg twins have been revealed in a number of ways. The least hazard is an inversion of asymmetrical organs, such as the heart, by which one twin becomes the mirror image of the other. In ten per cent of cases one twin is right- and the other left-handed. A worse case is where the heart of one takes over the work of the other in a joint blood-system so that one is born with a dead heart. It is when splitting has taken place late that it is incomplete. The twins remain attached in every degree between Siamese twins which can live a long life and two-headed monsters which are born dead. Such monsters are found among worms and fish and other animals as well as human beings, and for the same reason (see Figure 16).

Side by side with this gradation is an increasing tendency to mirroring. Normal one-egg twins show varying degrees of mirror-image resemblances. Siamese twins are always complete mirror-images even in the position of the heart and stomach.

TABLE 3

Range of types in one-egg twins

Order of Splitting	Degree of Fusion in Womb	Notes	Probable Order of Likeness at Birth
6 days	None	} also with	↑
12 days	Joint Attachment (Placenta)	} two-eggs	
18 days	„ Membrane (Chorion)	—	
24 days	„ Cavity (Amnion)	} show mirror	
30 days	„ Body (i) Siamese	} imaging	
	(ii) Monsters	}	

These variations in attachment and in mirroring are evidently due to variation in the time when the egg splits in two. It is not surprising to find therefore that a proportion, indeed a majority, of one-egg twins (as Verschuer determined by tests of similarity) split before the foetal membranes begin to be formed on the ninth day after fertilization. These then form separate membranes. Two afterbirths develop just as in two-egg twins. The proportion of all twins to have single afterbirths is therefore, not a quarter, but less than an eighth; and two afterbirths are characteristic both of two-egg twins and of the one-egg twins which should be the most alike!

Now the two sides of an egg develop at different rates. These differences in time of separation must therefore have detectable consequences. Late splitters should differ at the time of splitting. The twin from the left side of the egg will probably be the right-handed twin and in other physical and mental respects the more vigorous. Only one-egg twins which have split early and formed separate membranes should be taken as having nearly identical heredity and pre-natal environments as similar as those of two-egg twins.

If late-splitting one-egg twins differ, where does the difference come from? Certainly not from the nucleus and the chromosomes, nor from external conditions. It comes from the act of splitting itself! Twins are used to establish the contrast between heredity and environment. And they do so correctly, no doubt, in ninety per cent of cases. But the other ten per cent represents, by a strange paradox, the one situation in human life where heredity and environment are not separable. For the process of their origin is external to each but internal to the two.

The difference in character due to late splitting is the peculiar property of one-egg twins. If one is left-handed we can well see that that one is bound to suffer a ramifying disadvantage in the processes of upbringing. But other such differences will certainly be physically invisible. They express themselves in an emotional polarity which is characteristic of dissimilar one-egg twins. It is a polarity which grows as each becomes more important in the environment of the other. The discordances of intelligence and behaviour between one-egg twins appear indeed in the highest degree even when there have been no differences in the formal

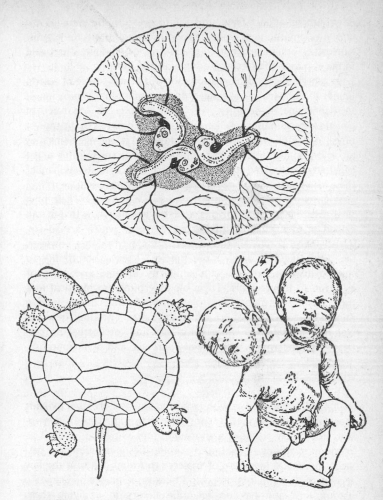

Figure 16

One-egg multiplets. Above, triplets in a fowl's egg split early and perfectly separated (from Newman, 1925). Below, turtle (from Bateson, 1894) and human twins (from Newman) split late and imperfectly separated. Note that the late splitting leads to dissimilarity of the two halves of the human twin even in the size of the head, although incorrectly they have been classified as 'identical'.

environment at all. They are not therefore a measure of the effects of environment as ordinarily understood, but the expression of errors inherent in the splitting of an animal egg and in the common life of the products of this splitting.

In general these considerations show that the degree of resemblance found between one-egg twins is a minimum expression of the 'influence of heredity', or, more strictly, of the force of genetic determination. Where we do find differences in rate of physical, mental and emotional development in one-egg twins they are to be ascribed sometimes chiefly to errors in the splitting of the egg. Later we shall see that there are chromosome mistakes in man: these also may lead to rare differences between-one egg twins.

What is the resultant similarity of one-egg twins? Their physical resemblance is notorious and few are unaware that it can extend to identical multiplets such as those which are so frequently photographed in the popular Press. Beyond this, however, the resemblance is much more precise. Their susceptibility to specific diseases extends to a similarity in time and place of infection in tuberculosis. Their blood groups are identical and their capacity for mutual transplantation of skin is unique among human beings. But most critical and significant of all is their outstanding similarity in those emotional and intellectual properties which determine their social character and behaviour.

TWINS AND CRIME

Among all social studies with twins the study of criminal twins is most fruitful for several reasons. Conviction, or lack of conviction, for crime provides a thorough, and impartial, as well as economical means of testing the similarities and differences between individual members of society: thorough because the law has exacting standards, impartial because it makes no scientific assumptions and has no scientific theory in applying these standards and arriving at its judgement. It is emotional and traditional rather than analytical or experimental. Conviction, of course, to some extent depends on luck; accidental other-level interference comes in. But the study of numbers can allow for this vagary. Again, examination of convicts in prison is much easier than that of the general public; and prison records are much fuller than any other public archives. And, finally, the origin and incidence of crime is a matter of great social interest.

The first and most serious study was by a German investigator, Johannes Lange, who examined thirty pairs of twins for their criminal records. If we put out the results he published in 1929 in the baldest way we reach the figures given in Table 4.

TABLE 4

Record of Lange's twins

With Crime Record	Type of Twin (all of same sex)		
	One-egg	Two-egg	Doubtful
Both	10	1	1
Only one	2*	15	1
Total	12	16	2

* The Ball and Hiersekorn twins.

These results by themselves might be regarded as enough to justify very simple and dogmatic conclusions. But the statistical statement is only the beginning. In the first place, the two-egg twins are of interest only in showing just the same amount of similarity that any brothers or sisters, sibs, as we call them, of the same sex, are expected to show. For the only pair where both have a crime record, the record is widely different in quantity and quality: one began earlier and became habitual, the other began late and did not become habitual.

What are important are the one-egg twins (Tables 4–5). How are we to explain the two discordant pairs (Table 4)? In both of these pairs the record of the two is entirely different. One of the first pair (Ball) murdered a girl who was expecting a child by him. His twin had lived over fifty years as a law-abiding peasant. In the second pair (Hiersekorn) one was feminine in appearance and behaviour and had been imprisoned for homosexual activity, the other was sexually normal. In one of these pairs injury at birth, in the other a head injury was held to be responsible for the changed character of the criminal member of the pair. A violent accident had altered the normal expression of heredity.

What strikes us first about the pairs that agree in both having criminal records is that they mostly agree so closely. They agree in their early history, in the age of their first conviction, and in the type of crime. Two pairs differ and the reasons are made clear. With the Schweizers, it is because they were both weak and one married a wife who kept him in order while the other had no such luck. With the Krämers, it is because one was hit very heavily on the head and knocked out before his career had properly begun. As for the rest, divergence in the number of sentences arises only from the fact that a long sentence interrupts the career of the twin in question; the length of the sentence depends as much on the character of the judge as of the judged.

What next strikes us is that the parents, brothers and sisters show the same low frequency of crime as do the two-egg twins of criminals. Of twenty known parents and twenty-seven known sibs, only four – and these were all in one family – show any serious delinquency. Moreover, as Lange points out, the one-egg twins, in consequence of their social activities, often rise or fall in the social scale with respect to their families, the Lauterbachs rising, the Ostertags falling. But they always rise or fall together, coming to the same level through their transgressions. The social level is thus genetically determined.

The conclusions that arise from this work bear on the study of heredity in general as well as on the heredity of crime. In sorting out heredity and environment as components of criminal conduct, Lange has enabled us also to sort out what is important in the environment, and also to show the unforeseen modes of interlocking of heredity and environment. Accidental injury is the most important of the purely environmental agents in determining the result, where crime is the result. Disease is another important agent in determining behaviour, but it is one which itself depends on heredity as well as on the accidents of infection. Companions are a third important group of agents partly genetic and partly environmental in the determination of their choice.

Different types of men are susceptible in different degrees to the effects of their companions. Some men are born to command,

TABLE 5. *Records of ten concordant pairs of one-egg criminal twins as determined by Lange up to 1927*

Name	Birth	Name	Age at First Offence	Convictions			Parents	Offences Sibs No.	Record
				No.	Type				
Male Ostetag[1]	1886?	A	23?	2	Fraud, embezzling, forgery, theft		No	1 B	None (had fits)
		K	26?	1	Fraud, embezzling				
Lauterbach	1890?	W	34	3	Company promoting, bogus invention, and title forgery		No	2 B? and 1 S	None
		H	36	7	*Ditto*				
Rieder	1890	J	14	c.8	Theft, drink, violence, begging		No	2 B	None (one in Institution)
		W	14	c.8	Theft, drink, vagrancy, illicit trade, procuring				

1. Both have diabetes mellitus.

251

TABLE 5 (contd). *Records of ten concordant pairs of one-egg criminal twins as determined by Lange up to 1927*

Name	Birth	Name	Age at First Offence	Convictions		Offences		
				No.	Type	Parents	Sibs No.	Record
Heufelder	1890	An.	14	10	Theft and burglary	No	5 B	None
		Ad.	14	8	Ditto			
Schweizer[2]	1895	F	16	3	Theft, embezzling, desertion, procuring, burglary	No	None (illegitimate)	—
		L	16	1	Violence			
Meister[3]	1899	G	18	2	Larceny, embezzling	No	2 S	None
		F	18	4	Ditto			
Maat	1903	—	—	0	Supported by homosexuality	No	?	'Excellent family'
		—	16	1	Ditto			

2. Separated at adoption at eight, but a difference arose only in 1920 when L married a strong-willed wife. Both are weak-willed. They both have a great number of illegitimate children.

3. Separated early. Both ran away from work at fifteen. Both operated on for appendicitis at seventeen.

TABLE 5 (contd). Records of ten concordant pairs of one-egg criminal twins as determined by Lange[1] up to 1927

Name	Birth	Name	Convictions			Offences		
			Age at First Offence	No.	Type	Parents	Sibs No.	Record
Diener	1904	K	20	1	Drink, manslaughter	No	3 B	One had 3 days' detention
		L	18	2	Drink, violence, theft			
Kramer[4]	1906	G	20	3	Drink, wounding	Father convicted often for wounding	3 B	All convicted for wounding when drunk
		A	16	1	Theft			
Female								
Messer[5]	1895	Ant.	18	—	Vagrancy, prostitution, procuring	No	10	None
		Am.	18	—	*Ditto*			
							29 sibs	

4. Both sexually undeveloped. G hit on head at eighteen, hence wide discordance in type of crime.
5. Separated at seventeen.

253

others to obey, and others again are intermediate. Those more inclined to command, and more capable of doing so, create the environment for those more inclined to obey. Amongst twins we therefore find the greatest resemblance in those of the strongest character – the most enterprising swindlers, the most aggressive gangsters, the most enthusiastic prostitutes. Among the weaker characters, the restraint exercised during childhood by a strong parent, or later by a strong husband or wife, has a powerful influence, although its effect lasts only while it is being exerted. The luck of adoption or marriage may therefore temporarily affect the course of a potentially criminal life. This is shown by the difference in behaviour of the Schweizers. Elsewhere there was no such agency to prevent one going astray when the other had done so, even when they had been separated in childhood.

Finally, economic conditions are of course important, but their mode of action is not what is usually expected. Poverty may make for larceny in one disposed that way. But in one not disposed that way many brothers may sharpen the wits and prepare for a useful life. An expensive education may develop a discriminating taste or it may encourage embezzlement. Wealth may promote idleness, drunkenness or swindling, or a deep sense of public duty. Economic circumstances alter the expression of vices as well as virtues. But they play no part in creating them.

The notion that we result from the reaction of heredity and environment has indeed given rise to another widespread misunderstanding. It is argued that an unpleasant environment will influence the result seriously – which is true – and always in an unfavourable way – which is not true. Would Dante or Chaucer have been better poets for living in the more splendid age that followed them? We may doubt it. Did the sufferings of Dickens and Dostoyevsky, of Laurence Sterne and Charlie Chaplin, of Benjamin Franklin and Jean-Jacques Rousseau, cripple their genius? Evidently not: on the contrary, suffering was responsible for bringing them to full development. Did Leonardo and Shakespeare suffer for being relatively uneducated men? Scarcely so. Rather, an inquiring spirit seems to have moved more freely with a lighter load of learning. Were Leeuwenhoeck, by being a draper, and Hofmeister, by being a bookseller, prevented from doing as good scientific work as their contemporaries who were cradled in ease and instructed by wisdom? Quite the reverse. Indeed, how often do we find that the sons of great men are given the best chances with the worst results!

The fact is we do not know which is the necessary or favourable environment for a particular genotype any more than we know which is the necessary or favourable genotype for a particular environment. Environments no more than genotypes are to be arrayed on objective scales of value. Our judgement is as much warped by our own prejudices, our own snobbery, in assessing the one as the other. Even a knock on the head may have very diverse consequences. Two one-egg twins have been described (by Aubrey Lewis in 1936) one of whom was over eight inches taller than the other. The tall one had suffered a head injury at the age of twelve, just before puberty, an injury which probably disturbed the pituitary gland and so altered the control of growth. By injury this boy became the better specimen.

The opposite effect, it must be admitted, is more usual. The Ball and Hiersekorn twins reveal that a man may commit a crime as grave as murder on account of the character determined by and in the fertilized egg. But he may also do so on account of the character determined by an accidental head injury at birth or after birth. And by *determined* in this case we mean that the crime is likely to be repeated by the individual, unless he is restrained, in both types of determination. In the one case the man owes his misfortune to his parents and will pass it on to his children. In the other case, neither parents nor children come into the picture. But from the point of view of the practical relations of society with the individuals concerned there is no difference: for the crime is not merely likely but, so far as we know, *equally* likely to be repeated in the two types of determination. This conclusion brings us to the most fundamental of all issues in regard to the theory of punishment. Is its purpose to improve living and present society? Or is it to benefit the society of the future? Both must in practice be affected and the two can be separated.

Clearly, to begin with, the two Old Testament notions of punishment, one as vengeance upon the individual, the other as retribution by heredity to the third and fourth generation, are both indefensible. Hence the forgiveness with which the New Testament attempts to temper these punishments is no longer needed. If there is nothing to revenge there is nothing to forgive.

Freed from these ideas we can approach the practical problem from a new point of view. Our evidence indicates that deterrence and reformation are of strictly limited scope. And where deterrence fails and revenge is dropped the distinction, always an arbitrary distinction, between sanity and insanity no longer comes in question. For the insane felon, if left at large, is at least as likely to repeat his felony as the sane felon. Neither has any choice in the matter.

For the old lag, in polite speech the 'recidivist', vengeance does not deter, and compassion does not reform. Prolonged imprisonment, of course, postpones the repetition of the crime and, what matters more, the propagation of the criminal. But since it costs society as much to keep the offender in prison for the sake of his past as to keep a student in the university for the sake of his future we need to ask ourselves what we gain by this policy.

What other courses then are left open to us? There are certain individuals we can well do without. No environment will make them useful to any form of society. Not wanting to put them away quietly, or to keep them all their lives under preventive detention at the public expense, we may inquire whether they need ever have been born. We could have known in advance. The study of their heredity indicates that in all societies some proportion of them need never have been born. How large a proportion it is our business to discover by accurate recording of the individual and of his family.

THE FUTURE OF TWINS

A vast field of inquiry will be opened to us when the opportunities offered by twins for studying the genetic determination of individuality come to be recognized.

Animal cells have a protein character specific to the individual. This character determines the kinds of 'antibody' which they produce when they react to the presence of alien proteins, the proteins of organic bodies which have arrived in the cell by injection or infection. This immunity-producing character, as it may be called, is responsible for individual variation in susceptibility to infectious diseases. It is also responsible for variation in susceptibility to anaphylaxis or specific allergy such as is shown by asthma, or hay fever, or by a pain after eating lobsters, or handling cats or primroses. Are all these differences in individual character, like the differences in blood groups, genetically determined, and if so, how? These are questions that twin studies will be used to answer.

The properties of antibody formation will be studied for one-egg twins and two-egg twins, and diseases such as anthrax and tetanus, in which there is no previous infection, will be used as the starting-point. The vitamin requirements of individuals will be studied and likewise the differences in the symptoms they reveal with vitamin deficiency. Great differences will be found in responses to dietetic variations, except of course in one-egg twins. Variation curves in the electrical activity, as well as differences in the total energy consumption, of the brain will be studied individually and in relation to the genetic determination of crime and other forms of social behaviour. One-egg twins will be used to discover how far disease and diet and drugs can modify the genetic determination of temperament by way of the hormone secretions. A new era of medical research will arrive when medical inquiry makes use of the full resources of genetic technique with twins.

Another field for twin studies is education. On the one hand, we must never forget that an unfavourable environment may prevent the full development of the genetically determined character. No one expects a child who has been deprived of hearing by brain fever in infancy to develop his musical talents. On the other hand, we have to realize that every one of us has carried, from the fertilized egg, defects in heredity for which no environment that we shall ever have at our disposal will compensate. By studying the education of twins we can discover just what is either significantly favourable or significantly unfavourable either in the environment or in the heredity.

The whole of our efforts in the three great humane departments of health, education, and the treatment of crime, could be multiplied, nay transformed, in value and effect if we were to study, measure and record the similarity and differences of our great population of twins in these three aspects of living. Indeed, by these methods we should get something of more practical use for our survival than by any other invention of the human mind.

INDIVIDUALITY

Notwithstanding that we cannot make experiments with human beings we have now got to know heredity in man about as well as if he were an experimental animal. Pedigrees and populations, chromosomes and twins, the copious records of history and geography, of crime, education and medicine, have told us more than is known of any other organism.

From what these things have taught us we can now enlarge the catalogue of properties described so forcefully by Darwin as inherited, or rather genetically controlled and determined, as follows:

1. The rate and duration of our growth; and hence our ultimate size, structure and quality in bone, flesh, brain, blood, etc.

2. Our hormone systems and hence our temperaments, whether sanguine, melancholy or choleric; timid or courageous; observant, reflective or impulsive. Hence our social habits, whether solitary or gregarious; affectionate or morose; settled or nomadic, useful, deranged, or criminal; hence also the company we keep, and our capacities and directions of love and hatred.

3. Our perception and appreciation of taste, touch and smell, sound and colour, harmony and pattern, our capacities and qualities for memory, whether for sound, sight, number or form, our kinds and degrees of imagination, visualization and reason. Hence our understanding of truth and beauty, hence also our educability in all these respects, or lack of it, and our capacity and choice in work and leisure.

4. The structures producing our voice; hence the pitch, timbre and strength in which we produce it; hence, in conjunction with our sensitivity and range of hearing, the educability of our voice and the range and defects of our speech.

5. The times and patterns by which we gain and lose our hair and teeth, our deposits of fat, and our perceptual, intellectual, and reproductive powers.

6. Our requirements of water, salts, sugars, fats, proteins and specific vitamins, of sleep, of sunlight and of exercise. And like-

wise the advantages and disadvantages we derive from drugs, and our susceptibility to addiction to drugs, of various kinds and amounts, whether nicotine or alcohol, strychnine or cocaine.

7. Our susceptibility to every disease, infectious or non-infectious, that flesh is heir to. Our abilities to receive, or coagulate, or reject, an infusion of blood or a graft of skin: these all depending on the types and varieties of our cell proteins.

8. And above all, or beneath all (by means we shall consider later) our sex, whether male or female, our sexual capacity and interest, our fertility or sterility, our love of children.

In all these respects our properties are limited and prescribed in the fertilized egg. They are inherent in almost every cell of our bodies. And they are carried in them from conception to dissolution.

Physical structures, chemical processes and physiological arrangements mediate this determination. They do so in ways which we only partly understand and their understanding, as we increase it, will be of great interest for those whose business it is to treat the sick or to reform the delinquent, to teach the young or to govern the whole community.

Now what do we mean by this *determination*? There are a multitude of possibilities for misunderstanding this potent idea. On the one hand, we mean that in all these respects (that is to say, in every respect) our reactions with any given set of outside events are decided before they occur. On the other hand, we mean that, taking all possible circumstances into account, and allowing for an infinite variety of circumstances, there are certain limits to what the product of a particular fertilized egg can do and these limits are laid down by the chemical and physical structure of that egg.

This principle means a great deal for men and for mankind. What it means we shall have to devote a few chapters to considering. Meanwhile it constitutes, as timid souls will quickly declare, a sentence of predestination. But, to bolder minds, it is also the charter of individuality. The indelible character and personality which in greater or less degree we each possess is what John Locke called the *principium individuatum* and what we call individuality. The mother recognizes her own accustomed offspring, as Darwin pointed out, from among millions, whether she is a human mother or a ewe or a mare. And a father or a friend may do likewise. We ourselves (unless we happen to be one-egg twins) are at least as conscious of our individuality as others are. It rests not, as John Locke and Bateson imagined, on an 'immaterial substance', but, as we have seen, on the genetic substances in the fertilized egg.

If we were infinitely plastic and malleable, reflecting our surroundings with intelligent, or unintelligent, fidelity there could be no such variety of known persons preserving from their first, right through to their second, infancy their peculiar and infallibly recognizable behaviours and appearances, dispositions and talents, each too with his own degree of self-esteem and proper pride in his or her own behaviour and appearance, disposition and talent. Each of us may give himself some latitude in interpretation, attributing his successes to a good heredity and his failures to a bad environment. But others know that our individuality is not in fact so conveniently plastic. They can predict what we shall do even if we ourselves cannot. They will freely assert that the leopard cannot change his spots and that what is bred in the bone comes out in the flesh.

Nor is the recognition of individuality a mere matter of civility: it is, or should be, the foundation, both of the working of law, and the practice of medicine. In law, all responsibility of the individual depends on the recognition of the permanent character and separateness of individuals which even the institution of marriage may blur but cannot suppress. In medicine, on the other hand, individuality has not always been accepted as the first principle of diagnosis and treatment. Indeed, the modern practice of medicine has tended to suppress the recognition of individuality of men, which was better understood when less was known of the specificity of microbes. The terrible problem of individual diversity which confronts the medical profession has been submerged under an extravagant technical curriculum. But it remains. And, when medicine wakes up to the existence of biology and rediscovers a philosophy, the genetic individual will be restored to his place.

The reverse side of the picture of individuality is shown by the differences in the aspect of the world as seen by different individuals who know how to express what they see. Owing to differences in our inborn characters we live in different worlds even though we live side by side. We see the world through different eyes, even the part of it that we see in common. We consequently speak, as we often say, different languages even if they are the same dialect. It is this diversity that gives the colour and brightness to living in the genetically mixed communities of great cities and in travelling to different lands. It is this diversity also that speeds up the cultural evolution of those who enjoy it. Variety is indeed the spice of life. But, so far as man and his works are concerned, it is a genetically determined variety.

All our differences have a genetic component. They may be reduced by social experience in some respects, but in how much more vital respects are they enhanced! The children that may tolerate one another's company at five or six will find it unbearable twenty years later when their individual capacities have been developed. Why? Because these individual capacities have developed by the individuals' initiative often in sharp divergence from the wishes and hopes of their pastors and masters.

It is above all our parents who are partly successful but largely unsuccessful in providing the environment which they hope will mould our characters. When a former king recently explained, 'My father could not understand why I was not more like him', he was pointing to the difficulty that has troubled millions of fathers and sons since long before Oedipus. The biographies of men who made their mark are full of conflicts between them and their parents, especially conflicts with regard to the career of the child.

Without Mendelian recombination it would have seemed absurd to attribute a conflict of parent and offspring to heredity! Yet it is now obvious that such conflicts are genetically determined in a high degree. The parental environment has failed to overcome the predisposition, the genetic individuality, of the child – notwithstanding the fact that the child has a better chance of being like the parent than anyone else in the world.

The fifty-seven Bachs who were musicians, the thirteen Wyatts who were architects, and the eight Bernoullis who were mathematicians owed their gifts to heredity. Environment sometimes favoured them but often it did not. Johann Sebastian Bach is merely the most splendid of many examples of heredity being preserved by assortative mating for several generations in a musical community. Those members of such closely assorted families who did *not* follow the examples of their parents show, conversely, the failure of the most favourable environment to educate an unfavourable heredity. The descendants of Bach today are no longer musicians.

Western civilization during the last 300 years has fed and flourished on a tolerance of individual differences, limited and intermittent, to be sure, but continually recurring. This tolerance is of course born of respect for individuality. We complain that there is 'nowt so queer as folks'. But we admit that 'it takes all sorts to make a world'. A rich culture demands a genetically diverse society.

Now we are in a position to justify this empirical understanding by our knowledge of genetic determination. But in the circumstances of individual differentiation something more than mere tolerance was needed if life in the heterogeneous communities of great modern cities was to be possible. Variety is stimulating. Up to a point it stimulates. Beyond that point it irritates. It leads to friction. Friction is in fact relieved by two important agencies. First, there is the subdivision by the assortment of trade, craft and profession into small social and mating groups. And, secondly there is the family whose members, although distinct genetic individuals, are mutually chosen or genetically related and are therefore usually capable of a greater understanding among themselves than can be expected outside.

Thus the relationships of the individual and the family, the mating group and the nation offer us a self-perpetuating system capable of a state between stability and instability, that dynamic equilibrium on which the development of human culture depends. The basis of the dynamic equilibrium is found in genetic recombination, assortative mating and natural selection. How these work in human society we must now proceed to examine.

14

Man in Society

WHEN Darwin hinted in the *Origin of Species* that man had sprung from a lowlier stock the full implications were seen more quickly by those who were prepared to differ than by those who were prepared to agree. Religious writers were quick to denounce the proposal of affinity with the apes. Indeed, the charge of sacrilege probably did as much to concentrate the thoughts of Thomas Henry Huxley on this problem as the polemics of his zoological colleagues. The results of this concentration were his essays on *Man's Place in Nature*.

Huxley's argument was not fresh when it was written. But its implications are still far from being accepted today. The educated, no less than the uneducated, masses refuse to believe that the study of the human species can be based on principles derived from the lower animals.

Huxley was concerned to show above all that the human brain, man's outstanding exhibit in the museum of evolution, varied as between different races over a range nearly as great as that which separated it from the ape's brain; further, that between the smaller brains of some modern races of man and those of the apes there were brains of fossil men belonging to races that were now extinct. Since mental capacity (using Galton's methods) is found to be correlated with the size of the brain as between individuals, races and classes, it was likely that there had been a gradual increase in intelligence of man by a not very slow process of natural selection. This is the view we accept today. We can indeed see amongst individuals, classes and races of men today all the variation, all the materials for selection, that are needed for further tremendous changes in the evolution of human intelligence.

Huxley having broken the teeth, if not the spirit, of the opposition the way was open for a second advance. Darwin could at last apply to the classification of men the knowledge he had gained from a broad and deep consideration of animals. 'Now', he writes, in the *Descent of Man* (taking his courage in both hands), 'let us apply these generally-admitted principles to the races of man, viewing him in the same spirit as a naturalist would any other animal.'

Darwin had spent five years travelling round the world and he had watched with an observant eye more different peoples in different states of evolution and civilization than it falls to the lot of most men to see. And, whatever other faults he may have had, as his books show, he was prepared to look at them with an open mind and to ponder what he saw with patient deliberation. The races of man differ, he says, in every physical character in regard to which individuals are known to vary. Further:

The races differ also in constitution, in acclimatization, and in liability to certain diseases. Their mental characteristics are likewise very distinct; chiefly as it would appear in their emotional, but partly in their intellectual faculties.

Everyone who has had the opportunity of comparison, must have been struck with the contrast between the taciturn, and even morose, aborigines of South America and the light-hearted, talkative negroes. There is a nearly similar contrast between the Malays and the Papuans who live under the same physical conditions, and are separated from each other only by a narrow space of sea.

Are these different races then, Darwin asks, to be regarded as distinct species? Their differences have been 'nearly constant for very long periods of time'. They correspond in geographical distribution with distinct species in other groups of mammal. They even have distinct species of parasites like bed-bugs and lice, so much so, that, as we know, *Cimex lectularius*, the bed-bug of the white man, has a different number of chromosomes from *C. rotundatus* of the black man. And, as Darwin points out, lice from Hawaiians that stray on to English sailors die in three or four days. Such a distinctness has not arisen between the parasites of different breeds of dogs. For the dogs have been differentiated by man himself more recently than man probably within the space of 20,000 years.

These considerations point to the view that the human races are distinct species. One thing makes Darwin doubt. The different races are probably all interfertile. This circumstance had led to the production of the cross-bred populations which already in his time occupied a large part of the New World.

Darwin also remarks – and he does not regard it as a cause or a consequence of this interfertility – that the races of man 'graduate into each other'. Hence no two authorities agree as to how many races or species of men there ought to be. Are there, 2, 3 or 4? Or are there 10, 20 or even 60? Or is there only one? The answer, it turns out, as in so many other cases (with due respect to Linnaeus) is a matter of convenience. But what is not a matter of convenience is whether we asssume that the races of man are descended from one, or more than one, common stock at a particular remote and pre-human period. From one stock, Darwin says; and no doubt he had in mind some stock like that of the chimpanzee consisting of ten or twenty thousand families and living in some warm region of the Old World 1,000,000 years ago, and already perhaps differentiated into races.

Darwin's greatest puzzle is to explain how the differences between human races have come about:

They cannot be accounted for by the direct action of different conditions of life, even after exposure to them for an enormous period of time. The Esquimaux live exclusively on animal food; they are clothed in thick fur, and are exposed to intense cold and to prolonged darkness; yet they do not differ in any extreme degree from the inhabitants of Southern China who live entirely on vegetable food and are exposed almost naked to a hot glaring climate.

Nor can the differences between the races of man be accounted for, except to a quite insignificant degree, by the inherited effects of the increased or decreased use of parts. . . .

And finally since 'not one of the external differences between the races of man is of any direct or special service to him' natural selection cannot be held responsible. 'There remains one important agency, namely, Sexual Selection . . .'

(*Descent of Man*, p. 246).

In this regard Darwin discusses the differences between the sexes in animals and man. He points out the distinction between primary sexual characters in the sex organs necessary for reproduction, and the secondary sexual organs or characters such as the beard and deeper voice of men and the breasts of women.

He also points out that these secondary sex characters are highly variable. Among Australian blackfellows (and also he might have said many Europeans) the male is 65 mm. ($2\frac{1}{2}$ ins.) taller than the female, while among the Javanese the difference is more than three times as great. In all series of measurements of races the men are more variable than the women. The beard, for example, is fully developed in hardly any men except those of the white races. The greater size of the man than the woman Darwin attributes to selection having favoured the stronger man in fighting for the woman. Working, however, may have been as important as fighting in maintaining a bimodality of the sexes.

Man, according to Darwin, is the more intelligent and aggressive, woman the more affectionate and self-sacrificing of the two sexes. All over the world beauty plays some part in sexual attraction, but the standard of beauty is different in every region: hence the divergence in appearance of races. On the inheritance of good looks, Darwin also quotes the painter Lawrence, 'who attributes the beauty of the upper classes in England to the men having long selected the more beautiful women'. The same process, apart from some details, Darwin accepts as the basis of physical improvement in certain West African and other peoples who have habitually sold their worst-looking slaves.

Conversely, Darwin admits, many African tribes have selected their women for the enlargement of the buttocks. Standing them in a row they would always by preference make their choice of wives from those who projected furthest behind. Thus, in his view, the buttocks, having no doubt first developed as a safeguard for the future of the mother and child in time of famine, had eventually become for prospective fathers an end in themselves (loc. cit. 2, p. 346).

The most striking and general change which Darwin ascribes to man's selection of woman is the loss of hair on the body. In this case, to different degrees in different races, selection of the female has reacted on the character of the male. The two sexes, having twenty-two pairs of chromosomes in common are naturally not entirely separable in variation; selection of the one will therefore shift the character of both (loc. cit. 2, p. 377).

Loss of hair in human evolution has probably taken place independently and in parallel in the great and, according to Coon, ancient human races, black, white and yellow. So also has the reversal of mating posture which has accompanied the gradual straightening of the human body. This new attitude has, no doubt, as Haldane has suggested, directed man's interest to the face of his mate and led to the change from an older to a newer version of Venus. It has also led to possibilities of injury from coitus. The development of pubic hair in both sexes may be looked on as a response to the need for protection: like the milling on the coin it serves for both *decus et tutamen*.

In all these matters Darwin was not far wrong so far as he went. But we can go further.

MATING GROUPS

Our knowledge of heredity enables us to get out of the chief difficulties that baffled Darwin. The facts with which we are faced, the differentiation and adaptation of human races, and of the two sexes, have accumulated. But they are little altered from Darwin's description. The theory of sexual selection is as necessary and as plausible as it was when Darwin put it forward. The underlying explanation however, is changed. It is changed by one fact of which Darwin was unaware: the Mendelian ratio of chromosome propagation. As we saw, in each generation one quarter of the chromosomes will reappear in the progeny twice, one half once, and one quarter will not reappear at all: they will be altogether lost.

This is the most important of all Mendelian ratios for it is the Mendelism of race. On it the course of evolution depends. For selection, by permitting the survival of some offspring and not of others, determines which quarter of the chromosomes will be doubled and which will be lost. Selection had no such power in Darwin's mind, no such resources to exploit. Nor had it the power to sort out all the recombinations of maternal and paternal pieces of chromosomes that arise from the crossing-over and separation in which chromosome reduction actually consists. Nobody could realize, before this chromosome shuffling was seen under the microscope and demonstrated by breeding, what tremendous stakes selection could play with.

Now this process of selection acts not merely on genes and

chromosomes and individuals; it also acts on the group of individuals, the community whose complements of chromosomes can, as generation succeeds generation, exchange their members and, after crossing-over, their parts; the community whose chromosomes form, as it were, a pool from which individuals are begotten and into which they throw their lot in begetting. In this process the pairing of individuals is the external and visible agency. It is what we have always seen. But the pairing of nuclei, of chromosomes and of genes, the invisible part of the universal mixing, is what in a finer sense determines the results.

We thus reach the third level of genetic thinking. We have been forced to admit the existence of the gene. We have faced the reality of the individual. We now have to uncover the community. All these are ancient ideas, of course, but their meaning and relationship only become clear when we consider them as the genetic particle, the genetic person and the genetic pool.

Let us not suppose that we finally understand what these ideas mean. But we are approaching an understanding. What is the genetic pool? It is a reservoir of gene exchange, a continuum. It corresponds to a group of individuals within which genetic movement, genetic recombination, is possible. In nature, when we know least about it, we call this group a population. But when we know more we have more definite names. In domestic animals it is the breed. In wild animals it is the race. What is it in man? That now becomes the focus of our inquiry. For whatever this community is, it must be the basis of the differentiation and evolution of mankind.

In animal species we often find a great complexity in the division and subdivision of the breeding groups which accompanies a fine, and sometimes, apart from the chromosomes themselves, an invisible, differentiation of appearance. But in man the complexity of subdivision is greater, far greater, than in any other organism. The reason is not far to seek. Choice of mate in man depends on his intellectual processes. As his means of livelihood have become more elaborate, and more diversified, his intellectual powers of discrimination have become steadily more refined. And he has not failed to use them.

In man, fertile mating is apt to take the permanent or repetitive form of marriage. How does he choose his mate? 'Marry one who lives near you', said Hesiod. But men and women who marry require one another to be not merely, like animals, within geographical range and perhaps of a similar age. They also require one another (as a rule) to speak the same language, even the same dialect and with the same accent. They require, as a rule, to be of the same religious sect, even though the sect may be small, and to be of similar social and economic status, even though the status may be rare and exalted. They are also very likely to marry within a community of a similar craft or trade or profession. The tests they apply to one another all have a large genetic component. They are sometimes very crude, but sometimes very sensitive. Indeed we may doubt whether the words of the poet or the instruments of the scientist are capable of describing or measuring the modes of discrimination to which mateable youth will eagerly submit itself in the process of human courtship.

To be sure, the unromantic aspects of these restrictions are largely disregarded in the fairy tale where the king may marry a beggar maid. In real life, however, the king does not marry the beggar maid. In real life the rules are not often disregarded, and in a stable society they are never disregarded with impunity. The same is true, in a rudimentary way, in all large outbreeding species of animals and plants. Now large parts of the world for long periods of time have been, and will be, populated by stable societies. In such societies these restrictions operate with increasing force up to the point where the society breaks down and new communities are constituted. The communities or mating groups that are separated in this way consist of our chromosome pools. The separation is mitigated by a trickle or a stream of contamination, a kind of social osmosis. Each group then undergoes selection and adaptation to the special way of life and special natural conditions which it finds for itself.

How this system works was discovered for a single gene by Galton. He was considering the Quakers, a group of people from whom he was derived, a group who, until 1870, were forbidden to marry outside their community. This is how he describes his discovery:

Colour blindness ... is nearly twice as prevalent among the Quakers as among the rest of the community, the proportions being as 5·9 to 3·5 per cent. We might have expected an even larger ratio. Nearly every

Quaker is descended on both sides solely from members of a group of men and women who segregated themselves from the rest of the world five or six generations ago; one of their strongest opinions being that fine arts were worldly snares, and their most conspicuous practice being to dress in drabs.

Human Faculty, 1883

Galton here takes the first steps in demonstrating the genetic sequence of civilization. The sequence is that the genetically fixed capacities of individual men first influence their beliefs and secondly their social behaviour; thirdly, having done so, they in turn influence the groups in which the individuals will mate; and fourthly, the mating group selects and concentrates the genetic capacities of individual men.

By this circular sequence we can now see that the differentiation of society is established on a genetic basis, of which the people concerned are unconscious; and with the genetic means, by the separation of breeding groups, of perpetuating, accentuating, and finally even overdoing, this differentiation. Galton could not see all this himself because he did not know how genes recombine. He merely saw the first and the last terms of the series. What is true of one gene in the Quakers is true of all genes in all communities of all plants and animals. Galton had uncovered the process of racial differentiation in its simplest instance much as Mendel had uncovered the process of recombination in its simplest instance.

Primitive societies of men consist of single mating-groups usually with a uniform character maintained by the instinctive custom of avoiding outbreeding: or as we may say, by assortative mating. Advanced societies have existed only since the origin of agriculture less than 10,000 years ago. They arose in the first instance by the meeting of different races or by technical inventions whose practice selectively disrupted society. They are differentiated into mating groups. These groups, which are now social classes, are kept apart by their preference for mating within the group rather than between groups. The classes, like the tribes, are preserved by assortative mating which is seen in the stratified societies of modern nations. How do these societies in fact maintain themselves?

The formation of a mating group by people who are mutually

attractive and culturally and genetically alike has cumulative or self-exaggerating effects. For amongst human beings, as distinct from any other animal, such a group provides an important part of the environment of its members. It provides the cultural environment. Indeed the formation by man of mating groups of unprecedented discrimination is due to the working of a general biological principle, that every organism seeks, or rather is adapted to find, its proper environment. It is due to that principle working in an organism with the necessary powers of discriminating between environments. Its working need not be enlarged upon here since the whole of the imaginative literature of mankind is concerned with expounding its vicissitudes.

Thus the environment with which a man's genotype reacts is itself in its most profound character, the creation of men of like genotype. Those who come to study human biology without understanding fundamental genetic principles are bound to find this analysis baffling. They assume that man's culture makes him. They do not realize that a whole community working for generations is needed to make the culture which only then reacts with an individual of the same community, with one of its own genotypes, to give the harmonious working which is represented amongst other things by what we may be permitted to call 'love of one's country', a characteristic to be reckoned with among ordinary men so long as they dwell in stable communities.

Throughout history there has been a crystallization by inbreeding – that is relative inbreeding – of tribes, classes, castes and races. Ever and anon this crystallization has been interrupted by the opposite process of melting and fusion when the barriers to mating break down and new groups are formed following conquest, revolution, famine, pestilence and adventurous migration. Such a breakdown has led to the processes Darwin observed of race mixing in the New World which are continuing at the present day side by side with the formation of new races, and the stratification of new classes, as stable societies are re-formed in freshly settled territories. Always the same principles of sexual discrimination are at work, the efforts of men and women throughout the ages being continually aimed (so far as modesty will allow them) at displaying their personal attractions to one

271

another within mating groups which are both culturally and genetically conditioned.

Sexual selection therefore follows the same rules but takes a different shape today from that which Darwin described. Every choice in mating is a part of the great pattern on which natural selection acts. It has two aspects in regard to its long-range or evolutionary consequences. The first, which was what concerned Darwin, affects the differentiation of the sexes and the evolution of each sex. The second affects the differentiation of mating groups classes or races. Those making the choice, although it is an entirely conscious choice, are entirely unconscious of the divisibility into the two aspects. The two together have been, and, we may venture to predict, always will be an indispensable agent in human evolution. The two together we see explaining, not merely the structure and diversity of human societies today, but also the brilliant and changing patterns of their past and their future.

SPEECH AND SOCIETY

The relations of speech to society are now clear enough to be worth describing. Their intrinsic value in the understanding of society is great but their value in serving as a model of how to apply genetics to the study of society is even greater.

Human speech began, perhaps 100,000 years ago, in a section of the already diversified human species. Or, perhaps it arose independently in several sections. As a means of transmitting culture and as a basis of social unity it must have conferred an advantage from its very beginning on those whose genetic properties of tongue, teeth, throat and ear made speech possible. It would spread therefore by natural selection probably accompanied by hybridization between speakers and non-speakers. The forms of speech would rapidly become diversified as space and culture divided the speakers into genetically isolated groups and created incipient speaking races.

The processes of evolution that would follow can be verified from the varieties of human speech today. The form that speech takes is modified by the diverse genetic character of the separated races. The traditional basis of every language handed down by imitation is changed as the genetic character of the group, the nation, which speaks it, changes following conquest and hybridization. The genealogy of sounds is traceable through these changes on the principles of etymology; but the grammar is changed with the intellectual character of the people; and the sounds are shifted by the changing structures of their vocal organs. The etymology which distinguishes groups of languages (such as Aryan and Semitic) therefore has almost no genetic meaning. The grammar has a little meaning. The phonetics, as Brosnahan has shown, has much meaning.

These historic changes must, of course, all be genetically determined but the determination shows a novel relationship between the individual and the society in which he lives and speaks. Every individual has his own genetically determined character of speaking. This individual character he tries to suppress so far as sounds are concerned, and even to a large extent so far as style and construction are concerned. This is a concession which the individual makes to the community in order to be understood by them and to get what he wants from them. He keeps, in general, as few idiosyncrasies of sound as possible although an enterprising individual may venture to make innovations of sound and of idiom; instead of accepting the language he may change it.

The genetic determination of the forms of language thus operates through combining the interests of a whole group of individuals extending over many generations. In small groups, nearly all these individuals are closely related and similar; they are therefore able to imitate one another easily. But when a national language emerges, with its greater extension in space and time, more diverse individuals combine and only strict education can enforce a conformity to a standard language. Hence we find the survival of dialects as distinct from an educated language. These dialects are phonetically conterminous with mating groups. Hence, also, we find the persistence or recovery of particular speech sounds even when they have been submerged by a change of language, when, for example, the Celtic speech was replaced in England and the Basque speech in Spain.

The genetic determination of the character and changes of speech is, however, only half the story. Languages are continually being adopted by groups of people who did not invent or even inherit them. These people will always change the speech they have adopted, as the French changed Latin, unless a governing class is ready and able to impose the educated speech immediately as a national language. Whether the language is fixed or changing, however, it fixes the limits within which it facilitates mating and beyond which it hinders mating. Language has thus become with advancing civilization the most powerful agent in the formation of mating groups: that is to say, in determining the size and shape of the genetic pools within which the genes and the characters of the human species are recombined.

Linguistic discrimination, as we may call it, by its elaborate genetic effects has helped to shape the pattern of history. Its greatest interest, however, is that it is effective in separating, in different ways, both races and classes. In a new community arising from migration and revolution, like the United States, it only begins to take effect after other causes of differentiation. But in well-established communities like those of Western Europe it separates both classes and races by accent and dialect. Its action is, of course, complex. On the one hand speech separates different classes in the same region, making marriage between classes impossible. Yet its geographical effects are quite different within different classes. For it may separate even neighbouring villages among the uneducated classes, while among the educated and multilingual it does not even entirely separate different nations.

By considering these genetic relationships of speech and society we can see many social, cultural and historical problems in a clearer light. The most urgent help they give us, however, is in allowing us to clear away the litter of false theories and superstitions which have been foisted upon us in the last hundred years in the names of race and language. Race builds language. And language builds race. But they build very slowly and both can be destroyed very quickly when languages are mixed and races are crossed. The principles of building and destruction we understand. By applying them we shall undoubtedly gain knowledge of practical value to the government of all human societies. But their application is not to be undertaken without the labours of historical study and genetic observation and inference.

RACE AND CLASS

Mating groups taken out of any species of experimental animal always differ from one another in ways that can be described at different levels. We can speak of differences in respect of individual genes, differences in respect of the whole genotype, differences in respect of the external appearance or phenotype. Moreover, separate mating groups always vary internally in all these respects. The phenotypic variations fall into normal curves which in quantitative respects may or may not overlap for different mating groups. And we can explain their properties in terms of individual genes and of genotypes.

These situations are exactly paralleled for human races and classes so far as the appearances, the phenotypes, are concerned. We find absolute differences like those in colour. We find overlapping, statistical, differences like those in height, speed of running, brain size and intelligence. We also find that overlap applies to each difference, but not to all differences, if they are taken together.

We cannot pursue our study in man with complete precision from the phenotype to the genotype. For one thing we cannot breed him experimentally. But there is also another difficulty. The records of human inheritance show that a large proportion of human gene differences do not express themselves with the simple regularity of genes in a Mendelian experiment with peas. Many people may have the gene we mentioned in connexion with Gratio Kelleia, the gene which seems to determine the possession of extra fingers in their uncles, grandmothers and children, but which does not cause them to have extra fingers themselves. We may say that they have modifying genes or polygenes which prevent the major gene expressing itself. This complication arises to an unusual and overwhelming degree in man. Why should this be so?

The answer is that human genetics is complicated because most human mating groups are large and variable. Scores, perhaps hundreds, of differences are being recombined in every family. The Mendelian situation and the Johannsen system of standardized lines cannot occur without repeated brother–sister mating.

The clean segregation of single differences therefore cannot arise. We may discover a massive difference which overrides the modification of other gene differences and gives a 3 : 1 or 1 : 1 segregation in one family. But this difference will not necessarily override all others in another family. The only class of effect in which one can be sure of finding direct and simple Mendelian behaviour is where the genes act directly in producing cell-proteins. Such are the special blood-group genes which prevent the transfusion of blood between genetically different people; and also the haemoglobin genes which, as we shall see, confer resistance to malaria.

The peculiarities of heredity in man are explained by his intermittent capacity for outbreeding. But, by a strange paradox, the differentiation of his races and classes is due to his regular habit of inbreeding. It is, of course, a limited and not an extreme inbreeding. His avoidance of the extreme inbreeding which we call incest is nearly universal and appears to be instinctive in its origin. Its evolutionary advantage is not that it avoids disabilities in the individual. For there are plenty of successful societies like the Mennonites that are highly inbred. Its advantage is that it preserves his capacity to vary, and hence his genetic means of escape from difficult or changing environmental conditions. For this reason avoidance of inbreeding is encouraged by a variety of adaptive genetic mechanisms in plants and animals. It is a property of the breeding system which, as we saw of various properties of heredity, is universally favoured by natural selection.

RACIAL VALUES: COOPERATION AND BALANCE

All races, all classes, all mating groups and all social units composed of mating groups have their own genetic characteristics. They are all different. As soon as we answer this question and admit this difference we appear to admit the propriety of a second question: is one group better than another? In this general form, the question, although it seems so obvious, is inadmissible. When we ask whether one woodman's axe is better than another we mean better for felling trees. We may even mean for the use of a certain type of man, with a certain kind of training, felling a certain kind of tree. These implications are usually understood and do not need to be expressed. Nor are they invidious. But when we compare different men or different groups of men the implication that the men are to be used for a particular purpose is not understood. Indeed, unless the men are slaves, the purpose is partly within the power of the men themselves to decide and cannot be decided by others in advance. We can therefore compare men only for particular theoretical purposes defined for the sake of discussion. With this express restriction the comparison of men and races is of great value, indeed it is indispensable if we are to examine how humanity can manage its own future. Two examples will illustrate the possible conditions of inquiry and the kind of conclusion that can be drawn.

The United States serves as an experiment in the study of the values of races. Indeed it is the most important experiment of its kind in human history. It is important because we can see it in progress. That country owes its strength partly to genetic recombination between diverse races. But it owes its strength also, perhaps even more, to the unrecombined diversity.

In the southern United States there are now 10,000,000 Negroes and some 20,000,000 whites. The proportion of Negroes decreases as one moves north and the proportion of their admixture with the whites increases. On the same territory there were 400 years ago perhaps 100,000 American Indians. If no white or Negro had ever entered this territory there would still be about the same number of Indians. They were displaced by whites: it is doubtful whether they ever could, or would, have been displaced by Negroes in view of the warlike capacity of the Indians.

From the point of view of supporting a population of human beings there can be no doubt that the white-plus-Negro society is more efficient than the Indian was or ever could be. And the disparity is still increasing. Why? A white society alone would probably be little more numerous than the whites in the mixed society. A Negro society alone, even if not cut off from all intercourse with whites (to judge from the experiments in Liberia and Haiti) would support fewer Negroes or poorer Negroes than there are in the mixed society. The advantage of the white-plus-Negro society is that its two racially dissimilar elements are able and

277

willing (although only just willing) to help one another. The American Indian has been found not to be able and willing to help the other two. Their capacity and his capacity are both, of course, racial and genetic. They are determined and limited by heredity.

We now know that the long evolution from the most primitive hunting and collecting people (like the Bushmen in the Kalahari desert) to the most advanced urban peoples has been accompanied by two general types of change. The advanced people have lost or partly lost many of the faculties of perception and of temperament necessary for the preservation of the primitive people. For example, defects of vision, notably colour blindness, have increased as they have ceased to have fatal consequences for people living in advanced societies. Conversely these people, or rather some of them, have gained certain faculties of reasoning and temperament necessary or exceedingly useful for the maintenance of complex societies. They have also become vastly differentiated in their faculties and temperaments. This point is neatly brought out by an observation of Francis Galton on his travels in Damaraland:

> The herdsmen, he relates, 'seldom lose oxen: the way in which they discover the loss of one, is not by the number of the herd being diminished, but by the absence of a face they know' (ch. v).

The primitive pastoralist has retained the gifts of acute observation which he has inherited from his palaeolithic ancestors. They are gifts which have been very generally lost in civilization. But civilized men possess the whole range of skills in dealing with numbers; they possess them from the low level of the Damara up to the high level of Galton. In history, in the evolution of society, this range, this differentiation, has arisen by the combination and cooperation of races: by one kind of man helping another kind of man.

An important conclusion follows. One of the definable genetic characters and, as some would say, virtues, of human races and classes (as also of individuals) is the capacity for social cooperation. For the cooperation of genetically different groups permits the building up of more complex societies and cultures and the exploitation of the earth's resources by a more numerous population; and, what is most important of all, in the light of genetics, a genetically diversified population.

Thus we arrive at a paradox which timidity usually hides from us. The assumption of a genetic basis for race and class differences provides the evidence, the only scientific evidence, in favour of racial tolerance and cooperation.

It is absurd to pretend that water and vinegar are equal. Water is better for some purposes, vinegar for others. Vinegar is harder to get but easier to do without. So it is with people. For 200 generations the advance of mankind has depended on those genetically diverse groups, whether races or classes, which have been able to practise mutual help and show mutual respect. The future of mankind will depend on the continuance of such abilities and habits: a happy aim which cannot be assisted in the long run by make-believe, certainly not by a make-believe of equality in the physical, intellectual and cultural capacities of such groups.

Individuals and groups which are genetically similar are bound to compete with one another. Only when they are genetically different can help predominate. Whether they do help one another, of course, depends on heredity and education, but the education can be of no use if it does not depend on a recognition of the laws of nature.

A second aspect of the value of a race or class appears if we ask ourselves how many we want of any one kind of men. We should not want a world full of Fuegians or of Hottentots or even of Scotsmen or New Englanders. Nor should we want a world deprived entirely of any of these. It is not merely from sentimentality that we deplore the disappearance of the Tasmanians, the decay of the Cherokees, or the depopulation of the Scottish glens. It takes, we agree, all sorts to make a world. Every one of these racial groups had something to give to the rich diversity of human cultures. It also had something of genetic value to give to the sum and scope of human heredity and variation; something that might add to the possibilities of human hybridization in some later age 1,000 or 10,000 generations hence. For a race, whether it disappears by extinction or by hybridization, disappears none the less. It cannot be used up twice.

What is said of race is also true of class. Those small inbred groups, whether they are the flint-knappers of Norfolk, or the net-makers of Bridport, the leather-workers of Florence or the silversmiths of Isfahān, if lost cannot be remade in one generation or two. Such groups are of course continually being lost; and other new ones are being gradually made, fitted to the new needs of changing civilization through the selection of trades and of mates by the young men and women of each generation.

Following inbreeding, a certain degree of purity or homozygosity is found in any old-fashioned group and gives it a useful predictability of breeding-behaviour and fitness or adaptation to fixed conditions. This pure-breeding is lost by crossing between races and castes and even classes. The result of a single cross can be undone only by many generations of later inbreeding and selection. The objection to outbreeding, crossing or hybridization is therefore chiefly that it must be applied with moderation. It is not in itself good or bad. It has its value in proportion.

A balance is therefore needed between the genetically differentiated elements of every nation and of all the nations of the world. And a balance is also needed between inbreeding and outbreeding.

RACIAL VALUES: DISEASE RESISTANCE

Apart from their genetic differences, races are distinguished from one another by their dwelling-place, classes only by their occupation. There are several fields in which selective differentiation therefore applies to races with greater effect than it applies to classes. The most important of these concerns resistance to disease.

Darwin noticed that when groups which had long been separated from one another were brought into contact they introduced their diseases to one another, new diseases with which one group or the other had been unfamiliar. Darwin did not realize that his own principle of geographical isolation was here at work. The isolation of the peripheral groups of man from the central body of the Old World had prevented their becoming selected for resistance to the main body of disease: contact with these isolated groups did not occur in ancient times. It arose chiefly through the great navigations. Darwin was, however, setting on foot the inquiry whose pursuit led Archdall Reid to declare thirty years later, with abundance of evidence, that 'the Natural History of Man is, in effect, a history of his evolution against disease'. The general explanation is now clear. A large group is selected for

Figure 17

Map showing the general direction of the successive types of human expansion which have populated the world: (i) solid lines, movements by land starting from Southern Asia; (ii) broken line, main Polynesian sea movement of first millennium A.D., omitting Madagascar; (iii) dotted line, European sea movements following the great navigations. The last has given contacts and hybridization between discontinuous peoples such as the first has not given in historic times. *Note:* The land movements are actually composed of palaeolithic, neolithic, Aryan, Hamitic and Bantu expansions.

resistance to many diseases, a small isolated group for resistance to few. The ancient empires of the Old World were all part of one great human continuum: subject to regular exchange of genes by heredity and of germs by infection. In modern times civilized people from this great central group have suddenly come into contact with smaller isolated groups like the natives of America, Australia, New Zealand and the Pacific and Indian Ocean islands. Both sides have suffered, but, as we saw, the smaller groups have suffered most. A few of them have been saved by continued isolation. A few more have been saved, but not intact, by hybridization. The rest have been largely exterminated. A visit from a gunboat or a missionary, bringing the white man's diseases, has proved equally fatal (Figure 17).

Scales of disease resistance may be measured by the proportion of individuals attacked, the gravity of the attack and the frequency of death. These generally agree for any one disease. On this basis three generalizations can be made about the values of different races. First, every race is best adapted to resisting the diseases peculiar to its own region and its own way of life. Secondly, races that have been in contact with the main body of mankind will be more resistant to the diseases of the main body of mankind. Hence, thirdly, the isolated peoples will be less resistant to these diseases than their own cross-breeds. All these conclusions follow from the Darwinian principle of natural selection.

MALARIA AND THE BLOOD GENES

A number of protozoan parasites carried by mosquitoes digest the haemoglobin of human blood. They destroy the red blood corpuscles thus causing fever which in the weak and underfed leads to death. The most dangerous of these parasites is *Plasmodium falciparum* and it is carried by at least sixty species of mosquitoes of the genus *Anopheles*. The disease it causes is known as malaria, and of a special kind described as malignant or subtertian or falciparum malaria. It is generally distributed in the low-lying damper parts of the tropics long inhabited by man. It began in Asia or Africa but it has been carried, by the movements of men in recent times, first to Europe, then to America, and last of all to Australia.

Malaria, like many other diseases, probably became active and dangerous to man only after the great increase in human numbers less than 10,000 years ago. But unlike any other disease the profound evolutionary changes it has induced during this time happen to be genetically and chemically identifiable. How does this come about?

Alternative forms of haemoglobin have no doubt always been present in man as in cattle and other animals. The presence of malaria has given a selective advantage to certain forms which seem to be less readily digestible by the malaria parasite. It is in consequence of this situation that abnormal haemoglobins have spread. They now appear with high frequency in all populations subject to malignant malaria. A dozen different haemoglobins, labelled C, D, E, F and so on, together with the normal A seem to have arisen from A by gene mutation. They show different rearrangements of single amino-acids in one of the four chains of the haemoglobin molecule. And they are characteristic of different populations. There are several in tropical Africa which have been carried to America. Others are found in the Mediterranean and Southern Asia. In addition to these mutant alleles there are other genes which modify the production or utilization of haemoglobin with similar effects (Figure 18).

The various modifications of haemoglobin which make the human being more resistant to malaria do so at the expense of damaging the haemoglobin for the uses of its owner: they cause anaemia. The most widespread forms are known as sickle-cell anaemia and thallassaemia. Long after their recognition their mode of operation was explained by Allison in 1954.

The sickle cell anaemia is due to an allele s which produces wholly abnormal haemoglobin in the homozygote and hence collapsed red blood corpuscles. In the heterozygote it produces half its effect, with mixed haemoglobins and the corpuscles collapsing only with reduced oxygen supply. Thus, on Allison's view, a population with sickle cell anaemia will always contain three types of individual:

AA	AS	SS
Normal or A haemoglobin	Half A half s	Sickle-cell or s haemoglobin
Partly die of malaria	Resist malaria and survive	Die of anaemia in childhood

These three types of individual will exist in the population in proportions maintained by the incidence of malaria. Moreover, in consequence, populations exposed to malaria will show a general rise in the frequency of the heterozygotes, AS, between birth and maturity. This effect has indeed been shown. For

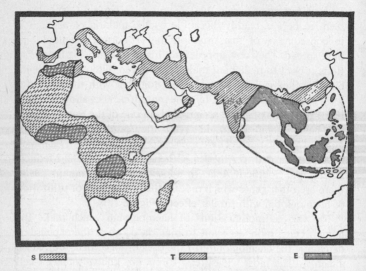

S ▨▨▨▨   T ▨▨▨   E ▨▨▨

Figure 18

Main areas of distribution of three of the principal genes supposed to control malaria through haemoglobin production in man: S and E, genes for sickle-cell and for the eastern type of haemoglobin; T, a gene reducing haemoglobin production and causing thallassaemia.

Note: (i) S probably arose first in tropical Africa, T in the Mediterranean, while E might have arisen only in South-east Asia.
(ii) These genes are found only where there has been malaria.
(iii) Several anti-malaria genes can exist together in mixed populations, e.g in Orissa, Nigeria and the Congo.
(iv) The absence of E in Madagascar, if true, is evidence that its spread is later than the Indonesian colonization 1800 years ago.
Mainly from Allison 1961.

example among different Congo peoples the proportion rises in the Baluba from 16 to 23 per cent and in the pygmies from 23 to 28 per cent. It is therefore from the AS individuals that the two types of homozygotes are continually being replenished. What is more the frequency of the s gene seems still to be generally increasing in Africa.

It might appear that the s gene is dividing or disputing the role of killer with the mosquito and the *Plasmodium*: it achieves the same effect by destroying the blood in a different way. So it does. But the parasites always come first. And in countries like the United States where malaria is diminishing, s haemoglobin diminishes also. Evidently the abnormal haemoglobins are maintained in the human population by the action of the malaria. By extinguishing one part of the population they are able to prevent the disease from extinguishing or crippling another and larger part.

The anti-malaria genes offer us therefore the most striking, because it is the most drastic, of all examples of how natural selection is working today in man. But they lead us beyond this, for they illustrate the principle that every geographical race of an organism is adapted to resist and to survive the attacks of its local diseases. It has its own protective genes. Every invasion, every migration, from one region or one habitat to another, is therefore resisted by the local diseases. It is this principle above all which has protected tropical Africa against the invasion of northern peoples. People from South-west Asia with their horses and cattle have spread without hindrance in temperate climates and in uninhabited continents. Until recently they have been prevented from crossing the barrier of equatorial Africa not by men as such but by the diseases they carry. We are now on the threshold of understanding, with the help of the protective genes, a great deal more about how men have moved in the past.

THE MEDICAL DILEMMA

Causes of disease and death of human beings may be distinguished between those with, and those without, an element of infection. In both there is, as we have seen, a genetic component. Where there is infection the genetic variation of the human victim concerns his resistance to the invasion of the microbe, or its propagation, or the consequences of its propagation. Where there is no infection the genetic variation concerns distortions of the chemical processes of life often giving rise to malformations, visible or invisible.

The second or crudely genetic class of disease takes various forms. Of the invisible distortions of the metabolism some, like haemophilia and phenylketonuria, are due to specific major genes; others, like diabetes, are polygenic. The same is true of the visible malformations, like mongolism and polydactyly; some are due to major gene or chromosome defects; others are polygenic. A few, as we know from the drug thalidomide, can be mimicked by external agents. In advanced countries where the estimation can be attempted 6 per cent of live born children are said to carry one or other of such genetic defects. This 6 per cent of abnormalities has been roughly assigned (by a United Nations report) to the following classes:

1 per cent: chromosomes and pieces of chromosome
1 per cent: specific major genes
4 per cent: unidentified polygenes

These defects are in a strict sense incurable: if the carrier reproduces they are liable to be handed down to all succeeding generations. Moreover, owing to the advances in the understanding of the causes of disease, of immunity to disease, and of the treatment of disease, a great increase has taken place, especially in the last twenty years, in the relative frequency of genetic disabilities not only as classes of disease but also as causes of death. First vaccination and inoculation, then sanitation and disinfection, and lastly chemical prevention and chemical destruction of microbes and insect carriers, have slowly reduced the loss from infectious diseases. The genetic diseases, mostly remaining constant in frequency, have mounted in the proportion of the damage they do (Table 6).

The possible means of reducing infantile mortality due to infectious disease have now been almost fully applied. The possible means of treating genetic abnormalities, however, are still in an early stage of exploitation. Treatment of diabetes with insulin, and the operation of relieving pyloric stenosis likewise, are little more than forty years old. Their effects however are already obvious. Both these abnormalities have an important genetic component. The individuals whose lives are saved are liable to have progeny with a higher proportion of these defects than the normal population. Whence, we notice, a new general principle

TABLE 6

Percentage causes of death in the Hospital for Sick Children, London, after C. O. Carter, 1956

		Non-infectious	
	Infectious[1]	External Malformation	Internal Errors[2]
1914	68·0	15·5	16·5
1934	51·5	32·5	16·0
1954	14·5	48·0	37·5

1. Including tuberculosis, pneumonia, gastro-enteritis.
2. Including pyloric stenosis and diabetes mellitus.

appears: the cure or palliative treatment of genetic abnormalities increases the frequency of these abnormalities in later generations. It thus increases the need for repetition of the original treatment.

The situation in regard to infectious diseases is sharply contrasted. As an extreme example take malaria. This disease is principally controlled by spoiling the breeding-places of the mosquito. When the disease is extirpated the human population suffers no hereditary damage. On the contrary, the drastic genetic means which it has used for controlling the disease, namely the production of abnormal and partly lethal haemoglobins, becomes unnecessary. The genetic lethals decline in the population which is restored to health *vis-à-vis* both the gene and the parasite.

In its evolutionary effect therefore the medical treatment of infectious diseases differs from that of non-infectious diseases. The incidence of both has a genetic component. But the removal of infection or its causes inevitably *diminishes* the source of propagation. The removal of purely internal genetic defects *increases* the source of propagation.

All medically and surgically curable genetic defects, we can predict, will therefore increase in the populations enjoying the full advantages of medical and surgical treatment, unless, that is, the community, or the medical profession, or the individuals concerned, aware of what is happening – that is, of the genetic principles concerned – take steps to avoid the disastrous consequences of their own achievements.

Such is the dilemma which confronts us today. It is an unfamiliar situation, especially for the medical profession, for it is the first moral dilemma they have had to face since the time of Hippocrates.

THE SELECTION OF THE ENVIRONMENT

The very essence of the experimental analysis of heredity is the notion of Galton and Johannsen that the properties of the individual depend on the reaction of nature and nurture. We may describe the contrast or polarity as one between heredity and circumstance, genotype and environment; or between what comes from inside and from outside the fertilized egg. Experiments in genetics depend upon separating, standardizing and controlling these opposed conditions. We keep one constant while we discover the action of differences in the other. But at the same time that Galton and Johannsen were introducing this necessary idea an opposite notion attached to the word environment was searching for expression, a notion which had a validity of its own.

In 1903 a young American zoologist, C. B. Davenport, was studying the population of animals on the beach of Cold Spring Harbor near New York. He pointed out that in such a place there was a whole range of environments open to the individuals of any one species. It was not proper therefore to consider the survival of the fittest members of a species without asking to which environment it was to be fitted. This is a question which cannot be answered in advance. Moreover, genetic changes might often arise in a population or group of animals in one environment which would fit later generations to a different environment. Adaptations might therefore appear (as Lucretius had pointed out) before they had a use. As we saw, in considering the evolution of heredity and of breeding-systems, the most important adaptations do arise in this way. And the fact that they do so constitutes an unanswerable objection to both parts of the theory of Lamarck.

The notion is, however, so fundamental that it may be put in many ways, each useful and effective. Davenport summed the matter up by saying that adaptation is reciprocal:

Adaptation of organization to environment has been effected by the double process of selection by environment of the most appropriate organization and by the organism of the most congenial environment.

Now this notion of variation in the available *natural* environment, and the consequent choice of environments among the varying individuals of a natural species, is diametrically opposed to Johannsen's notion of the standardized *experimental* environment. And, since at that time genetics depended for its very survival on the experimental situation, the natural environment failed to make itself felt: it was smothered by the rival concept, the alternative idea, attached to the same name.

Most of this book has been concerned with discovering heredity by Johannsen's method: by the use of the experimental environment. It is only when we are clear about heredity – that is, about the genotype – that we can put aside the experimental environment and look at the problem of the natural environment and the natural population that lives in it. This we can now do without (we hope) confusing our ideas.

If we are concerned with assessing the relative effects of changes in heredity and changes in environment under natural conditions our experimental standardization of the environment is misleading. A single gene so alters a plant or an animal that it alters the reaction of the environment to it. The separation of heredity from environment that we achieve is clean experimentally but not physiologically. The tall pea meets a different world from the short one. The hairy leaf registers the harsh affronts of wind and drought with greater or less accuracy than the smooth leaf. Even where there is no choice of environment it is thus clear that heredity determines what is effective in the environment.

Put a group of different human beings in a garden, in the same garden, in the same environment. One will be delighted with the colours of the flowers; another with their perfumes; a third will appreciate the songs of the birds and not notice the flowers at all; a fourth will set about at once to root up weeds, observing nothing but what offers work; a fifth will read a book or be content with his own abstract thoughts: he will not notice flowers or trees, birds or men, clouds or sun. And five such people may be found among brothers and sisters who have had the same chances and same encouragement in all these different directions. One may be bounded in a nutshell and count himself a king of infinite space. Another may command great space but still be bounded in a nutshell. Or, as Dr Johnson put it: one man will learn as much in the Hampton stage as another in the Grand Tour of Europe. In all organisms, differences in heredity create differences in their environment, however rigorously we may make it standardized and homogeneous.

To this model Davenport adds another dimension, the dimension represented by the choice of environments. Every animal that has the capacity for movement has the capability of making this choice. By virtue of exercising the choice, variation and natural selection, adaptation and the genetic stratification of societies, take on a pattern that is otherwise missing. Instead of an elimination of those which are unfit for the place where they find themselves, there is, first of all, a process of sorting out. Each animal seeks and selects the place, the environment, that fits it best.

This mutual or double selection, as Davenport calls it, must enormously increase the efficiency and speed of adaptive and evolutionary processes. It represents one of the great advantages of animals which move in the direction they choose over plants which are dispersed in all directions by chance. At the same time it supports the illusion that both individuals and races are moulded by an environment which they have actually chosen: variable animal species in variable environments are therefore often said by experienced naturalists to 'respond' to their environments with a wonderful 'plasticity'.

This type of casual inversion has become a systematic fallacy of social discussion today. We find, for example, social scientists reporting on Racial Problems that:

The one trait which above all others has been at a premium in the evolution of men's mental characters has been educability, plasticity. This is a trait which all human beings possess. It is indeed a species character of *Homo sapiens*.

Attributing differences to the environment which primarily spring from heredity is most widespread as a social fallacy. It has innumerable ramifications; they run into almost every common-sense opinion about life. We say a man is healthy because he takes plenty of exercise. Yet it is evident that men take exercise because they are healthy. Some men by heredity require much exercise: with little exercise they would fall ill. Other men require little exercise: with much exercise they would fall ill. And we are often surprised to discover that they have what we call a 'good constitution'.

Again we say that playing games in teams cultivates the team spirit. But children play games in teams because they already have the team spirit, by heredity. No amount of playing games will give a team spirit either to the imbecile or to the child with initiative and originality. Fallacies of this kind are made the basis of educational systems. They provide the vulgar excuse for suppressing individuality. But in heterogeneous societies biological rules have to be made to allow for individuals as well as for people in general.

For people in general, for us, the possibilities of life are multiplied beyond measure by the choice of environments. The civilized world into which we come, although formally one environment, is effectively an enormous diversity of environments, the creation of generations of genetically diversified men and groups of men. It is this diversity of environments which it is to a great extent the business of imaginative literature to render into the currency of interchangeable ideas. In this world no two individuals have to put up with the same environment: we have a choice. The choice is limited and determined by our individual genetic character. According to that character it may be very small or very large. It may be a passive choice in which we accept one of the possibilities that is offered to us. Heredity may then indeed be said to 'respond' to the environments as the textbooks tell us. But it may be an active selection. We may even create to a greater or less extent the environment we want. The gradation between the most helpless of mortals and a Caesar (or a Newton or a Shakespeare) is a genetic one. Shakespeare hits the nail on the head as usual when he contrasts Macbeth with the murderers (Act Three, Scene One):

FIRST MURDERER: We are men, my liege.

MACBETH: Ay, in the catalogue ye go for men,
  As hounds, and greyhounds, mongrels, spaniels, curs,
  Shoughs, water-rugs, and demi-wolves, are clept
  All by the name of dogs: the valued file
  Distinguishes the swift, the slow, the subtle,
  The housekeeper, the hunter, every one
  According to the gift which bounteous nature
  Hath in him clos'd, whereby he does receive
  Particular addition, from the bill
  That writes them all alike: and so of men. . . .

SECOND MURDERER: I am one, my liege,
  Whom the vile blows and buffets of the world
  Hath so incens'd, that I am reckless what
  I do to spite the world.

Thus the noble Macbeth attributes character and achievement to heredity; the base murderer attributes them to the environment. We can, however, go into more detail. The gradation in full shows individuals in four orders of capacity:

The first accepts the environment in which he finds himself.

The second seeks an environment that suits him.

The third changes his environment to suit him better.

The fourth changes the environments of others for his own and even for succeeding generations, for his own species and even for the whole living world.

This gradation of relationships is most evident in regard to our actions. It is no less momentous, however, in regard to our ideas, our beliefs. Most of us believe what we are told first or told most often. Some of us choose what we will believe from the opinions that we are given. A few of us venture to think for ourselves. And rare individuals go further. They raise their voices to persuade their neighbours or their nations or all mankind to believe in the word that has been revealed to them.

The same range is found in natural interests. There are some of us who have no concern beyond ourselves. Most of us admit an interest in our families, our communities and even our nations. And there are a few of us who extend our interests – both in space and time – to include mankind at large.

Finally, the crudely physical and physiological properties of the body combine with all its other genetically determined properties to decide the modes of life we choose. Our choice, therefore, in the whole sum of our activities forestalls the reaction of heredity and environment. That is the genetic view. If we repudiate it we can believe both in the freedom of our choice (a possibility to which we shall return later) and in the plasticity of our behaviour.

All this choice of environment has arisen as men, by creating new environments, have advanced from the Old Stone Age. With each one of us the choice grows with our own understanding. Take us back either to early infancy or to the Old Stone Age, and the choice of environment vanishes. We rejoice once more in our primitive appearance of equality. Every step in civilization is a step in exposing and exploiting the genetic diversity of men and their genetic gradation between what in poetic terms are called the creature of circumstance and the man of destiny.

The proportions of the orders in different groups and sections of mankind are different and naturally of great cultural significance. The second order is the most numerous in both sexes, in all races and, with rare and transient exceptions, in all classes. And there are some groups in which the third and fourth orders scarcely appear. Reproduction, again, stands by itself. Most men and women will rise to the second order in choosing a mate although they may never rise so high before or after.

In the fourth order a new relationship of heredity and environment makes its appearance. The genotypes of individuals begin to determine the environment in an absolute sense and to change the course of evolution. What are the fourth order of individuals? They are what we call, in ordinary speech, the Heroes of former ages, the Great Men of our own. Let us, by all means, agree with Tolstoy and distrust, disparage or dislike great men. Let us admit, too, that they are often great less by virtue of their copious talents than of their appropriate limitations. Best men, they say, are moulded out of faults. But let us not doubt that they change the course of history or that the character which enables them to do so is genetically determined. Particular individuals – individuals resulting from the exploitation of the uncertainty of genetic recombinations – have had immense effects on man's history, ever since the invention of speech. And it is this fact that gives its unpredictability to the course of human history.

15

Sex and Temperament

THE DETERMINATION OF SEX

ONE of the questions which has followed us down the ages is that of the determination of sex. It occupied the attention of Aristotle. Leeuwenhoeck claimed to have traced the cause to the production of two kinds of sperm. Our friend Jean Senebier, however, and, a little later, Darwin, both ignored his solution. They very properly ignored it because, although we now know that he was right, we also know that it was a guess and the wish, the animalculist's wish, was father to his thought.

There are two questions concerned in the problem of why a species should consist of individuals of two widely different kinds like the sexes in the higher animals. The first is a question of mechanics: why are the fertilized eggs of just these two kinds and in nearly equal numbers? The second is a question of development: how do eggs of each kind grow up into mature individuals having the characteristic form and behaviour of that sex? Let us take the mechanical question first.

The two sexes are in fact born in almost equal numbers because men and other male mammals produce sperm of two kinds in equal numbers. When they are ripe, we cannot, as Leeuwenhoeck pretended, pick out the two kinds under the microscope; but earlier there is a visible difference. Both kinds have twenty-three chromosomes; A, B, C, D, down to X, we may call them. But one of the two kinds has a short twenty-third chromosome. Instead of a large X chromosome there is a small Y chromosome, a third as long, which is virtually an X curtailed. If each small letter stands for a block of segment of genes their linear order may be shown quite simply as follows :

```
X   xxxxxxxxxxxxxxxxxooCoooo
Y                    yooCoooo
```

Then x applies to parts of the X chromosome alone, y to parts of

294

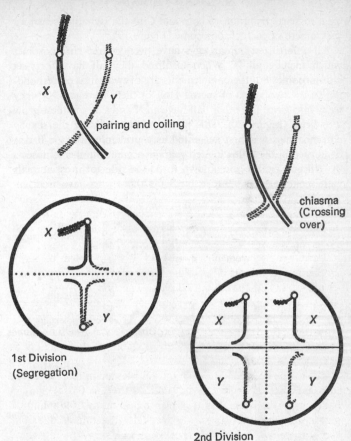

X Y
pairing and coiling

chiasma
(Crossing
over)

X

Y

1st Division
(Segregation)

X X

Y Y

2nd Division

Figure 19

The succession of movements of the two sex chromosomes at meiosis
in the sperm mother cells of man and other male mammals. The longer
X chromosome has a segment not represented in the Y. The two pair
and cross over in their similar parts, and, being held together by a
chiasma, are co-orientated at the first division passing to opposite
poles. At the second division the four daughter chromosomes have
passed to four sperm-making cells and all are of a different genetic
character, two male- and two female-determining, two changed and
two unchanged by crossing-over. The centromeres, represented by
small circles, split at this second division (see Figures 8 and 20).

Y, *o* to parts common to both and C to the dynamic centre or centromere of each chromosome (Figure 19).

All unfertilized human eggs have twenty-three chromosomes which include an X. When fertilized they all have forty-six chromosomes but the complements are of two kinds corresponding to the two kinds of sperm. Half of them have two Xs; they grow into girls. The other half have an X and a Y and these grow into boys (Figure 20). This means of determining the sex by chromosomes was first suggested as a principle in 1899. It was confirmed in the following ten years in a great number of insects by Wilson. This is now known to be the rule for most animals with separate sexes.[1] But in birds (as those who have bred sex-

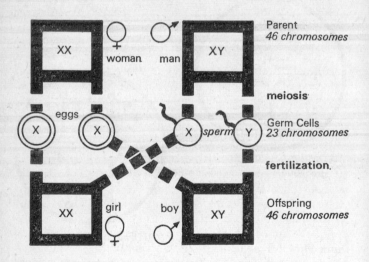

Figure 20

Diagram showing how sex is determined in the offspring by the formation in equal numbers of two kinds of sperm in which the twenty-third chromosome is either X or Y (see Figures 3 and 7).

1. The outstanding exception is in the Hymenoptera, the bees, wasps and ants, where the male develops from the virgin egg, the female from the fertilized egg: the difference is between haploid and diploid chromosome complements.

linked poultry know) and in butterflies, the system works the other way round: the male is XX, the female XY.

Thus sex is, as Mendel suspected, a special case of Mendelian segregation. In our own species the woman is true-breeding, the man is hybrid in respect of the X chromosome. He lacks a block of genes, or a 'supergene', from one of the two X chromosomes which every woman has. This applies to the egg from which he or she begins and to most of the 600,000,000,000,000 cells that make up the body he or she grows into.

The best-known consequences of XX–XY determination is the most trivial. It is that certain bad genes which lie in the xxx segment of the x chromosome show in a woman only when both her X chromosomes are the same in this respect: the bad genes have to come from both parents. And they are not likely to be the same unless her parents are closely related. But, in the man, these same genes can show when only one parent carried the bad gene because he has only one X chromosome which he gets from one parent only. Moreover, this parent is always his mother. Thus red–green colour blindness and haemophilia, whose genes lie in the xxx segment of the X chromosome, are ten or twenty times as frequent in men as in women, and the men have always inherited them from their mothers in whom they usually did not show.

The gravest consequence of the chromosome difference between the sexes is, however, that we have to regard the two sexes as no less different genetically than two related species. This notion is not a new one. John Ray long ago pointed out that the bull and the cow differ widely in form and function and are as different as two species. Offspring of opposite sexes may, however, arise not only from the same parents but even at the same birth. How this could happen had been one of the great problems of heredity or biological determination from the beginning. Here, for the first time, Ray puts it in a category by itself. The two sexes must always belong to the same species. Why? Because they may be born by the same mother? No. Rather because they breed together; because indeed they cannot breed otherwise. They have to take their chromosomes from the same pool.

The sexes may be alike or widely divergent. In certain fishes the male attaches itself in infancy to the belly of the female and there, incapable of independent life, it continues without further growth or movement, a parasite for the rest of its existence. The divergence of the sexes in man is less serious but still physically and mentally profound.

The two sexes are mutually adapted in regard to reproduction and are obviously inter-fertile. In our species they consequently share, and combine in creating, the culture and language and religion of each community. This sharing causes a superficial convergence of character; but underlying it there is a genetic divergence. On account of his hybridity, the male suffers many disadvantages. He is more variable than the female, as Darwin remarked, especially in his ability to live. His death rate is higher, both before and after he is born. And, as Aristotle noted, he is more often born defective.

The genetic constitutions of the sexes are so dissimilar in this respect of viability that their relative frequency, what is called the sex ratio, varies according to the relationship of the parents. In other animal groups than our own, where crosses can be made between species the XY sex, instead of being equal in numbers to the XX, is deficient in the hybrid. It may also be more or less sterile, although the XX sex is fertile. This difference is due to the fact that the contribution of the two parents is exactly equal in the XX sex. But the XY sex entirely lacks a piece of chromosome from one parental species, the xxx part of the X that is not in the Y, the little y segment being usually negligible. Inbreeding also may depress the XY sex. This is elegantly shown by a comparison of mice and men in Table 7.

TABLE 7

Sex ratios in mice and men: numbers of males to 100 females born (*Little, 1947*)

Experimental Mice		Men (New York Hospital)	
Breeding		*Parents*	
Inbred	103·5	from the same European country	104·5
		from different European countries	112·8
Outbred (between unrelated strains)	112·5	both U.S. born	118·3

A very broad principle may thus be stated: the best degree of relationship between parents gives the highest proportion of the XY sex. Either exceptional inbreeding or exceptional outbreeding upsets the delicate balance of the XY sex and reduces his relative vigour, numbers or fertility. The traditional system of breeding in any organism gives the healthiest – although not necessarily the most exciting – results.

At the same time the human sex ratios from New York make possible a very interesting deduction. The indication of racial hybridity when the parents come from different parts of Europe, and still more when they both come from the United States, as contrasted with intra-nation breeding in Europe, is unmistakable.

It is on account of the independent history of the X and Y chromosomes that the two sexes can, as Darwin supposed, to some extent evolve independently, differing much less in one race than they do in another. They take their other chromosomes out of the same pool but their sex chromosomes have to be one kind of pair or the other, XX or XY. How absurd it is therefore for us to speak of two sexes being equal! Clearly they are not. They overlap in particular respects. But, taken as a whole, they are different. Each has its value, a value best appreciated by the other, a value the result of long selection and adaptation. Just as with two races or two classes, equality can only be in relation to some particular scale, some particular terms of reference. The administration of justice or the theory of religion may require us to shut our eyes to all scales save one. But the interpretation of history, the practice of government, and the choice of a spouse permit us to apply our powers of discrimination to the question as a whole.

THE DEVELOPMENT OF SEX

Between the moment a fertilized egg arises with an XX or an XY pair of chromosomes and the maturing of the woman or man who is predestined to develop from it – according to whether it is of one or the other kind – many steps intervene whose effects can be separately identified. In a fly after ten hours the two sexes are distinguishable. But in the human embryo not until a couple of months after fertilization do the two types, now two inches long, begin to diverge. The sexual organs, whose rudiments are indistinguishable, begin to follow different lines, and at birth, although kittens may be hard to sex, living babies fail to show the external distinction between boys or girls less than once in a thousand times.

After birth the two sexes continue to diverge and to fall in with one sex or the other in temperament, in behaviour, in intelligence, and even in facial expression; the divergence being recognizable, as a rule, during the first few months. Such differences are all parts of the system of what we call secondary sexual characters. Some of these, like the growing of the beard, appear suddenly as sexual maturity approaches. Others develop more gradually, more gradually indeed than is generally realized. We think of the breaking of a boy's voice as a fairly sudden transformation. But it results from the lengthening of the vocal cords, a change which proceeds in both sexes from birth until well past sexual maturity. Authorities differ, but according to Marshall, at six the cords are on the average 10 mm. long in both sexes; between ten and fourteen a slight difference appears; at twenty they are 16 mm. in girls, 24 mm. in boys; and the proportion remains the same at thirty with 20 mm. and 30 mm.

These are averages. Each sex shows, however, a wide range of variation. Among women there is a continuous series from the contralto to the soprano and among men from the bass to the tenor and beyond. In the secondary sexual characters of all races, there are a small proportion who remain undefined and intermediate all the way through life. In their primary differences between ovaries and testes there is little overlapping of the two sexes but there is a great overlapping of their secondary differences. How can this be explained?

The practice of castrating, cutting off the two testes, of young male animals or of men captured in war, began in the middle bronze age. The castration of boys, for the purpose of recruiting male sopranos for the Sistine Choir, was continued by the Popes until the death of Pius IX in 1879. For the effect of castration is not only to prevent the formation of semen and (as the eunuch says to Cleopatra) to remove the ability to do anything but what is honest to be done. It also, if it occurs early enough, stops the development of the secondary sexual characters.

There are thus two steps in the determination of our sexual character. The first step, distinguishing which kind of sex organ, ovaries or testes shall develop, rests almost directly on the chromosomes and it takes place in the cells that matter long before birth. The second step depends on something produced by the ovaries and testes, something apart from eggs and sperm. This something may well vary in quantity or quality, subject not to a mere X–Y trigger but to the variation in all forty-six chromosomes. It is this something which leads to a much wider range of variation in the secondary sexual characters.

That the testis in fact produces things of two kinds is shown by the existence of a half-way house between castration and normality. In some boys the testes do not descend : they remain in the body cavity like the ovaries of a woman. Sperm are not then developed. Meiosis fails to occur, apparently because a lower temperature than that within the body is necessary for its success. But the secondary male characters are quite normal. And with these we have to include the production, by other glands outside the testis, of the seminal fluid in which the sperm swim. Intercourse can occur but it is bound to be sterile. It can be shown in the rabbit that when the testes are prevented from descending by surgical means, the same results follow.

Thus there are two sides to the determination of normal form and behaviour in the male. They can be related to two kinds of cells in the testes. One produces the sperm. The other composes an 'interstitial' tissue. This tissue remains normal and evidently continues to work in testes within the body cavity. And it produces some agent setting up all the secondary sexual effects.

It is now known that this agent is a chemical substance which is released into the blood and acts as a chemical messenger to the whole body, or rather to all parts which it may concern. Such chemical messengers are known as *hormones*. A corresponding and alternative series are secreted by the ovaries. And, of course, there are other hormones such as those produced by the thyroid, the adrenal and the pituitary glands which are similar for the two sexes.

HOW THE HORMONES WORK

What are these hormones? Between the fertilized egg and the

mature adult lie the processes of development laid down or planned, as we have seen in insects, by the pattern of the fertilized egg. During this development the whole trend, at first sight, seems to be towards the separation of different cells and tissues from one another so that they can exist as independent entities, parts capable of cooperating with other parts but avoiding any interference with one another's internal affairs. Over and above this principle of *autonomy*, however, there is an opposed principle of limited *intervention* which comes into action as animals pass a certain size and live beyond a certain age.

In plants and in insects different tissues already interact in development. They interact chemically by way of diffusible substances which are produced by one, and alter the work of another, tissue. In the higher animals, with our complex organization, the direct determination is not merely modified, but actually mediated, by a system of hormones. These substances, produced by particular tissues or glands, pass directly into the blood. Carried all over the body they produce their effects by reacting with other tissues, including nervous tissues or other glands, causing their growth, altering their activity, facilitating or hindering certain chemical processes such as the utilization of sugar, and above all interacting with one another's secretions.

In this way the properties of particular cells or tissues are no longer committed to an endless repetition of the same activity even after growth is complete. They can, so to speak, be put in gear and out of gear. They can be committed to limited tasks, such as cyclical growth, or disease-resistance; or cope with extreme efforts of body or mind. And when growth has reached its determined span, or when the emergency is over, their action can be stopped.

How did these things come to be understood? In the middle of the eighteenth century it was realized that the thyroid gland and the testes were 'ductless glands'. That is to say, they secreted something directly into the blood and not merely into special passages of their own. A century later the great French physiologist, Claude Bernard, referred to certain glands as producing 'internal secretions'. Later, the idea of 'chemical messengers' appeared. Finally, on 16 January 1902, Ernest Starling, working at University College, London, showed that the digestive ferment secreted by the pancreas of a dog was not produced as a result of a nerve message. On the same day he also showed that the agent was a chemical messenger in the blood. Two years later Starling gave these secretions – not only the digestive ones – their name of hormones. Their whole working is still understood only in a frag-mentary way. For the hormones are the instruments, not only of day-to-day activities like digestion, but also of many long-term processes of development. They are therefore an essential part of the means by which genetic differences between human beings express themselves.

The nervous or electrical system, to be sure, established a connectedness between the parts of very simple animals. In our bodies its immense structural elaboration makes it the seat of remarkable capacities for memory, association and purpose. But it is primarily a means of carrying out the daily work by the body. The scope of the hormone or chemical system, on the other hand, is much wider and deeper. It begins during embryonic life; it controls the development of all parts of the body including the nervous system itself; and it makes what we call the temperament. In actual working the nervous and hormone systems are con-stantly interlocked. Together they are the foundation of the mind. The brain conditioned by the temperament is what makes us think as we think and what gives the individual character of the mind.

The evidence of castration shows us the first principles of hormone action. The ovaries and the testes produce diffusible substances which influence remote parts of the body. If these substances begin to work before birth we should expect them to control the development of the accessory sex organs such as the womb and the penis. We know that they do so by a pretty experi-ment of nature. In cattle, twin embryos even of the two-egg kind form a joint placenta with connexions between their blood supplies. When the twins are of opposite sex the female is shifted in character in a masculine direction. She is born sterile and is known as a 'freemartin'. Evidently the male hormone of the brother has worked earlier or proved stronger than the female and has governed his sister's development as well as his own.

The sex hormones do not, however, work by themselves. Experiments depending first on surgery and disease, later on chemistry and genetics, have made it possible to piece together the mechanism of which they form a part. It appears that the fore-part of the pituitary is, in a sense, the master gland of the whole system. For it is the pituitary secretion which sets in motion the activity of the thyroid and these two cooperate in stimulating both testes and ovaries to produce their hormones. In childhood the pituitary is concerned with stimulating general growth. At puberty (by a mechanism we do not yet understand) it gradually switches over to stimulating the testes and ovaries, and hence the development not only of the secondary sexual characters but even of the sperm and eggs themselves. Injection of pituitary extract increases the number of eggs shed by the female rabbit.

Since the pituitary is, in a sense, an extension of the brain, it is well placed to convert sensory and intellectual stimuli into chemical messages. There is, indeed, reason to suppose that the pituitary controls externally stimulated variations in sexual activity. These are of many kinds. In birds the breeding seasons are known to depend on changes in light intensity. In all animals, and not least in man, mating is influenced by the senses. The presence and attractiveness of the opposite sex probably operates through the eyes, ears and nose, stimulating the pituitary. Its chemical message is passed on to the sex glands which are stimulated to produce more sex hormones.

Beyond these variations, applying to both sexes, there is in all mammals a sexual cycle in the female related to the shedding of the eggs. Here also the pituitary plays its part. The stimulation of the sexual organs of the female, the 'heat' or oestrus, depends directly on a hormone, the female fertility hormone, secreted by the Graafian follicle from which each egg is going to be set free a day or two later. After the release of the egg, a yellow body is formed on the site of the follicle and this *corpus luteum* produces a second hormone, the pregnancy hormone, which helps to implant the egg, if it has been fertilized, in the womb. Later the placenta itself takes over part of this business of hormone production. But if no embryo is formed the *corpus luteum* degenerates and the monthly cycle is resumed (Figure 21).

The effect of this monthly cycle in the lower mammals is to restrict mating to the one or two days in the cycle when it can be effective. In woman there is no such restriction; but the cycle of her hormone changes is responsible for a wider range of temperamental variation in women than in men. And at the change of life, when the shedding of eggs ceases (a process which is more gradual and less complete for the sperm in the male), a new balance of hormones has to be established.

The male, as we saw, suffers certain disadvantages from being the hybrid sex, disadvantages which are inherent in the genetic system of all mammals. The female, however, suffers two disadvantages which are almost peculiar to our species. Woman may reasonably complain that she is not in this respect the paragon of animals. Natural selection has fitted her for a higher fertility than she now needs. And the penalty of shedding the membranes of an unfertilized egg is a pain and loss of blood greater than any other animal suffers. This misfortune, however, as we shall see, is bound up with changes in human sexual life which were necessary for the final and crucial steps in the evolution of our species.

BETWEEN GENES AND TEMPERAMENT

How do the hormones stand in relation to the genotype of the egg and the form of behaviour, intelligence and temperament of the mature animal?

In the first place it is known that deficiencies of certain hormones lead to abnormalities of growth and behaviour in man. The cretin's condition is relieved by injection of thyroid extract. The distorted, heavy-boned, or 'acromegalous' giant, as was first discovered in 1889, has an abnormal pituitary. Such conditions are directly or indirectly genetic in their determination. And, in the mouse, genetic dwarfs can be made normal by pituitary injections. It is, however, from dogs that the fullest evidence comes.

The domestic dog is of great value for the student of man. It is not that his mind or body resembles our own very closely. There is a resemblance but it is the variation in the dog's mind and body that matters. The dog is much the oldest of domesticated animals and it is the only one that shares the social vicissitudes of man. The dog, like man, is derived from ancestors – different races or species – distributed over most of the world. He is at present, like man, living and breeding under largely artificial conditions. He exists in such inbred breeds or races as we saw described by Macbeth. Some of them are useful and continually selected for uses, specialized or unspecialized; others (like certain classes of human beings) are largely ornamental whether by beauty or ugliness. Like man, also, the dog exists in a great variety of un-

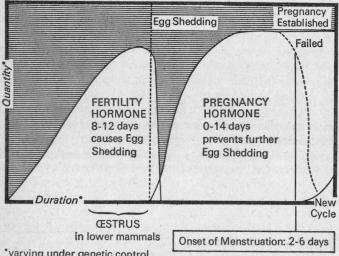

Figure 21

Diagram showing the cycle of events which underlies the release of the egg, allows it to be fertilized and if it is not fertilized, stimulates the release of another egg. Note that all quantities and times vary subject to genetic control. A sign of this variation in adjustment of the fertility hormone is the shedding of more than one egg at a time by a woman who will then be able to give birth to two-egg twins (after Bullough, 1951).

selected hybrid forms. His breeds differ in form much more than the races of man: in behaviour, instincts, temperament, and susceptibility to diseases, to about the same extent; and in dietetic requirements, in intelligence or educability much less than the races of man, but nevertheless more nearly approaching them than the races of any other species.

The first man to understand this was Darwin. It is to Charles Stockard of Cornell University, however, that we are indebted for its application. Stockard crossed the basset hound with the saluki, the alsatian and the bulldog; he also crossed the saluki with the pekinese, the dachshund with the Boston terrier and the Brussels griffon. The F_1s were in most cases, as expected, as healthy, or more healthy, than their parents. They were also uniform, even more uniform than the pedigree breeds. The F_2s, as a result of Mendelian segregation, showed a wide range of variation. The variation revealed some quite unexpected features. The short twisted-leg character of the basset and dachshund showed a partial dominance over the long and straight-legged types: it was due to a single gene difference. The axial peculiarity of the bulldog and the griffon which shortens and twists the muzzle and the tail proved to depend on several independent genes. And even the upper and lower jaws could be shortened separately in different F_2 dogs to give jaws that would not meet: non-occlusion as the dentists say. There was much loss of fertility, many stillbirths, and irregularities of development, such as harelip, and of behaviour, such as untrainability. The bulldog–basset F_2 was often quite sterile. In a word the bulldog jaw character is complex or polygenic. As we should expect, errors of the jaw leading to failure of biting appeared also in the F_2 between similarly long-jawed breeds like the Alsatian and saluki.

These observations of disharmony are interesting because they so closely resemble the disharmonies arising in later generations of human race crosses where one race does not predominate in numbers to give general back-crossing of the F_1 and a consequent restoration of balance. The worst results arise in man in such situations as Tristan da Cunha and Pitcairn where the genuine F_2 situation arises.

Stockard and his colleagues now studied the relationships of these skeletal abnormalities in dogs to the hormone system. They found that all the polygenically flat-faced breeds of dogs had abnormal pituitaries and arrested thyroids – the thyroid effect being no doubt subordinate to the pituitary. This correlation applied to the pedigree breeds. It also applied to the varying F_2 dogs in respect of the short muzzle although not in respect of the screw tail.

The dog-breeding results are complex enough to provide a good model of what happens with inbreeding and outbreeding in man. The principles are nevertheless, in regard to the heredity and development of body and mind, simple enough to be understood. Heredity does determine the hormone system and the hormone system does control growth, temperament and intelligence. But the control of growth, temperament and intelligence is not only by way of the hormones. The hormones react with structural foundations in every organ – above all, in the brain – which are more directly determined by gene variations.

There is, we can now see, a basis for the classical division of temperaments into choleric and lymphatic, phlegmatic and sanguine. There are fluid humours. But the fluids are not the basis of the mechanism. They are worked by particles. The hormones are controlled by genes and chromosomes. And this division by humours does not describe the whole situation. Nor does it cleave mankind in unjoinable groups like the division between the XX and the XY sexes. On the contrary, the humours may serve to join together what the chromosomes have put asunder. As an example, take Little's experiments on changing the sexes of mice.

In man, and in all farm and laboratory animals, we find that castration of the infant prevents the growth of the sexual organs and the appearance of the secondary sexual characters. But in some special strains of mice that Little had selected for the genetic character of cancer production, castration had certain quite unexpected effects. Tumours developed, where they never normally appeared, on the adrenal gland. In one strain the tumours were benign and they led to a shift, quite a regular shift, towards femaleness in the castrated males. In another strain the tumours were malignant and they caused an irregular shift to masculinity in the castrated females.

Little's experiments show diagrammatically some of the main properties of the hormone-producing and genetic mechanisms connected with sex determination. In the first place, the chromosome difference between XX and XY has no sex-determining effect beyond producing the rudimentary sex organs of the two kinds: already before birth, in normal individuals, the whole of sexual development begins to be taken care of by the hormones released by the testes and ovaries. In the second place, the sex hormones in both strains are preventing tumour formation in uncastrated individuals. In the third place, the plasmagene mutations which are causing tumours in the adrenals are also causing the new tumour tissues to produce hormones, one of the male, and the other of the female, type – each in both XX and XY mice.

A derangement of the hormone system by injury can thus alter the whole character of an individual. Such a derangement may arise with similar results, intentionally in an experiment like Little's, or by the kind of accident revealed by the one-egg human twins who grew to different sizes. The same consequences can arise from severe illnesses, including of course tumours of the hormone-producing glands. It is indeed, so far as we know, only in these ways that profound changes of character can overtake human beings. The manifestations of these changes will depend on the structure of the brain. But it is in human individuals who, like some of Stockard's F_2s, have an unstable hormone balance that conversion and the enthusiasms of novel beliefs may lead to striking transformations, especially at the beginning and at the end of sexual life.

What we have seen from one-egg twins, and in other ways, has shown that the character of the individual, his property of behaving in one way or another in all the situations of life, is determined by the fertilized egg. Can we now visualize this determination?

In any emergency the perceptions of the senses and the processes of the brain determine the release of hormones which in turn determine feelings of love, hate, fear, anger, or desire. These in their turn guide or direct the intellectual processes. The sympathetic nervous system conveys a message of danger electrically to the adrenal gland which, secreting adrenalin, prepares the mind for anger and the body for action. Intellectual and bodily activity are bound up together, and, as the gestures and habits of different individuals and races inform us, they are bound up differently under genetic control.

The emotions can therefore be expressed as chemistry operated by genetics. Apart from emergencies, however, it seems that the supply and balance of hormones must give direction or policy to the intellectual activity of the individual by guiding his conduct. The delayed and cumulative interaction of chemical and electrical processes gives him a direction in time and hence a dynamic character or initiative which we recognize (when it is present) as personality. Irregularities of behaviour are, to a large extent, traceable to irregularities of hormone production. But these irregularities in themselves partly arise from intellectual processes, or from a lack of them.

Differences in temperament – and hence social behaviour – affecting, for example, wildness or tameness, have been shown to be hereditary in a great variety of animals: rats and mice, sheep and dogs. The albinism of the ferret is an exceptional short-cut method of getting human control by making the animal dependent. Elsewhere, intelligence, as determined by the structure of the brain, must always play some part. But the hormone system is even more important. Variations in the adrenal gland, governing the emotions of fear and anger, and the thyroid, influencing alertness, are bound to be the basis of selection, whether it is for aggressiveness in the game cock, or for docility in the cow or the rabbit or for either in man. The genetic properties which mark out fighting tribes from peaceful agriculturists, the extinct North American Indian tribes from their amenable survivors, the untameable Kurd from his tameable neighbours in Tabriz, the Pathan from the Bengali, and have been necessary for the survival of each, no doubt express themselves as much by way of differences in hormone balance as in the structural adaptation of the nervous system.

Summing up: we are only at the beginning of understanding the complete relations of genotype, hormones, temperament and intelligence. In experiment we can change all four and show their effects on the others. The genotype, of course, cannot be changed by the others. While we find that hormones and intellectual processes interact in governing temperament, the capacities of all the reacting agents are determined genetically. And we do not need to know how the intermediate processes have worked, for example, to produce identical results in two one-egg twins. It was merely useful, in the rare case where the results were not identical, to know how a knock on the head could produce the difference.

INTERSEXES

In ancient times it was commonly held that individuals, herma-phrodites, might occur combining perfectly the functions of both sexes. The combination in fact occurs but it is always imperfect. Probably about one in every few hundred in most human popula-tions is of this kind, as we may say, of intermediate sex. Such persons have the most varied characters and careers and they provide a good example of the meaning of heredity and also of the possibilities of marriage. They may marry as males or as females. They are usually sterile but they have normal parents and ancestors. Their abnormality is not therefore hereditary in the accepted sense. It is nevertheless to be regarded as determined as a rule in the fertilized egg so that we must call it genetic. Natur-ally with human beings we cannot make the complete study that we could with experimental animals. But by analogy we can understand well enough what is happening in these cases.

Intermediate individuals sometimes arise, we may suppose, through loss of a whole or part of a sex chromosome either at the first or at a later mitosis of the egg. They may also arise through a novel gene combination which leads, as in Little's mice, to the growth of a tumour and hence to secondary changes in the sex organs. The best-defined group of between-sexes, however, are what we call intersexes, individuals who change their sex in the course of development.

A particular kind of intersex has been accurately described from medical cases classified as hermaphrodites in different parts of Europe by a surgeon and a geneticist in Sweden, Pettersson and Bonnier. The individuals concerned have been found in 5 families, 8 in one, 6 in another, 22 in all (see Table 8, pedigree). Externally they appear to be normal women and they often have enough sexual interest to get married. Internally, however, they have no womb, the vagina is blind; menstruation is represented only by a monthly nose-bleeding; and instead of ovaries there are what appear to be sterile, half-descending testes. The condition seems to be due to a gene in the X chromosome. This gene has begun to act before birth, and, having converted testes into producers of female hormones, converts males (with an X Y chro-mosome outfit) into spurious females.

Thus, if the abnormal X is labelled x, the normal mother of the intersexes has the constitution Xx. It is worth noting that, in her mating, the eggs as well as the sperm will be of two kinds and the X–x segregation will be the means of determining the difference between two *apparent* sexes in union with Y chromosome sperm. Evolutionary changes in sex determination can happen in this way.

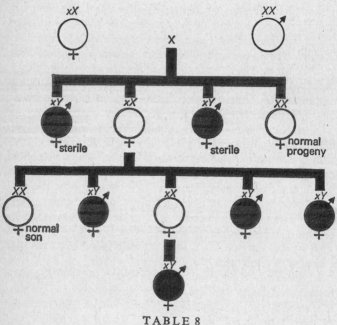

TABLE 8

Pedigree of Intersexes ('hermaphrodites') from Pettersson and Bonnier (1936)

X and Y, normal sex chromosomes. x, an X chromosome with a feminizing gene, carried by half the females. ♀ and ♂, normal female and male. ☿ intersex.

The abnormal result, the xY individual, is legally a woman. Although she is sterile, and may be told that she is sterile, she is nevertheless allowed by law to marry as a woman and the marriage can be legally consummated. Her condition can be brought to medical notice only by a hernia resulting from the delayed descent of the testes. Such cases may be much commoner than is recognized. But they are nothing like so common as the next group.

CHROMOSOME MISTAKES

Students of mental defect have recognized for over thirty years (indeed since 1929) that defects of the mind are genuinely of two kinds. One is that of the imbecile, often going with physical abnormality; the other is that of the feeble-minded, usually normal in appearance. Gradually this contrast has been associated with heredity. On the one hand, imbeciles are born into families of all grades of intelligence: they appear as though they were due to mutations in major genes. Their occurrence, although genetic, is not hereditary in the popular sense. On the other hand the feeble-minded are born into families of a lower range of intelligence related to their own: they appear as recombinations of differences between genes of small effect, indeed between polygenes. Their occurrence is genetic and hereditary in every sense. This explanation, which we owe largely to Fraser Roberts, has been illustrated and confirmed by the discovery of the chromosome basis of a number of mental defects in man. How does this come about?

All plants and animals vary in the frequency and distribution of crossing-over between chromosomes at meiosis. The limit of this variation is reached where two partner chromosomes fail to cross over. They fail then to form a chiasma and to orientate themselves as a pair and pass to opposite poles of the spindle. In consequence, germ cells are formed which have 2 chromosomes of a particular kind or none.

Thus at meiosis in a man, instead of the normal 23 chromosomes in the chromosome sets of a sperm produced, there may be 2 or none of a particular kind, making 22 or 24 in all. Eggs fertilized by such an abnormal sperm will then have complements with 45 or 47 chromosomes. Number 21 is the chromosome most often affected. And although it is next to the shortest of the chromosomes, its loss is fatal – and, probably, quickly fatal – to the egg which a defective sperm fertilizes. The 45-chromosome embryo dies. But the sperm or the egg with an extra chromosome no. 21 gives an embryo with 47 chromosomes in all. This 'trisomic' embryo survives with scarcely reduced chances, to birth.

This kind of error happens in all organisms with a frequency of the order of one per cent. But the shorter chromosomes are the most affected since they have fewest chiasmata. And since they also do least harm they give the trisomic individuals which most often survive.

It is at meiosis in woman, not in man, that chromosome no. 21 most often fails to pair. It evidently does so with increasing frequency as women get older. In the youngest class of mothers the frequency of error is about one in a thousand and these are not due to ordinary failure in pairing so much as to other kinds of abnormalities. But in the oldest class, over forty-five, the frequency rises to about one in ten of all births. The resultant average frequency among all births is about 1 in 400.

To quote one example: Charles Darwin's tenth child, born when his wife was forty-eight, was a mongol which died in infancy. The mental defect of the child is related to the age of the mother. It is not related to the intelligence of the parents.

The abnormal trisomic child is recognizable at birth. It has a mongolian eyelid, broad hands and a narrow palate. As the child grows its intelligence fails to develop. It has the character of a 'mongolian idiot' and many and variable secondary abnormalities begin to appear. Most of these are defects of the heart or skeleton, often corresponding to known specific gene defects like polydactyly. Mongol children succumb heavily to heart and lung complaints in the first year but a small and (with medical care) increasing fraction survive to an advanced age. A few women of mongol type have been known to breed and they have the expected fifty per cent of mongol children.

The trisomic abnormality in the mongol child helps us to understand the second great class of chromosome mistake. Chromosome no. 21 is a short one. But the sex chromosomes X and Y are short also as concerns the length of chromosome which can pair in the heterozygous sex, in the XY male (Figure 19). It is for this reason partly that men, perhaps all men, produce, in addition to X and Y sperm, also a small proportion of O and XY sperm. Women however, also produce, less commonly, O and XX eggs (O meaning without X or Y).

Thus, in respect of the sex chromosomes, not two, but four, types of embryo arise in approximately the following frequencies:

	Female		*Male*	
Normal	XX	49 per cent	XY	49 per cent
Abnormal	XO	1 per cent	XXY	1 per cent
	(Turner type: under-sized)		(Klinefelter type: oversized)	

The two abnormal types are sexually undeveloped. They are also mentally undeveloped. Together they form a small proportion of the total cases of sterility but a much larger proportion of the total cases of mental defect. They have indeed been largely brought to light from the chromosome study of patients in mental hospitals. They are extreme examples of the ineradicable genetic determination of mental deficiency. But they fall into a special class of those who offer no danger to society from their propagation: they are – fortunately – sterile.

Extreme examples these are and they provide an illuminating contrast with their opposite extremes. For at the other pole, still within the mutational or major-gene type are forms of mental defect like that arising from phenylketonuria. Here is a defect due to a simple error of the metabolism in infancy. It is potentially curable. And it is not only genetically determined but simply inherited as a mendelian recessive condition. Such mental defects with care or with cure could be readily increased in frequency in the population. The chromosome mistakes, however, are almost entirely dead ends. They are irremediable. But they are also untransmissible. And in mere physical survival they are at a hopeless and complicated disadvantage.

The poor survival of men and women with abnormal chromosome complements, notably the mongol type, makes us wonder what proportion of mental defectives of the mutational or major-gene type is due to such chromosome mistakes. If we look at the evidence of death rates now and formerly. in the normal and in defective populations, we see that defectives generally fail to have a normal life span. They fail to have a prime of life with a reduced death rate. The resultant curve of survival is quite different from that in the normal population. This is true even if we go back a century to when infectious diseases took a heavy toll at all ages (Figure 22). Mental defectives as a whole indeed show an intermediate behaviour between the whole chromosome mongol type and that of the normal population. A large proportion of them, perhaps about half, may be due to losses of segments of chromosome occurring at meiosis in their immediate parents. Such individuals probably constitute the class of imbeciles of mutational type whose mental character has no relation with that of their parents.

SEXUAL BEHAVIOUR AND HUMAN LOVE

These observations teach us about certain properties governing sexual behaviour which man shares with all the higher animals. In the first place, the determination of the characters of the individual is not wholly direct for each cell in the body. Rather, it depends in part upon an organized series of reactions sometimes operated at a great distance in time and place. Further, these remote controls operate especially between the genes in the chromosomes of the fertilized egg and the temperament of the mature individual, which, in this way, varies under genetic determination. And, just as it varies between the sexes, so it also varies by the same gene-plus-hormone control between individuals of the same sex. Thus sexual behaviour, interest, desire and performance are likely to be correlated but are certain to be capable of independent genetic variation among males and among females. Every individual will have his or her determined sexual character and individuality, a character whose dynamic aspect is the will.

The question now arises how far these animal characteristics can be related to what we regard as the nobler, richer and more beautiful types of relationship which we know at least among some human beings and to which we give the name of love; not platonic love, or Christian love, but specifically sexual love. We can now see, and even represent, how human sexual love is based on the ascertainable properties of the animal mind and body. In order to explain how this is so we can represent the animal situation with a simplified diagram which we may call the Diagram of Love (Figure 23).

The Diagram of Love shows the separate agents or instruments whose activities are bound to underlie the development of love.

The sensory perceptions of eye and ear, the central nervous system coordinating, recording and accumulating these perceptions, the sex glands, secreting the hormones which govern in-

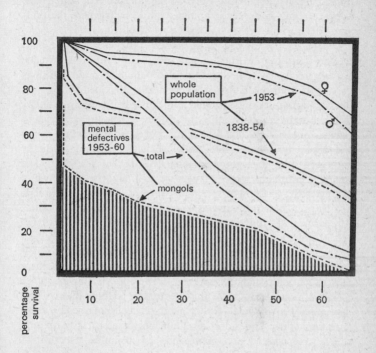

Figure 22

Curves of survival for men and women in England and Wales from the Registrar-General's reports (cf. Tizard in Clarke & Clarke, 1958), for mongols up to ten years from C. O. Carter (1958) and after ten years from hospital data of the Registrar-General (1954–9). These are uncorrected estimates valid merely for general comparison.

terest in the opposite sex and direct the sensory perceptions, at the same time that they accumulate the means of sexual fertility – all these work together in all animals conducing to the same result, the propagation of the species. In many animals sexual union is preceded by elaborate courtship, both preceded and followed by a preparation for the hatching or birth of the young. In most animals these complex instinctive reactions are subject to the cycles of climatic change. But this relationship has largely disappeared both in domestic animals and in man where the pressure of natural selection has ceased to favour it.

Where, then, is the crucial difference in these respects between man and the animals most closely related to him? It lies in the human mind. The development of the human brain, with its capacity for consciousness, its complexity of coordination and discrimination, its memory and its foresight, its multitudinous faculties and interests, all these have been, as it were, harnessed to the machinery of sex, the development of the individual repeating the course of evolution, intellectual elements becoming gradually embodied with the emotions long after sexual maturity. The period of courtship, which in the lower animals serves merely as a barrier to the crossing of species or, at most, of races, has gradually become in man the means of creating finer and finer systems of choice, and (conversely) of barriers between groups, or exclusions of choice.

The consequences of these evolutionary developments are felt at two levels. On the one hand, as concerns the individual, there have arisen emotional relationships more elaborate than any other species of animal could possibly create. It is to these that we give the name of love. On the other hand, as concerns society, there have been finer and finer developments of assortative mating which have created and maintained the complex structure of stratified societies.

In man, therefore, the sexual relationship is not only the basis of the whole social relationship; it also develops from it. Our social lives depend on discovering other individuals who resemble us closely enough in inborn character to make it possible for us to live and work together. This search for compatibles reaches a crisis of urgency when sexual maturity approaches. It is made vastly more difficult by the fact that a new genetic variation, variation in rate of sexual maturity and in degree of sexual development, is superimposed on all others. Some European children mature at twelve; others at twenty; others never mature at all. And they all express their maturity in different ways. And in all

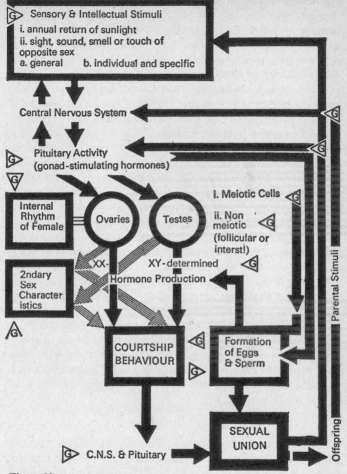

Figure 23

The Diagram of Love: a simplified statement of the processes and reactions involved in consummating the sexual relationship. G indicates the chief points at which genetically determined differences occur between individuals, in respect of which concordance is necessary for the maintenance of the relationship. This scheme works separately for each partner, thus giving another dimension to the possibilities.

these respects races vary as well as the individuals who compose them.

When the boy of twelve or twenty takes aside a girl of the same age, puts his arm round her and declares that he loves her, she may run away in terror. But if, undeterred by this set-back, the boy tries the same experiment with another girl he may find that she is disappointed that he does not know how to take the next step with which she is already quite familiar. These differences of behaviour – attributed by their elders to education – occur between sisters and between brothers. They are genetically determined.

The differences in mental attitude to one another of the two sexes can be expressed in terms of the difference in physiological habit. In the male the production of the sexual hormone directs him towards the female, the production of semen provides the motive power. The rhythm of male activity therefore derives from sexual intercourse. In the female, strongly in a chimpanzee or less so in a woman, there is a monthly cycle. The maximum secretion of the female fertility hormone takes place, as we saw, at the time of the shedding of the egg. But the effect of the female hormone in creating desire is more dependent on the availability of a worthy male than is the opposite condition in the male.

No doubt, therefore, it is usually true, both in the whole history of the individual and of a mere episode, that in man love springs from desire while in woman desire springs from love. The point of beginning the cycle in our Diagram of Love is different in the two sexes. It is also usually true that –

> Man's love is of man's life a thing apart,
> 'Tis woman's whole existence.

But all these rules refer to the middle part of the normal curve of genetic variation. The importance of the genetic interpretation of man is that it teaches us to understand why these rules break down at both ends of the curve. It teaches us to accept his genetic variation and hence his individuality in these as in all other matters. All rules break down, and even the rule which divides the species into two sexes breaks down, when applied to separate characteristics of individuals. Just as some otherwise quite normal men fail to grow a beard, so some otherwise almost normal women develop a masculine rather than a feminine kind of intelligence and temperament. Not only the sex chromosomes, and the hormone systems set in action by them, but all the other chromosomes, also varying, play their part in governing the whole character of a man or a woman.

16

Marriage and Fertility

MARRIAGE

A LARGE proportion of mankind, like pigeons and partridges, on reaching maturity, having passed through a period of playfulness or promiscuity, establish what they hope and expect will be a permanent and fertile mating relationship. This we call marriage.

There are many views on what makes marriage successful and therefore permanent. We may well warm our hearts with the words of Tertullian, the literary founder of Latin Christianity, when he exclaims, 'How can we find words to describe the happiness of that marriage which the Church brings about, the Oblation confirms, the Benediction seals, the Angels announce, and the Father ratifies?' (*Ad Uxorem*, ii. 8). But when Chaucer's merchant explains that 'wedlok is so esy and so clene' we hear another side of the question. We have to give heed to the voices of both the prophet and the poet.

The development of marriage in man has been favoured by a series of genetic changes in the course of evolution. These changes, beginning with the monkeys, concern physiology, intelligence, and instinctive behaviour. In the mammals generally the ovary of the female releases eggs into the womb during limited breeding-seasons or at intervals throughout the year. At these times for two or three days she attracts the male and mating takes place. If fertilization fails, the eggs are shed again later: after five days in the mouse, after forty-five days in the gorilla.

In female monkeys and apes, after the entry of an egg into the womb, membranes develop as though in preparation for the growth of an embryo. If fertilization fails, or the embryo dies, these membranes are shed with some loss of blood. This is the menstruation which provides evidence of egg-shedding, but, in women, occurs after a delay of usually a fortnight.

Side by side with this evolutionary change another step took place in the monkeys. The period of heat at egg-shedding became somewhat less pronounced than in other mammals. It also became less obvious to the male and mating began to be extended throughout the period between menstruations. The gradual replacement of strict rutting-seasons by continual sexual interest reaches its limit in man. But the beginnings of it existed before man. It was a pre-adaptation, a property (as Lucretius puts it) waiting to beget a use, or to be exploited. It has been exploited by the gradual slowing down of the development of the human child.

The coordination of changes necessary for the evolution of the family, each favoured by natural selection, can now be seen. In the first place, the occurrence of sexual intercourse has been extended from the period of heat to the whole month. Consequently sexual interest is continuous. In the second place, as the infant's intellectual development has increased, it has been extended in time, and the intellectual and emotional interest of the parents in the child, and in one another, has also been extended. In the third place, the love of companionship, instinctively established in this way, has been extended forward in life in the pre-mating period, thus lengthening the time of discrimination in the choice of the spouse.

These immense advantages have been achieved at a certain cost which we can reckon within certain limits of error. For every conception effected, coitus occurs from ten to a hundred times more frequently in man than in other animals: a man produces not 10^8 but 10^9 or 10^{10} sperm for each egg he fertilizes: pleasure has superseded propagation.

The institution of marriage and its stability would seem to depend on the coordination of these evolutionary changes, all favoured by natural selection. The coordination itself would be favoured by a number of ancillary circumstances. Equality in the numbers of the sexes, reducing competition, would favour a monogamous habit. The permanent interest of the father in his family would ensure a profitable exploitation of the male in the economy of the whole species. Among the lower mammals the contribution of the male is generally less than that of the female although he is stronger. His special attributes developed under the stress of sexual selection are otherwise wasted. In the evolution of the human family and of a continuous society the capacities of the male are at last fully utilized. It is not only that in this way the male has become a useful member of the community. Masculine intelligence has become a special object of natural selection and has thus acquired a special responsibility in the recent development of civilization.

Choice of mate, as we have seen, so far as it is based on socially recognizable characteristics, gives rise to the differentiation of individuals, tribes, classes and races. And, so far as it is based on sexually recognizable characteristics, it gives rise to the secondary differentiation of the two sexes themselves. Choice of mate is also further elaborated by these two kinds of differentiation: the action is reciprocal, as we may see in the following way. The fixed union of marriage and its absence, which we call promiscuity, equally depend on the recognition by the parties concerned of the fixed quality, the genetic individuality, of the persons concerned.

Choice of mate also constitutes a choice of parents. It has therefore become the chief means of carrying on the specialized skill and knowledge of tribe and class, whose accumulation in a space of a few hundred generations has built up the sum of human culture, indeed everything that matters in human as distinct from animal life. In addition to these evolutionary processes, on the choice of spouse in marriage depends that ephemeral detail, so much and so properly discussed by poets and philosophers, the well-being and happiness of the bulk of the individuals of whom mankind is composed.

Thus an elaborate fabric of movements and processes arises from a single foundation, the propagation of the species, which itself consists of a sequence of three events: choice of mate, sexual intercourse, and the generation of offspring. All these three events are closely bound up with the property of genetic determination, in a way we must now examine.

Of the choice of mate in its social aspects, that is, in courtship prior to intercourse, the whole world is well informed. Its discriminating character, and the consequences of discrimination, we have noted. One other aspect is worth recording. Each spouse has a belief at the beginning, a belief which deepens with experience, in the individuality of the partner. Rare exceptions to this rule are known: if one partner is feeble-minded; or if one is an identical twin. But these exceptions only prove the force of the rule. That this conviction of the unique and unchanging character of the partner is not an illusion of wish-fulfilment, but rather an observation of a reality, is shown by the fact that only too often he or she is found to wish it were otherwise. In a minority of marriages, an unhappy minority, the parties after a certain time might well wish one another different; they might well hope for some mollifying influence of the environment. But their hopes are disappointed unless the error has been due to ignorance which can be corrected or disease which can be cured.

The success or failure of a marriage thus has a large genetic component and it is worth inquiring how this component is made up. In the first choice of a mate, the social choice, the two individuals do their best to measure their compatibilities of temperament and intelligence, culture and physique. Into this judgement comes obviously an assessment of the secondary sexual characters, including sexual behaviour. Unfortunately these give an imperfect measure of actual sexual performance in marriage.

If we examine the Diagram of Love and see the immense complexity of the workings of mind and body in regard to which two individuals have to be adjusted, we get some idea of the magnitude of the problem which each couple has to settle. But even this gives no measure of the genetic problem of sexual fertility on which depend the biological, and even the social, success of marriage.

COUSIN MARRIAGE

Primitive peoples by custom and advanced societies by religion and even by law reject the practice of close inbreeding and we condemn it by the special inflexion we give to the word *incest*. The Oedipus relation of mother and son is universally abhorred but mere marriage of cousins, first, second or third cousins, may be condemned. The reasons given are sometimes social but usually genetic: it is said that the progeny will deteriorate. Darwin, having married his first cousin and being much interested in systems of breeding, wrestled unsuccessfully with this problem.

The genetic argument against inbreeding seemed to be brilliantly confirmed in 1902 by the observation of Archibald Garrod. The disease of alkaptonuria was due, according to Garrod, to an 'inborn error of the metabolism'. Failure to oxidize homogentisic acid in the urine, which consequently darkens on standing, appears in pedigrees of families so as to suggest Mendelian inheritance. If it is determined as a recessive character, Garrod argued, it should be more frequent in progenies of cousin marriages than in the general population where people usually marry cousins too remote to trace. For first cousins have one eighth of their chromosomes in common by virtue of their common grandparents. He found in fact that though one hundredth of our marriages are between first cousins, one third of all alkaptonurics are produced by them. This sharp contrast between the results of inbreeding and outbreeding is due to the great rarity of the gene. One person in 1,000,000 shows the disease. One chromosome in 1,000, approximately, therefore carries the gene; and 1 person in 500. The chance of two parents being heterozygous for it should therefore be 1 in 250,000 for ordinary marriages, 1 in 4,000 for cousin marriages.

The traditional view of inbreeding seemed to be vindicated by this argument, which has governed most later study of the problem. But a little thought shows that it is based on assumptions which are not completely water-tight. Our population is not divided into two kinds of people, those who outbreed and those who marry their first cousins. The outbreeders are of many kinds. There are within our complex society innumerable groups which are in effect, and with varying effect, breeding-groups. These groups depend to varying degrees on economic standing and local residence, on religious affiliation and professional interest. They are accordingly of varying stability and size. Most are, in modern urban conditions, highly outbred. But a few are highly inbred. Clearly, therefore, the effects of cousin marriage must be related to the existence of these groups. Its distinct effect should be noticeable within outbred but not within inbred groups. It should be the change in the breeding-system that is important rather than the system itself.

Study of the effects of breeding and changes in breeding can yield interesting results in relation to specific Mendelian characters like alkaptonuria. But what matters is their connexion with fertility and survival: that is, with the basic properties of life, death and reproduction. Fortunately we have vast records of these basic properties which enables us to decide the issue. And sexual fertility, which is enormously variable, is also highly hereditary, as

Galton, Pearson and Fisher have successively demonstrated (Table 9).

TABLE 9

The fertility of daughters in relation to that of their mothers as measured by the numbers of children born to them (after Fisher, 1930, from Pearson and Lee)

Mothers (individual)	1	2	3	4	5	6	7	8	9	10	11	12–15
Daughters	3·0	3·5	3·1	3·4	4·0	3·9	3·9	4·1	4·2	4·4	5·1	6·4

If there is an important genetic component in fertility how are we to discover the effects of inbreeding or outbreeding on fertility? Clearly we shall need to know the numbers of children born not to the cousins themselves but to their children and even to later generations. Clearly also we shall need to compare these results with outbreeding results both in previously inbred and in previously outbred families.

Fortunately there exist in family records, including those of royal families, the materials not merely for mass comparisons of these kinds but also for individual and experimental comparisons. There are numerous records of men and women who, having married twice, have raised families from both cousin and non-cousin marriages. These double-test marriages, as we may call them, have happened both in outbred families and in families from small religious, commercial and dynastic groups which are known to be inbred (Table 10).

The double-test marriages show that the effects of cousin marriage are quite different in outbred and in inbred families. The traditional assumption about the deleterious results of cousin marriage is true of the outbred families. It is not true of the inbred families. Indeed the reverse is true: it is outbreeding which impairs their fertility. In both groups it is not the particular breeding-system but the change in the breeding-system which leads to loss of fertility.

327

The contrast between some families which lose, and others which gain, fertility begins in the second generation. It is magnified in the third. Why? Because the difference of fertility is, in the first place, hereditary. And, in the second place, it is the subject of assortative mating. Men who want children marry women who want children. Those who don't want children marry for money.

TABLE 10

Results of double-test marriages, cousin and non-cousin, in first, second and third generations (c, gc, ggc) *of inbred and outbred families* (*from Darlington 1960*)

Family Breeding System	Cousin			Unrelated			Ratio of increases
	c	gc	ggc	c	gc	ggc	C : U
Outbred	17	7	5	12	20	45	0·3 : 3·7
Inbred	15	27	61	12	13	22	4·1 : 1·8

What then are we to say of the fertility of strictly inbred groups? The most notable of all these are the Mennonite communities in the middle western United States. These people having long enjoyed a regular agricultural life and, being pledged to mutual help in all the vicissitudes of life, have reached almost a climax of adaptation to their own conditions. Homogeneous they naturally are in every genetical property. This includes intelligence, industry and fertility. Whether their intelligence and industry are still rising we may doubt. But their fertility has only barely reached its maximum. Over the period from 1920–1950 the average number of children born per marriage rose from 9·2 to 10·9.

The disastrous consequences of marrying heiresses, a habit practised in all governing classes, have been observed since the eighteenth century, notably by Erasmus Darwin and Francis Galton. But sometimes this habit was combined with first cousin marriage. In the Hoare family of Stourhead in Wiltshire, as three lines of descent in succession over a period of 150 years inherited the estate, they married first cousins or heiresses and extinguished themselves in this way: the family continues but only in the descendants of the fourth son.

Whether it arises genetically from inbreeding or outbreeding or the accidents of recombination the immediate causes of loss of fertility and extinction in a family are diverse. They may be structural or physiological, physical or mental. They may express themselves in the impotence of John Ruskin or in the homosexuality of Edward Fitzgerald, in the feeble-mindedness of some, or in the physical defects of others. All that is excluded is the chromosome mistakes which fall in a class by themselves.

One problem remains. If inbreeding is not in itself deleterious why has the revulsion against incest been implanted successively in our instincts, our morals, and our laws? The answer is that outbreeding is indispensable for maintaining the variation of a group. Without outbreeding, as we saw in considering the evolution of genetic systems, any group becomes homogeneous and thus loses the differences between which selection can occur. It can therefore no longer adapt itself to changing circumstances. How easily this happens in human societies, even with our outbreeding rules, we know only too well. For the attraction between those of similar interests, habits and beliefs, provides a basis of discrimination in the choice of mate more powerful than is known in any other organism.

The opposite side of the picture, the rejection of exceptional outbreeding, is not peculiar to man. But he is more diverse in his behaviour than any other animal. Extreme disturbances of the sex ratio, extreme economic differentiation of races and classes, conditions of conquest and slavery, all these lead to sudden changes of his breeding habits. Different races and classes differ widely in their attitudes. But we can make a number of assertions about the consequences of wide outbreeding or race-crossing. It differs from inbreeding in producing results which are both more variable and less predictable, and in which heredity therefore not only appears to be, but actually is, less important. Now heredity is necessary for the carrying and conservation of culture. Only those with the right hereditary gifts can transmit the culture that is handed down to them. But only by recombination from outbreeding can new kinds of ability, and with them the means of creating new kinds of culture, arise.

In general the human preference for inbreeding as a regular practice and wide-crossing as an irregular practice is well justified by these considerations. For it takes several generations of inbreeding to restore the predictability that is destroyed by one generation of out-crossing. Broadly speaking, therefore, our breeding habits, founded on a mixture of reason and instinct, are peculiarly adapted to the needs of our own species, the most diverse species so far evolved.

THE SCOPE OF SEXUAL VARIATION

If mankind were all alike, all mates would be equally compatible. It is the fact that we are all different that makes the difficulty and the significance of correct assortment, of compatible or suitable mating. We need to know how widely men and women vary, what kind of variation matters most for their happiness in marriage, and how this variation is caused or determined, how far therefore it may be remediable or irremediable. For all these purposes a genetic study of the situation is of paramount interest.

Fertility itself in man and other male animals depends on several independently varying conditions. All of these conditions are genetically determined and, unless deficiency of vitamin E is responsible, they have little possibility of modification by treatment.

In the first place, the sex interest shown by sexual behaviour depends, as we saw, on the production of sex hormones. In the second place, sexual desire and capacity at any moment depend on the accumulated supply of semen, not mostly produced by the testes themselves but by the prostate and other glands. In the third place, sexual fertility depends on the sperm: it depends on the number produced, and their concentration in the semen; it also depends on their mobility and viability, or capacity for living in the seminal fluid; and finally it depends on their capacity for fusing with the nucleus of the egg and thereupon producing a viable product: that is, an embryo capable of life. These different factors vary to a certain extent independently of one another. How great is the variation?

One kind of incompatibility may be physical. Men and women in all races vary enormously in the shapes of their bodies and consequently in their modes or preferences for sexual union. Our modes of copulation have certainly undergone a revolution in the last 100,000 generations and we are no doubt still changing our average forms and habits as a species. Kissing, a recent invention though parallel to the billing of birds, has no doubt diffused through a part of the human species by the improvement of fertility it conferred on its inventors with a whole succession of mental and physical consequences which are still taking effect through natural selection.

Our serious knowledge about the range of variation of sexual behaviour in man we owe to the pioneer studies of Raymond Pearl, Marie Stopes and recently of A. C. Kinsey of the University of Indiana. They have collected evidence by inquiries with statistical safeguards from large numbers of men and women of all ages, classes and professions over a large area of the United States.

These studies show that the range of sexual interest and capacity among individuals is far greater than is popularly imagined, although not greater than was known to the author of the *Kama Sutra*. There are men who will have sexual intercourse thirty times a week. And there are others of the same age and equal opportunities who will be satisfied with intercourse once in thirty weeks. The difference between the two is evidently genetically determined : and likewise between both these extremes and the bulk of mankind, the so-called 'normal' people who lie in an intermediate position nearer the mode and the mean of Galton's normal curve.

Another large individual variation is in duration of sexual activity, which as a rule begins in the male between ten and sixteen and continues to between thirty and ninety. It is interesting to note that those who begin early continue just as late as the others. There is indeed no evidence that sexual indulgence of any kind impairs the health. Some may suffer for duty but none for pleasure.

The third factor in the success of marriage is that which concerns the production of sperm and of eggs, the immediate basis of fertility. Its variation we know best from the behaviour of bulls. The study of cattle has the advantage that the obvious objection raised to human evidence does not apply. Bulls do not boast.

Their achievements in artificial insemination are impartially recorded.

Artificial insemination was, of course, invented by Lazzaro Spallanzani. When he succeeded, by his own intervention, in getting a spaniel bitch in pup, he well knew what a momentous discovery he had made. Never, he declared, had he received greater pleasure upon any occasion since he first cultivated experimental philosophy. It is through Spallanzani's invention that we have now come to know so much about these vital matters.

The practice of artificially inseminating cows is now carried out in many countries under technically controlled conditions. In cattle the production of good sperm has become an industry. For the first time in the whole of evolution every sperm counts – and, in samples, is counted. The result has been to show that the potential fertility of healthy and sexually active animals varies from zero to hundreds of thousands of times the fertility that is realized or required in nature. In what we may call private life, the average British bull fertilizes seven cows per annum. He is kept for ornament rather than for use. The average prize bull fertilizes fifty cows. An insemination centre bull may fertilize no more than fifty; in which case he is quickly turned to baser uses. He is Class o. But among those that are kept on the rota the range of fertility if enormous. In 1949–50, the 245 outstanding bulls fully employed in the English A.I. service had the records indicated in Figure 24.

At one extreme there is a bull which fertilizes 72 per cent of over 4,000 cows, thus begetting 3,000 calves. At the other there are some which (with all the help of science) cannot beget any offspring at all. Variation arises both from differences in sexual appetite, as measured by the production of semen, and from differences in the number and fertility of the sperm it contains. In appearance there is no means of distinguishing the eight classes of bulls. They are all show animals, prize beauties of excellent pedigree, much admired by practical men. They are all in the prime of life and would fetch similar and high prices in the market. They all have the best diet that experience can devise and affluence afford. The variation therefore occurs among individuals raised under like conditions and of a like age. It must therefore arise through genetic differences between individuals. It must be genetically determined.

The reports of Pearl and Kinsey show the same variation in sexual appetites among men and among women as these figures show among bulls. For fertility, examination of human semen and consideration of numbers of offspring reveal also the same variation between the born eunuch, Class 0, and Class VIII. Once again we have Galton's normal curve of variation. But it is a curve of unusual breadth (Figure 24).

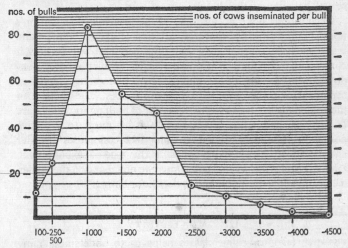

Figure 24

Normal curve of skew type showing the frequencies with which bulls selected for their physical excellence fall into classes 0–VIII in regard to sexual capacity and fertility: derived from the Records of Artificial Insemination Centre Bulls, selected for capacity to give more than 100 inseminations per bull per annum and a conception rate of more than 45 per cent. Milk Marketing Board, Production Division Report for 1950.

Such a variation occurs, of course, also within the life of one individual between the hot desire of youth and the cold impotence of age, between May and December, between Romeo and Prospero. Within the individual its effects on the moral outlook have been expounded by the greater of imaginative writers: Goethe, Tolstoy and John Donne all unconsciously reveal the transition from passionate enthusiasm to pious disgust, partly in what they did but even more in what they wrote. Those who have recorded the doings of the Empress Theodora have not even been unconscious of the transition. Others again, beginning very near the end, have no such transition to make or to reveal. These differences that may occur within the life of one individual demonstrate how important must be the genetic differences which distinguish individuals in their youth in governing their social, as well as their sexual, behaviour and outlook.

Once more we see an example of the principle that Galton's normal curve affects all natural variation of plants, animals and man. But here, more clearly than anywhere else, we see how it conflicts with the universal popular belief – which Aristotle endowed with the dignity of a philosophy – that average qualities, average sizes and average behaviour are the best. The doctrine of the golden mean, the proverbial precept of nothing too much, are the average man's law of prudence and his retort to excessive powers or abilities of others. Anything to excess causes disorder and disease. Particularly, of course, is this true of sexual excess. Understanding the normal curve must we not abandon the golden mean and allow the individual to decide for himself?

INCOMPATIBILITY

The division into sexual classes helps us to understand many problems connected with marriage. To begin with, which partner plays a greater part in making the choice of mate? First, possibly the male has a general advantage in initiative. Secondly, the less numerous sex also no doubt has a special advantage. But, thirdly, the partner nearer the middle of the sexual scale probably has an advantage over one nearer either extreme. Intellectual discrimination is perhaps at the lower end of the scale, initiative at the upper; hence the most effective combination is near the modal type. Natural selection will favour it.

Another aspect of genetic variation in sexual appetite is the wide range in the character of successful marriages that must result from it. Those of I–I and of VIII–VIII types may be equally happy and, with birth control, equally fertile. But what can there be in common between the social or business or dynastic partnership of a I–I marriage, a union of William-and-Mary, and the consuming passion of an VIII–VIII relationship of the Romeo-and-Juliet type? Again, generalizations about marriage are confidently and continually offered to us by moral and medical experts; but which of them can possibly apply to both extremes of harmony or, *a fortiori*, to the extremes of disharmony?

Why should the reproductive capacity and sexual temperament vary out of all proportion to other physical characters? Why is the normal curve of sexual desire so broad? The reason is that other physical characters would vary just as much, but the extremes are cut off before we grow up, or even before we are born. They are represented by miscarriages, stillbirths and infantile mortality. Reproductive incompetence is not eliminated at any age in the individuals concerned. It is eliminated only in the stock – that is, by the absence of progeny. To put the matter in another way: of the many hormones which are accurately understood today none is of less importance for the survival or health of the individual than the sexual hormones. None is of more importance for the success of a marriage or the survival of a family.

Reproductive competence thus has little effect on the life of the individual until after he or she grows up. Its effect arises in marriage. For those who are concerned with the success of human marriage, variation in sexual capacity, which is undiscovered at the time of marriage, is indeed the cardinal fact of life. It does not matter whether we measure success by the happiness of the parents, their fertility, or the well-being of their progeny. An extreme divergence in sexual capacity of mates is incompatible with successful marriage and is irremediable. Something can be done by goodwill but no amount of goodwill will turn Class I into Class VIII, Leonardo da Vinci into Benvenuto Cellini, Erasmus into Luther, William III into one of his Stuart uncles, G. B. Shaw into H. G. Wells, or vice versa. Nor will it enable them to see life through the same eyes or speak of it with the same tongue. A good deal is said by those who are unhappy in marriage about economic difficulties. That is because people understand more about money than about themselves. Money is not, however, the first source of trouble in these matters: it is the last. As the proverb tells us: Better is a dinner of herbs where love is, than a stalled ox and hatred therewith.

Here we come to a paradox. Men and women in pursuit of their mates take every precaution to choose one like themselves, and therefore suitable to themselves. But they have a difficulty in discovering this suitability in the one character of all which is most variable and in which compatibility is most important for the success of marriage. They have this difficulty until long after the union has been made legally binding and, in some societies (such is the nature of our conventions) irreversible. This is especially true if the partners are led to believe that sexual deficiencies are not irremediable, but can be made good by experience or goodwill, by medical treatment or private prayer. For a sexually undeveloped or homosexual man or woman may beget or bear many children but does not thereby correct his or her genetically determined disposition. And, as we saw, an XY intersex may seem to be a perfect woman but she certainly cannot feel as a woman. Nor can she breed as a woman for she cannot breed at all.

Apart from similarity of sexual behaviour there are other more complex incompatibilities of sexual relationship immediately concerned with fertility. Of these less is known but one can be mentioned. Only one sperm is necessary to fertilize an egg in any mammal, provided that the sperm can get at the egg. As many as 2,516,000,000 sperm have been estimated (by Edwards) in the genital tract of one young buck rabbit – nearly equal in number to the whole human race. But these would not fertilize the same number of eggs. In mammals the egg, as it passes down the tube which conveys it into the womb, is protected by a layer of sticky cells. This coat can be dissolved from it only by a large amount of a ferment provided by the sperm. And the egg dies in a few hours if it is not fertilized. A large supply of semen with a large number of sperm is necessary, therefore, at the right time and place if fertilization is to be secured.

The penetration of the egg may be affected by incompatibility of which we still know little. There may be unfavourable reactions between the proteins in the semen of a particular man and the eggs of a particular woman. These would be reactions like those which prevent the exchange of blood by transfusion between certain individuals. There are certainly such reactions affecting the survival of the embryo in the womb, the so-called Rhesus reactions. Such 'immunity' effects will cause inter-sterility, a specific sterility of two people each of whom would be perfectly fertile with other mates. Although much more is known about these forms of sterility, whether individual or relational, in plants than in animals, we can be certain that, like the sexual divergences already discussed, they are all genetically determined, individual and quite irremediable – except, of course, by taking new partners.

The success of marriages is governed by natural genetic variation. In the absence of an experimental approach, therefore, we must expect that a proportion, some five or ten per cent, of marriages will fail. Many will be predestined to fail, because they happen to be between individuals who have attempted to achieve the impossible at opposite ends of the sexual scale. In a I–VIII marriage there may well be more abstinence for one side or acquiescence for the other, than pleasure for either. In these circumstances which are we to pity more – the undermated or the over-mated?

DIVORCE

When disharmony makes marriage intolerable, which is to be regarded as the guilty party? For it is a convention – in this case, a fiction – of our law (which every plaintiff in divorce is bound to sustain if he wishes to avoid the suspicion of connivance, collusion or condonation) that one party must have always been guilty of an offence against the other. But we have seen that certain genetic properties decide the success or failure of a marriage both from the point of view of the individuals concerned and of the community. It is in the interests of the community, therefore, apart altogether from the happiness of married couples, and considering only the children that have been, or might be, born, that the small proportion of marriages which are genetically doomed should be dissolved when the incompatibility has been demonstrated. Its demonstration, of course, demands not a conflict at law but a collusion and cooperation of the two spouses with one another and with the law.

It is proper that there should be, as there is in our own country, a third party to the contract of marriage: the State. The view of the State is, however, in England and in some of the United States, based on the fictions of Church Law. These fictions were invented, we may recall, in the dark ages by a largely celibate priesthood, impressed by the splendid sentiments of Tertullian rather than the practical wit of Chaucer; a priesthood in grave doubt as to whether woman possessed a soul of her own but quite certain that she might conceive by the wind and by various wild beasts. It is now time that the State based its intervention in marriage not on such myths but on opinions that can be verified. A society which is bound to maintain itself by sexual reproduction is more likely to survive if it seeks to understand the facts of life and apply that understanding to its customs and its laws.

Differences and indeed conflicts of opinion will always exist on the conduct and status of sexual life. They are bound to arise from the divergence of sexual capacity between young and old and between high and low sexual classes. What is natural and even frivolous in the abundance of maturity appears sentimental or sacred to the extremes of innocence and of age. Heredity and development determine these principles. By recognizing their inevitable action in causing misunderstanding we may resolve it.

We have to remember that if the sexual act were not delightful it could not be the basis of reproduction. And if it were not capable of becoming sacred it would not be the basis of the family and hence of the development of society and of race, class and culture. An examination of these relationships in the light of genetics provides the means, the only means, of reconciling the interests of the individual with that of the community in what is the fundamental problem for the propagation of our race and the survival of our society.

HOMOSEXUALITY

The outstanding property of the human species is an immense range of genetic variation, combined with a great range of breeding-systems with which it deploys this variation. The greatest range of variation, for the reasons we have seen, affects the reproductive activities and leads to a wide spread in the sexual character of each sex: the normal curve is flat and broad. The segregation of x and y chromosomes acts as a trigger which releases development, with the rare exception of intersexes, along one of two sexual channels. But these channels are broadened by the variation occurring among all the forty-six chromosomes. They are broadened in respect of the secondary sexual characters.

We find men of pronouncedly feminine temperament and physique. We find women of pronouncedly masculine temperament and physique. Such men and women are often more interested in their own sex than in the opposite sex.

Over and above this variation, leading to overlap in secondary characters, there is the primary variation in sexual capacity which ranges from what we have called Class 0 to Class VIII. It might be thought that to sort out the reactions of these two kinds of genetic differences with different environments would be beyond the wit of man. But it so happens that observations of sexual behaviour and our experience of one-egg twins agree in showing us how the heredity–environment reaction expresses itself in this field. The problem of homosexuality is clarified by the realization of the two ranges of genetic variation underlying it. It is also clarified by the principle of the selection of environments.

On the one hand there are unalterably determined homosexual types. They are what we may call *positive* homosexuals. They are men and women of normal or high sexual capacity with the secondary sexual characters, emotionally and sometimes physically, of the opposite sex. On the other hand there are individuals whose secondary sexual characters are similarly intermediate and who are therefore not highly attractive to the opposite sex, but who are at the same time of low sexual capacity. These may be described as *negative* homosexuals. The first choose their own environment; the second have it chosen for them.

Between the positive and negative extremes of homosexuality there is of course a range of genetic variation, variation which the study of twins would help us to understand. The range of homosexual behaviour, as we should expect from this account, is as great as that of normal or heterosexual behaviour. It is not merely the range between active and passive homosexuality, between passion and mere social convenience; there is also the whole range between reciprocity and exploitation which occurs in normal sexual life.

How the environment works is also fairly clear. For a few years before puberty, which varies much in the time and speed of onset, boys and girls are more interested in their own sex than in the other. At this stage the passive homosexual may be said to be arrested. The segregation of the sexes, as happens in schools, colleges, and also professions, which attempt to reproduce the conditions of monastic life, favours the practice of homosexuality. Further, all segregation favours the coming together of people who are genetically disposed to avoid the opposite sex. To put the matter plainly: every barrier, every discouragement, to intercourse *between* the sexes is an encouragement to intercourse *within* the sexes.

Some of these barriers are put up by nature, others by society, and others again by both. Unequal numbers of the sexes arise in Europe from war, in India from child marriage. An excess of boys has often existed among primitive peoples both now and formerly, owing to the common habit of relatively neglecting or even exposing female children. Some barriers, again, are put up by nature, such as the fear of conception and disease, which have been, or could be, taken down by society. Isolation of men from women leads, not only to homosexuality, but also (in rural communities) to intercourse with animals.

Nothing will make intercourse within the sexes attractive to those who are of a contrary disposition. And homosexuals, like sterile neuters, will always constitute a minority of society since homosexuals are usually disinclined to reproduce and the difference in their character has a genetic component. Nor should we pretend to like persons or practices that we genuinely avoid. We can, however, clear our minds greatly by considering the social history of our feelings and opinions. Westermarck has pointed out that homosexuality has usually been disregarded in women while in men it has been thought admirable, abominable or negligible according to custom or superstition. The active homosexual's interest in his own sex has often been regarded as nothing short of magical while the passive homosexual's lack of interest in the opposite sex has made him an object of contempt.

Moral feeling on the subject has grown up only in the last 3,000 years among the bearded men of South-west Asia and Europe. These are the men who pride themselves more than any others on their virility and who (as Professor Muller has pointed out to the writer) have developed gender so strongly in their language. This feeling has no doubt a high genetic component.

It has been exploited in succession by Hinduism, Zoroastrianism, Judaism, Christianity and Islam.

This remarkable chain of events may best be seen in terms envisaged forty years ago. Carr Saunders, in examining the population explosion of modern man at that time, pointed out that palaeolithic man, like most stable species of animals, and like his survivors today, must have planned and limited his reproduction. He must have kept it in relation to a habitat which he was accustomed, and indeed genetically adapted, to preserve. The coming of agriculture 10,000 years ago led first to an increase and then to a stabilization in food supplies which destroyed this ancient adaptive mechanism. The advantage among the new races of cultivators and herdsmen then went to those who were genetically willing and able to reproduce most rapidly. The old methods of limitation by infanticide, abortion, polyandry and homosexuality were then slowly suppressed or abandoned. And those religions which denounced all the practices of limitation propagated themselves as well as their followers most successfully. It was their seed which inherited the earth.

Thus the economic revolution of agriculture changed the genetic character and the religious and moral outlook of its inheritors. Religious teachers accelerated and exploited the resulting change. They defined the rules which they thought fitted to ensure the highest rate of reproduction as well as the highest rate of survival. Their moral rules were in turn borrowed by political authority always eager to distract public attention from misgovernment or calamity. In this respect we owe most to Justinian who discovered the value of sexual deviations in providing society with a scapegoat. The homosexual, so the argument runs, is different from the rest of us. His behaviour has been condemned by the prophets. The Cities of the Plain were destroyed for tolerating him. Let us therefore burn or bury alive, drown or mutilate, the guilty ones. We shall then turn aside the plagues, remedy the famines, and avert the earthquakes which the wrath of the Almighty has brought upon us. Such was the reasoning of Justinian and perhaps of his spouse Theodora. And it was from this reasoning or, shall we say, feeling, that the law of England was derived by which, until 1861, sodomy was supposed to be punishable by death.

People have been able, by banning books on the subject, to pretend that homosexuality, of males or females, does not exist. Indeed it was possible for Lecky a hundred years ago to write a history of morals in Europe expressing this childish belief. The public as well as the private problems of sex can, however, be approached from a new angle when we understand the range and force of genetic determination. On account of his special genetic character the homosexual is genetically fitted for some, and genetically unfitted for other, social functions, quite apart from their sexual character. For example, positive homosexuals among men have made their mark in history. Throughout the ages they have made a characteristic and valuable contribution to the artistic and intellectual side of human culture.

Four homosexual Kings of England, William II, Edward II, Richard II and James I, and one of France, Henry IV, proved to be in various degrees inadequate to their responsibilities. Yet, on the other hand, Alexander the Great, the Emperor Hadrian, Richard Cœur de Lion, Charles XII of Sweden and Frederick the Great of Prussia were all of a predominantly homosexual tendency; and they were, either in peace or war, rulers of achievement. Nor should we forget that, for over five centuries before Napoleon destroyed them, the homosexual Mamelukes governed Egypt. And during the first half of their rule they compared and competed favourably with their contemporaries, the heterosexual rulers of Christendom and of Islam.

The positively homosexual type of woman also makes her mark. Her private life is of little interest to the community. Her public work is of great importance, for in the twentieth century she has become, by her own faculties and by her own choice, the mouthpiece of the less articulate and more feminine part of her sex. In communities where women enjoy political and social influence it is she who predominates in publicly exercising that influence. She is notably masculine in her type of intelligence yet she is responsible for what is happily called 'feminism'. It is she who is responsible for moulding the lines of the education which her (in this respect) less fortunate sisters have to suffer. This education, as Newsom has pointed out, is based on the assumption that women have a similar type of intelligence to that which is possessed and needed by men. Girls are therefore prepared for a life which most of them will never follow, or wish to follow, and which it would be disastrous to the community if they did follow. They are prepared by teachers of a sexual type widely differing from the mode or the mean of varying types in the population, teachers whose attitude towards men is not conducive to marriage. If we understand these conditions we may avoid their worst consequences and improve the lot of one half of mankind.

CELIBACY

There have always been, and the normal curve of variation indicates that there always will be, a proportion of men and women who feel no inclination for a sexual life. They are those from the lower end of the curve of variation. To some cultures and religions this attitude appears shameful, reproduction being a sovereign virtue. To others it appears as a sign of peculiar grace and the gift of continence is held to be the key to a holy life, and to salvation in the world to come. In consequence a special provision has been made, first in Buddhist, later in Christian, and lastly even in some Mohammedan communities, for the establishment of orders and institutions where men and women take vows to refrain from sexual activity. These systems of asexual grouping are most instructive in showing us the social consequences of the genetic variation in reproductive capacity.

It is very common for those who have no wish to take vows of celibacy themselves to imagine that such vows can never be kept; or that they are kept only by a painful effort of the will. It is suggested that monks and nuns must always indulge in clandestine intercourse, perverted or normal. From what we have seen, however, this opinion is wide of the mark. There are always likely to be two or three in every hundred individuals in whom the embers of passion glow with such a faint heat that the consequences of bringing them to a flame will not repay the effort. The Class o individual will be much more comfortable if left alone by the opposite sex. And the company of similar individuals of the same sex will be less disturbing than even a Class o–Class o marriage with its public reminder of obligations and expectations that cannot be fulfilled. In a word, the institution of celibacy acknowledges the propriety, and cares for the comfort, of a relationship other than marriage, a relationship which would otherwise appear both improper and uncomfortable. The institution of celibacy, by making a virtue of what cannot be avoided, will, if maintained with prudence, increase the sum of human happiness. The achievements of Fracastoro and Spallanzani, of Mendel and Janssens, show that it may also come to increase the sum of human knowledge.

Celibacy, however, has its pitfalls, no less painful than those of marriage. It may not be uncomfortable for a would-be Mahatma at the age of thirty-five to take a vow of celibacy. He knows his own feelings and he can neglect those of his wife. But the novice who commits himself or herself to a monastic life before reaching an age of maturity, before any classification by sexual needs or endowments can declare itself, is likely to be shouldering a woeful burden.

Marriage is a public ratification of private joy. As such it absolves the happy couple from the feeling of guilt inherent in entirely private happiness. Such a feeling of guilt, a consciousness of sin, is instinctive. It is part of our body of social instincts, which we shall consider later. It depends on no arbitrary invention of society but on an inherent reaction like that which makes us, as it made the Greeks, think that pride brings down the wrath of the gods. The revulsion that develops as we get older against enjoyment of a sexual orgasm without intercourse is another aspect of the instinctive feeling of guilt in private happiness or pleasure. Body craves for body, soul also craves for soul. When there is no object of craving, or yearning, or desire, or love, the body must find some outlet for its emotions and the male must find some outlet for accumulated semen. Most children and, still more, most grown-ups, all indeed who are sexually mature, require the relief of sexual stimulation. When they are compelled to sleep alone they have to obtain this relief alone. And after maturity stimulation leads to an orgasm. No one who has grown up needs to be told that such a satisfaction of sexual impulses, without an object of love in the form of another human being, is a poor substitute for the joy of sexual union. It is a waste of the opportunities of life – that is, if life has any opportunities. If it has none, then the only solution of the problem is masturbation or what medical cant has named 'solitary vice'. It is the solution adopted by man as well as all the other animals whose reproduction he controls. And, in a state of nature, in parthenogenetic species of earthworms, which have lost the faculty of sexual reproduction, mutual masturbation of hermaphrodites is a condition of the development of their virgin eggs.

Any mature male above the bottom of the reproductive scale must have some form of sexual outlet. Those who are impotent on account of physiological or psychological defect or mere age have often tried to persuade the young that all available forms of sexual outlet are sinful; or, for those who have taken vows, any form of sexual outlet whatever. They are led to invent fanciful arguments. They have suggested, for example, that masturbation is unhealthy and may even cause madness. If this were said of *coitus interruptus* it might be excused. As we may learn from spring fever in elephants it is more likely to prevent madness than to cause it. Masturbation is, of course, the standard practice in artificial insemination with the results shown in our fertility curve. These falsehoods arise from the old habit of deducing biology from morals, instead of deducing morals from biology. Which is what we must learn to do.

THE CRISIS OF PROPAGATION

All forms of pleasure – those associated with sex, art, and humour, no less than those of physical and intellectual achievement – are by-products of the useful aptitudes. The satisfactions gained from manual dexterity, vocal performance, sexual intercourse, or the mere appreciation of form, pattern, or harmony, are the direct or indirect products of natural selection. They are derived from the adaptation of primitive man to the necessity of survival by achievement. Already, when the caves of Altamira and Lascaux were painted, the by-products were becoming ends in themselves. And in civilization they exist in all degrees of independence from any original use.

In the evolution of plants and animals there are many analogies. The entrance of the sperm into the egg was originally the act determining its development. But so closely was the proximity of the sperm associated with its entrance that it often became convenient for this proximity alone to determine development.

It is then found in many plants and animals that, when proximity is *not* followed by entrance, the egg, although unfertilized, can develop. The egg *anticipates* its marriage. Virgin birth or parthenogenesis follows. The antecedent has taken the place of the real thing and become an end, or, what is the same thing, a beginning, in itself. In every group of plants and animals there are species in which this illicit device has become the sole means of reproduction.

So it is that in human society, arising from an abrupt reorientation through the development of the human mind, all kinds of by-products of useful activities have acquired new uses and have become ends and beginnings in themselves. In the opinion of the less civilized or less complicated societies or individuals many of these new uses seem trivial distractions from the great primary ends of existence. To them, art must always have an obvious ulterior use. To them, sexual intercourse must always have the purpose of propagating the species. To them, also, humour should never intrude into the serious affairs of life.

To all such views an opposite has been expressed. Art for art's sake is the only perfect art. Not only intercourse, but marriage, is sufficiently justified by the pleasure of the individuals. And in some circumstances it may well appear that there are no serious affairs in life. An alternation, or a compromise, or, best of all, a balance, between such extremes as these seems most likely to favour the well-being of human societies. There is, however, one respect in which failure to achieve a compromise seems likely to endanger the survival, not of one society only, but of all mankind: it concerns the *duty* of reproduction.

The greatest ancient religions, Hinduism, and Judaism, and directly or indirectly most forms of ancestor worship, have fostered a belief in the duty of reproduction or, at least, the necessity of becoming an ancestor. This belief, as we saw, held by a coherent racial group, favours the survival of both the race and the religion. Indeed, the Christian religion would not have survived if St Paul had not compromised between his own principles and the Old Testament view of the virtue of reproduction.

Belief in the virtue of reproduction has had a high selective value in the past since those who held it were bound to multiply more than those who did not. It must have a large genetic component, but, within limits, it will be modifiable by education or persuasion – the mass heredity modifying the individual habit. The same is probably also true, as we saw, of the particular method of reproduction by outbreeding. This recognition of a duty of reproduction led to the Jewish, the Hindu and the Chinese peoples increasing their numbers in the face of adversity and even catastrophe during the last 3,000 years. The Jews and Brahmins, for their part, held their own against the worst danger of all, contamination: Judaism and Hinduism became genetic religions depending for their maintenance on a correct theory of racial differentiation by inbreeding. But all three held their own against the constant drain of loss from famine, war, pestilence and persecution; and, above all, loss from the high death-rate of children in hot climates and among dense populations.

Now, the science and techniques of western civilization have freed the eastern peoples of a part of these perils. In 200 years of British rule the population of India increased from 150 to 450 millions. The same increase occurred in Britain but with us the advance arose from our own advance in the techniques of production. In the East it did not. The result is an increasing starvation of an increasing population. Moreover, we ourselves, having reached the limit of what our land will carry, are restricting our population with another western technique, that of birth control, which India has failed to learn, and indeed partly declines to learn.

This situation compels us to take a serious view of the future of mankind. In the past the mode of human fertility has no doubt usually agreed with the mode of human intelligence: average people have multiplied faster than the more intelligent or the less intelligent within each society. As between societies, the more intelligent or more capable have always gained at the expense of their competitors. This has allowed scope for natural selection to improve the average intelligence of mankind by the failure of survival of backward races. During the last century the advance of medicine and the practice of birth control have upset the ancient equilibrium. They are both inventions of the technically advanced classes of technically advanced societies. The first, but not the second, has been given to the technically backward classes and societies. The opportunities given to the last two generations have shown that these classes and societies are technically backward in part for genetic reasons. The mode of fertility has shifted to a lower point on the normal curve of intelligence, of heritable educability, of mankind as a whole.

The new direction to be expected of evolutionary change has already become defined. The growth of population is ceasing to be limited by famine and disease. Races, classes and individuals of technically less enterprising types, which would not be capable of surviving unassisted, are now multiplying. They are multiplying out of proportion to those races, classes and individuals to whose enterprise they owe their ability to multiply. Surely this is a hazardous situation.

The dangers of over-population were first pointed out by the Rev. Thomas Malthus, the author of, among other things, the law of diminishing returns. Malthus objected to the Utopian views which were current among intellectuals in his time, as they are today. He published his views in 1798 in *An Essay on the Principle of Population as it affects the Future Improvement of Society*. In his view, expanded in successive editions over a period of thirty-four years, the human population always increases to the limit of the subsistence available. Charitable doles therefore have the effect of aggravating by merely postponing the situation they are intended to correct. This situation has always been remedied in the past by war, famine, and disease, but it might be remedied in the future by a reduction of the birthrate.

The full dangers of propagation unrestricted by disease were not realizable before the end of the nineteenth century. But Malthus's discussion suggested the idea of natural selection to both Darwin and Wallace. The dangers of genetic decay and the possibilities of genetic improvement had been indicated by Plato on the basis of a theory of selection. They were made clearer by Darwin. With their specific social implications they were expounded by Galton in his three great works. But again the full force of his observations could not be realized until fifty years later when birth control became widely practised by better-educated classes and peoples. Now, the over-population predicted by Malthus and the decay feared by Galton are coming upon us suddenly and together. The population of one half of the world is standing still while that of the other half is increasing by several millions a month. And not all those millions will be able to feed or care for themselves.

To put the matter in another way: the limit to the population of men that the earth will carry is set by the physical character of the earth and the genetic character of the men. A few men may by scientific discovery greatly advance the possibilities of exploiting the growth of plants and animals on the soil of the earth. But these possibilities can be realized only by men with a certain genetically limited technical capacity; a capacity lower than that of the inventors but higher than that of the agricultural populations of the world today in almost every part of every country. The limiting factor at the present moment is therefore not agricultural research, not soil, plant, and animal research, but human research. The important means of increasing food production in Europe and in Asia is to breed better farmers and to put them in possession of the land.

In England, for example, it was not lack of research which limited food production during the last war, but the genetic unfitness of a large part of the tenant farmers, the legally secured occupiers who were organized to keep better men off the land. There was also unfitness above, to be sure, which rejected artificial insemination and preserved 1,000,000 bulls who were eating the food which might have been eaten by 1,000,000 cows.

The principle that is being applied to meet this crisis is the principle that the State – and even the World State – should accept responsibility for the nutrition, health, and education of all human beings from the time of conception to the end of life. This principle can be easily and immediately justified by the view that individuals who are not properly cared for in these respects are an incubus, and may be a danger, to society. But it is a principle with a corollary. The State or mankind cannot accept a responsibility which goes back as far as the fertilized egg without one day claiming the right to go further and control the quality or proportions of gametes which go to make the fertilized egg. Fertilization is, as we have tried to show, an important event. But it has antecedents, the processes, in fact, of heredity. And as we come to understand them better we shall come to reject the view that all responsibility should begin after fertilization, and none be allowed before it.

How this control can properly be exercised is one of our deeper problems. But although deep it is not remote. If we fail to think it out we shall be faced with the old methods of preserving balance. We shall be faced with war, famine, and disease, according to the rules laid down by Malthus. Now, however, war is likely to be the predominant agent. Equipped with new types of explosives which depend upon splitting the atom, man is able for the first time to make war by breaking the chromosomes and exploding heredity – for that, as we have seen, is the way atomic radiation kills. It is by this means that civilized men are now in a position to kill one another without any invidious discrimination.

PART FIVE

THINKING AND KNOWING

Our knowledge of the genetic processes at work in the development of the mind is inconsistent with such illusions about how the mind works, as its selfishness, immortality, equality, and free will. The development of biology, while admitting the importance of various kinds of chance, leads us to favour the deterministic school of physics. In conclusion, we find that human studies in history, medicine, psychology and the social sciences have failed to keep in touch with the changing knowledge of the facts of life. They have continually set up freely floating systems of determinism by repudiating genetics. These practices are responsible for errors, which can now be remedied, in these branches of thought.

17

The Irrational Element

STEP by step we have come to see the processes of life moving by rules and developing through the ages by evolutionary change which itself has rules. We have seen our ideas becoming coherent on a basis of determinism and of uncertainty controlled by processes of natural selection. We have now reached the point at which we can ask ourselves how far the human mind, which has discovered these rules and ideas, can be understood as the result of their operation.

In excavating the inner core of heredity we have had some experience of probing what seemed only a few years ago utterly inaccessible to scientific inquiry. The human mind is something we may admit to be yet one degree more inaccessible. In attacking heredity we had two powerful points of vantage. One was the ability to study it in action by experiment at the same time that we studied it in structure under the microscope. The other was that with heredity, as we could show with good reason, we were dealing with the same principles for all plants and animals and for man himself. For the study of the human mind our present points of vantage are less commanding. We can study under the microscope the thousands of millions of cells which do the work of the mind. For by *mind* we mean simply the brain in action. But their structure helps us very little to understand how the whole thing acts. We know also that in bare esentials the human brain works like that of an ape or a dog. The human temperament, like the dog's temperament depends on the activity of chemically identified hormones. And both mind and temperament in man and dog may be deranged by injury, by disease, and by heredity – of genes and of chromosomes. But the growth of the cerebral hemispheres in the 100,000 generations which separate us from apes, and the capacity for memory, association, prediction, and all the other peculiarities of human consciousness which they have thereby gathered together for us, have given the human mind a unique character, so much so that its study must, to some extent, be a thing by itself.

The development of the science of the mind has reflected these difficulties.

The internal or genetic component determining animal behaviour is described as instinct. But we have to move cautiously in approaching the notion of instinct. It is deeply embedded in thought and speech, whether of the farmer or of the philosopher. The one might say his instincts were what made him act as he does without the need of thinking. The other would say that his instincts were 'congenitally organized patterns of behaviour'. Neither of these answers has a practical application and, in terms of genetics, neither of them has a precise meaning.

In terms of genetics all behaviour is genetically determined; but it is also environmentally determined. It depends on the genotype-environment-genotype sequence of reactions. Differences of behaviour within different groups of people (like differences of structure) vary in the importance of the genetic and the environmental components in their determination. This view, however, is not the one that has guided the opinions of psychologists. It is worth studying the confusions of thought that have baffled them.

MacDougal's method of classifying instincts to fit classes of behaviour – flight, repulsion, pugnacity, assertion and so on – has long seemed, like Bateson's idea of the unit character, a little naïve. It follows the popular belief that types, or elements of behaviour, are units of cause as well as effect. The objections to instincts and to unit characters had similar consequences: they led to a contraction of the ideas. But the contraction of instinct entailed another series of fallacies. New-born infants vary so little in the desire to suck (without which they can scarcely live) and their environments vary so little in offering them the opportunity to suck (if they are to live), that, it is argued, human infants have a genuine, universal, inexpugnable sucking instinct. So far so good. Jung has, however, discovered differences among new-born babies in their sucking power. Now, it was argued, a mental property which varies among individuals of a species cannot vary by heredity: it must vary as a result of the action of the environment. It cannot therefore be an instinct. So we poor humans alone among animals are left with no instincts at all. Taking instincts as imaginary units of behaviour, and failing to reckon with the total genetic-environmental reaction, psychologists have been led into an absurdity.

It would, in the light of our knowledge, be ridiculous to suppose that flight, pugnacity or sucking are related to particular units of heredity or groups of genes. They are each characteristic of individuals as working wholes in particular situations. Nor is there any sharp boundary between instinctive and rational behaviour since behind human actions there is every gradation of thought. The idea of instinct is therefore a temporary convenience. It belongs, like the medical term 'congenital', to the pre-analytical stage of discussion. But it does not belong to the pre-genetic stage. For, in acting on the mind, natural selection does not discriminate directly between determinants or even between the structures they determine. It discriminates between activities. It acts through the results. These results are the instincts. The difficulty comes from the fact that in the long chain of mental processes the instincts are a necessary half-way house between the genotype and the phenotype.

How then are we to use the idea of instincts? At one end of the scale, the comparison of the behaviour of different species, and, at the other end, the studies of human one-egg twins show that there is a genetic component in all animal behaviour. On this basis every species of mobile organism, whether a slipper animalcule, a brandling worm, or a baboon, has its own characteristic instincts distinguishing it from other species. These will depend on the structure of its central nervous system, its relationship with the body as a whole, and especially its chemical regulation by hormones. For all of these together constitute the mind. The individual members of species vary to a greater or less degree in their instincts. Apes, earthworms, and animalcules vary enormously between their several species, although little enough within them. Dogs (that is, domestic dogs) and men, on the other hand, vary enormously within the species.

Every breed of dog has its own instinctive character. If it is a working breed this character depends on a coordinated muscular and nervous organization which has been selected for some practical purpose. Its instincts are patterns of behaviour. If it is a show breed, bred for the purpose of winning a prize, the co-ordination may, of course, be absent. In first crosses between similar breeds we still get the coordination, and often a useful one, as poachers have discovered in breeding the lurcher from a cross between the collie and the greyhound. But in the second generation or later derivatives of dog crosses, as we know from common experience, and as Stockard showed by his experiments, we get the uncoordinated genetic recombination in respect of mind as well as body which has given the mongrel its poor repute. Its instincts are often thrown out of gear.

What is the situation in regard to man's instincts? If we are to use our knowledge of human variation, breeding systems, and twin behaviour, we should expect that the human population would show the same variety as the domestic dog populations. As Galton puts it:

The instincts and faculties of different men and races differ in a variety of ways almost as profoundly as those of animals in different cages of the Zoological Gardens; and [he adds, with discernment] however diverse and antagonistic they are, each may be good of its kind (1883).

But how are these instincts in fact distributed among different breeds and races and men? There should be some relatively pure breeds selected for some long-established practical purpose – a humble purpose like that of the peasant or fishing community, or a more refined purpose like that of the skilled craftsmen of the older civilizations. There should be other relatively pure breeds selected for some unpractical purpose like those over-ripe governing classes, mentioned by Darwin, which would take prizes in the show ring for good looks together with their own cattle. There should also be products of crossing in the first and later generations, some showing useful new coordinations of behaviour adapted to new ways of life, and others showing a lack of coordination. Does this catalogue give a picture of humanity somewhat as we find it today? It goes some way, but not so far as it might.

It is clear from what we saw of the specially high variation in sexual character of all animals, including men, that no type of variation – within or between breeding-groups – will be so important as that in the sexual system. Differences in the production of sex hormones in the course of life, differences between individuals at the same time of life, and between opposite sexes at all times of life, are enormous. Behaviour, and the character of the mind governing behaviour, its instincts, will vary in dependence on these differences. The greater the importance of the sexual life, the greater will be the importance of these variations. And it is quite certain that in some individuals the sexual instincts, sexual behaviour, sexual life, have no importance whatever. They are neuter; they are vegetative; they have minds and bodies but the joys and miseries, desires, satisfactions and frustrations, of sexual life touch them in no cell of their bodies and in no part of their lives. These are things that genetics and physiology teach us. But the direct study of the mind, the sorting out of its activities by comparison and experiment, reveals a new world which, at first sight, seems to have little to do with the old one we have been studying so far.

THE TEACHINGS OF FREUD

The four great minds we have studied in this book were all bent on reaching conclusions. But, while Darwin, Mendel and Pasteur began from the fewest beginnings, the fourth, Galton, was in one respect even rarer, for he was willing to start where he had little hope of finishing. Like John Ray, he began several sciences. The last of these that we meet is the study of the mind itself. His gift for treating numbers and measurements had put him in the way of measuring the qualities of the human mind to which we give that composite name of intelligence. His studies, first of primitive peoples and later of twins, had revealed the genetic determination of differences of intelligence and temperament, and in consequence of individuality. And in the end he came to apprehend the relation between what he called the 'ante-chamber' of consciousness and what we regard as our ordinary processes of thought. He discovered that peculiarly human distinction between what are now called the conscious and the unconscious mind.

Towards the end of the nineteenth century this notion came

into sudden prominence and a prominence entirely separate from the rest of Galton's ideas. The study of hypnosis had made it clear that human actions could be based on mental processes of which the individual concerned was unaware. Under hypnosis it is possible to remember what in ordinary life has been forgotten. Something is there in the mind, a whole world of knowledge, thought and purpose, which is ordinarily prevented from coming to the surface of awareness. A man told to shut a window, or to do anything else unnecessary but not too outrageous, under deep hypnosis, will later, when returned to himself, do what he was told. He will follow the suggestion and will invent an excuse, a seemingly logical reason to justify his doing so, to rationalize his action. On these foundations, but using suggestion without hypnosis as a basis of his experimental method, the Viennese Jewish physician, Sigmund Freud, set to work to build a theory of the action of the human mind.

On Freud's view the properties of the mind must arise from something that had happened to it in the course of development. Inquiry and hypothesis were concentrated on development. Thus the unconscious part of the mind is something repressed, or expelled from, or allowed to exist outside, the knowledge of which we are aware. It acquires this position because it is disagreeable, or because our parents said it was wrong. It can find its way round the censorship of the mind by transferring or sublimating its purpose on to other lines. Sexual desire frustrated may thus express itself as creative art or Christian charity. The unconscious mind will express itself also in other ways, in slips of the tongue, and, with great distortion, in dreams. That is in adults. But the correction of infants for playing with their pudenda may lead to complexes of repression that will end in an upset of mental balance perhaps long after sexual maturity.

The conflicts or tensions set up by the supposed repression of the unconscious were, according to Freud, responsible for disturbances of the mind, for what we call nervous disorders. And, further, he was of the opinion (based on his own practical experience in treating neurotic and deranged individuals in Vienna) that the important desires could be entirely related to the sexual system. Sexual activity must thus be supposed to operate in the mind in infancy long before it operates in the body; and also in individuals in whose bodies it will never operate at all.

The method, work and theories of Freud are of profound and permanent importance for the understanding of the human mind, and for the interpretation of life and of history, including the history of science. His attempt to express his views in general biological terms was hampered, however, by absence of much elementary biological knowledge in his day. Yet they must be so expressed if we are to exploit them for the purpose of understanding nature as a whole.

Freud was naturally working all the time with the notion of instinct. But is an instinct individual? Is it genetically determined? Has it an adaptive value? To answer these questions we need to concentrate all our experience, and all the resources of biological method, on Freud's problem. In a discussion of instincts, *Triebe und Triebschicksale* (1915), Freud writes, if we may translate him:

We have often heard the opinion advanced that a science should be built on clear and sharply defined ideas. In fact no science begins with such definitions.

The science that we have been discussing, however, does begin with definitions. We are prepared to define what we mean by mind and instinct, heredity and environment. We are prepared to define their evolutionary origin, their structural basis, their social function. Our definitions may have to be changed but we are capable of stating them explicitly. It is true that the preparations for making a science need not *begin* with definitions. But they must aim at definitions and until they have achieved this aim their claim to be a science, and to correct or ignore other sciences, is not to be accepted. Freud's failure to define his idea of the mind in the beginning meant that in the end his general theory grew into vitalism, a theory in which the mind can be the beginning of everything.

Freud's argument was based on a rigorously deterministic view. Everything that men did was determined by some property of their minds. But what constituted the mind in the beginning he left open and undefined. It was not clear what it contained beyond an uncertain amount of 'racial memory' and a potentiality for reacting in the way, the Freudian way, in which all other human minds would react under given conditions. Thus Freud's determinism, like Marx's, excluded the basis of biological determinism. It was a determinism having all the aggressive capacity for hypothesis and discovery that determinism can give. But it was a determinism of limited liability. One could draw on it to any amount so long as one did not touch the heredity account.

The repudiation of heredity by Freud repeats what we have seen in every other field of human science. But it is of particular interest in psychology since the science which Freud developed had its foundations, as we have seen, in the work of Galton himself, who first connected psychology with the determinism of heredity. How does Freud succeed in wrenching himself loose from these foundations?

Heredity, says Freud, we do not mention because 'others have done so'. In any case, 'we can do nothing to change it'. Freud's business, again like Marx's, was not so much to understand nature as to change it. We, however, shall be happy enough if we can understand it. In order to do this our first necessity is to assess the action of the genetic component in any mental condition. If we know how close are the resemblances of one-egg twins in their behaviour, both normal and abnormal, both when separated and when kept together, we do not expect too much from the treatments of psychiatrists. We know, as Freud says, that they cannot alter heredity. Now we know, from the data of Eliot Slater, that chronic depressive mania is twenty-five times commoner among the brothers and sisters of afflicted individuals than in the general population. Hence we infer that its genetic component is very high. And we are not surprised to learn that treatment by psycho-analysis has never been known to relieve this condition. Again our genetic expectation is verified.

Not only does Freud exclude heredity in principle with a halting excuse. He excludes every manifestation of heredity outside the field of his immediate technique of mental inquiry. He excludes, and he admits excluding, the study of the health. The student of the mind is not supposed to inquire into the state of the body! This attitude in practice is supported by the exclusion in theory of all interests in the mental processes of animals. Social attitudes in man have no relation to the gregariousness of animals. Sexual desire has no relation to natural selection. Thus Freud voluntarily surrenders the help he could receive from the general body of biology, whether in the study of heredity, variation or evolution, development or physiology. He admits merely that there is a difference, a remarkably trivial difference, between the two sexes. On this narrow foundation (and an old version of it) everything is built.

Like all the specialists of this century, Freud wanted to reach conclusions without wasting time on evidence outside his own field. He could do this by assuming a standardized normal type from which we all diverged after birth owing to our experiences. He was bound to rely, for inferring this normal type of mind, on the study of more or less abnormal minds. From what we have seen of the extremely wide range of physical variation in reproductive capacity it is obvious that mental derangements are very likely to arise with regard to sex. They will be most serious in our Classes I and VIII. It is at either extreme that we are likely to get fixation of love on the parent. But the derangements of Class I and Class VIII will have little to do with one another. Infantile eroticism and the Oedipus complex are not the basis of normal development : they are the basis of the derangements that occur in a proportion, probably a small proportion, of individuals.

The attempt to express mental idiosyncrasies in terms of the accidents of birth and infancy becomes ridiculous in the light of our knowledge of one-egg twins. Refusing to admit the genetic basis of mental characters, Freud could be quite unrestrained in his assumptions about the effects of the environment. His successors have been even more unrestrained. The practical mistakes into which his theoretical errors have led his disciples cover two main fields, those of education and crime. Their argument has been as follows : If delinquency and derangement are the fruits of early unkindness then why not reverse the proposition? Why not say that early unkindness will unfailingly lead to delinquency and derangement? We are told with great confidence that any lack of understanding, any frustration, any injustice, will lead the young into the horrors of abnormal psychology. Their minds will become maladjusted and the way will be prepared for mental and moral breakdown. What was first intended for cure is now, therefore, used for prevention.

We are also told that the criminal, if well enough understood by the psychiatrist, can be put back on the right path from which unkindness has forced him to depart. For this view it is the business of the psychiatrist or clinical psychologist to obtain evidence. It is not his business to examine the theoretical foundations of his subject. How does he go to work? Take a British example. He is concerned with juvenile delinquency. He compiles the circumstances of delinquency with laborious statistics. He examines the results in pursuit of a cause and a remedy. He begins by eliminating heredity. After all, it is well known (he argues) that there is no heredity of mental qualities. Heredity is only a 'potentiality'. It is not a real thing. He then finds that no recorded circumstances conduce to delinquency except (strange to say) the possession of numerous delinquent brothers and sisters. What does this mean? he asks. Are they the consequence of his heredity? By no means. They are evidence of his environment.

Faced with the alternatives of heredity and environment as the basis of explanation, the learned have for many ages found themselves in the same quandary as the unlearned. Without the microscope, and without experimental method, heredity was as much beyond the inquiry of the physician as of his patient. They had to rely on the basic fallacy that brothers have the same heredity. The environment must therefore be held responsible for all differences in respect of which brothers vary. The impotent man has a fixation on his mother? Then his impotence is the result of his fixation. The homosexual (like André Gide) has an antagonism for his mother? Then his homosexuality is the result of his antagonism. Thus in every situation it is possible to give priority to the disembodied mind, to remove the study of the body and of heredity from the problem. Thus, indeed, it is possible to reverse the natural order of cause and effect according to the historic procedure which we have earlier seen working so successfully for the development of superstition in general.

INSTINCTS AND MORALS

Man's social history must be expected to have had some connexion with the evolution of his mind. It is of no use for a species to have individuals of two sexes, supplied with reproductive apparatus mutually adapted for their propagation, if the individuals are not endowed with suitable genetically determined impulses.

The potential parents must also have instincts prompting them to desire one another and to provide for the resulting young such care as they need for their survival. For man this means, as we have seen, far more care than his ancestors bestowed or enjoyed. We in fact notice that, while in heterogeneous communities like those of modern cities the mating and parental instincts are very variable in degree, in homogeneous inbred and simple communities they are as strong as the constant selection favouring their propagation would lead us to expect. This is a special example of the principle whereby the unit of selection is extended beyond the individual to its reproduction and to its racial character, which, as we have seen, is responsible for the evolution of heredity and of the genetic system.

Darwin and his followers could not understand the effect of selection on larger units and longer periods than the individual and his life. They also did not reckon with a selection of environments. Both these failures led to an error in their social arguments, an error which has had an abiding effect in the world ever since Darwinian doctrines came to be disseminated, vulgarized, and applied to man. All the paraphrases of the idea of Natural Selection throw the same emphasis on the individual as the ultimate and sufficient unit of evolutionary change. This emphasis was dramatically effective but analytically disastrous. Spencer's Survival of the Fittest and Malthus's Struggle for Existence equally ignored the stock or the race, the group or the community, as entities. They equally implied also a standardized environment. Haeckel fulminated against socialism with 'many are called but few are chosen'. With complacency and even satisfaction he was able to point out that the great mass of mankind 'starves and prematurely perishes in misery'. Darwin heartily declared: 'What a foolish idea seems to prevail in Germany on the connexion between Socialism and Evolution through Natural Selection' (1879, *Life and Letters*).

Darwin and the Darwinians were by no means uncomfortable under the regime of nature red in tooth and claw. They were not interested in disturbing a social order which had so much to commend it. A connexion, which Karl Marx had wished to emphasize by dedicating *Das Kapital* to Darwin, existed, of course, between the theories of evolution and of socialism. Both required change, and not least a change of thinking. To Marx the connexion was a matter of political expediency. Its scientific sense first came to the mind of the founder of Eugenics.

Galton had not lived among the Hottentots for nothing. He suggested that gregariousness was an instinct of value for the survival of societies of men as well as of cattle. He argued that some kind of social selection had encouraged its development. His disciple, Karl Pearson, took the matter up. In 1892 (and again in 1897) we find him pointing out that there is a struggle of society against society, and hence:

The socialistic as well as the individualistic tendency is a direct outcome of the fundamental principle of evolution.

Grammar of Science, Ch. 9

This idea might seem to be a clean break from Darwinian tradition. Darwin himself however had considered the point. In the *Descent of Man* he had argued that moral feelings and the corresponding feelings of guilt for transgression were shown by dogs. A dog selected for obedience and understanding will show feelings of guilt when it has failed to obey or understand. Such reactions were the product of natural selection diversely developed in different breeds. Further, he argued that in man social instincts and moral feelings were subject to inheritance and hence to selection. We have already seen how this principle helps us to understand the evolution of the human breeding system with its rejection of incest. We have also seen its bearing on methods of population control, with their powerful examples of the subjection of the individual to the authority of society. These views are all related to the ideas which, more than forty years later, germinated, under the impact of a great war, in the mind of Wilfred Trotter.

Trotter published his famous book, *The Instincts of the Herd in Peace and War* in 1915. Here he pointed out that man must have been selected and adapted to act as a social animal. In consequence his instincts must have been modified to conflict in some respects with his needs or his interests as an individual. For the purpose of this consideration, Trotter, unlike other psychologists, defines what he means by instincts. He does so conformably with genetic methods of analysis. They are 'inherited modes of reaction to bodily needs or external stimulus'. He makes it clear how hard these modes of reaction are to get at:

... it is just those fundamental propositions which owe their origin to instinct which appear to the subject the most obvious, the most axiomatic and the least liable to doubt by anyone but an eccentric or a madman.

Moreover the obstacles to inquiry become all the more important with the growth of the mind:

Intelligence ... leaves its possessor no less impelled by instinct ... but endows him with the capacity to respond in a larger variety of ways.

Hence in heterogeneous races of man different individuals will differ in their instincts, although having certain racial instincts in common.

We must now see how these views are related to the determination of human behaviour and its great environmental component, religious teaching.

THE GENETICS OF SELF-INTEREST

The view that a good man is naturally interested in his neighbours, or can readily be persuaded to love and serve them is one that has been inculcated by religious teachers since the Bronze Age. It has stimulated, no doubt, the opposite view: that man is instinctively and ineradicably self-interested; his own advantage, it is asserted, however much he may pretend otherwise, must always determine his actions. This view has been advanced by a long line of thinkers. And they have shown as a rule a greater intellectual coherence than their opponents. The opinion of Epicurus was translated by Hobbes with his: *Amicitia bona namque utilis*; and La Rochefoucauld said the same thing at greater length. The line continues through Marx with his economic determinism and Freud with his amoral unconscious.

Self-interest in this way has come to be regarded as a supremely rational motive. On the other hand, any departure from self-interest appears to derive from religious teaching, from unpractical 'idealism' or from the delusions of a Don Quixote. Salutary as are these repudiations of make-believe they are unconvincing in certain awkward particulars. They leave something out. When they are stripped of all hypocrisy, human beings can still be shown to be incorrigibly interested in things, and persons, and mere ideas, which do not touch their individual advantage.

The limiting case is one which we can all appreciate. All of us are interested in material and in intellectual conditions that will exist when we are dead. We are interested, in varying degrees, and in so far as we have any, in the fate of our property and our progeny, and, above all, our intellectual property and progeny. Some of us are also interested in our country, our people, and our culture. We are interested in the survival of things we value and even of the race from which we have sprung. And we are interested in the opinion that our fellow men, or at least some of them, will have of us when we are dead.

So long as the mental faculties remain, this interest is not diminished: it is even increased by the instant expectation of death. Our interest in life as a whole is, in this respect, like our interest in one of the particular jobs of which life is made up. We are interested in everything connected with ourselves, even though it no longer concerns us as individuals. Moreover the most intelligent human individuals in the most advanced societies are the most concerned about a future which does not concern them as individuals. For this reason special departments of government, administered by charity commissioners and public trustees, are appointed in advanced societies to take care of the posthumous affairs of men.

How do we acquire all this deep-rooted and, as some might say, irrational, interest in things beyond ourselves? Is it the inspiration of God or the voices of the Prophets that make us wish to improve, or instruct, or endow, succeeding generations? Is it the teaching or example of our parents that makes us take so much care in our testamentary dispositions? Not at all, says Trotter: 'Man is altruistic because he must be, not because reason recommends it.'

Why must man be altruistic? The human mind, as it has increased in power, has also increased in foresight. It has become adapted to take an interest in the future of things, persons and ideas, first in the family, and then in the community. This adaptation has arisen by natural selection. The first father to foresee the requirements of grain from one year to the next made the fortune of his family. The first steward to look ahead and foresee the requirements of grain for seven years ahead secured the destiny of his race. Indeed, we may well ask whether the higher species of human culture could ever have taken root without a genetically determined interest among our ancestors in the perpetuation of this culture by and for their posterity.

Interest in the remote future is an extension of interest beyond the individual. It is, of course, only one aspect of the social adaptation of instinct, of the genetic mind, in man. We may venerate the recluse and the hermit but we do not imitate them. Man is not a solitary animal. Ordinary men delight to assemble in solemn troops and sweet societies. A harmonious society could exist, according to Trotter, only if the individuals were instinctively adapted to take interest in one another and to react, as the members of a herd will, to any common danger or common advantage. At the same time such instinctive interest must have strengthened, and been strengthened by, the union of man and wife and of parent and offspring which make for the permanence of the human family. The instinctive basis of parental love is well shown by the fact that parents love their children more than children love their parents. This attitude, which Swift attempts to explain in our opening quotation, cannot be based on reason. But, if genetically determined, it is bound to have been favoured by natural selection. Thus, if the social instincts are more powerfully developed in man, and more intellectually elaborated, than in any other of the higher animals, there are good reasons why they should be so.

This instinctive herd interest has, on Trotter's view, brought with it profound, and increasingly profound, consequences for the evolution of man and woman. First, having founded the family, it made possible, as we have seen, the continuity, and hence the cumulative possibilities, of human culture. Secondly, it must have been the instrument of the formation of mating groups based on discriminating assortment with the interlocking cultural and genetic implications that we have seen. Thirdly, it must have brought about that primary concession of the individual to the community, the adoption of a common speech. And beyond these it must have been the basis of that *esprit de corps* which drives the fighting tribe or the political party, which gives authority to the king or the magistrate, and which betrays only too clearly its detachment from self-interest when it is used to support with equal enthusiasm (either now or in ancient Hellas) the heroes of military or of athletic exploits.

All social or herd instincts, we can be sure on general genetic grounds, will vary in quality and amount with the temperament, intellectual capacity, and social character of individuals. There will always be some more sophisticated or less exuberant people to agree with the elderly poet in saying:

> I wish I loved the Human Race;
> I wish I loved its silly face. ...

The great mental conflicts which take place in the unconscious mind are, according to Trotter, due to the antagonism between individual interests or impulses (of which Freud's favourite sex instinct is one) and restraining forces. These forces are partly external, as Freud would say, and partly internal, as Jung would have it. The external restraining forces arise from the action of society (itself genetically determined) on the minds of individuals who are, from their internal or genetic social adaptation, highly susceptible to such restraint.

As Trotter says:

The individual of a gregarious species can never be truly independent and self-sufficient. Natural selection has ensured that as an individual he must have an abiding sense of incompleteness. ... This is the psychological germ which expresses itself in the religious feelings, in the desire for completion, for mystic union.

IMMORTALITY

We now begin to see how our genetic character, our instinctive composition, may react on our beliefs and on our existence as individuals. We are conscious of an inability to curtail our interests within the limits of our mortal span. How easy, therefore, to admit that the mortal span is itself spurious! We wish to explain our enduring interests. We therefore assume an immaterial, an intellectual, a spiritual survival. A belief in immortality is thus a consequence of our genetic constitution. It is also a necessary condition, in some form, of the development of our civilization.

This argument and this conclusion conflict with the doctrine of the traditional materialists. At the same time (we may hope) they would be gratified to notice one of its results. For it enables us to explain, on materialistic assumptions, how the intuition of immortality comes to be adopted by natural religion and later exploited by revealed religion. It enables us to understand how the theory of the after-life, the grand science of eschatology, has been built up side by side, in the very same societies, with the growth of culture and the flowering of the human intellect.

Other arguments rationalizing the idea of immortality are merely parallel consequences of its primary causation. There is a sense, of course, in which we survive in the culture to which we may have contributed; or in the hearts of men, as the Sufi poet puts it. But again the culture is the consequence rather than the cause of a belief in immortality. Our genes, or at least the good ones, may also be said to have the capacity of living for ever. But their survival has nothing strictly to do with the survival of an individual or a personality.

If we wish to tremble for a moment on the brink of mysticism, we may say that man has realized and created the notion of time by the power of his own mind. To other animals, there may be a yesterday, but tomorrow is meaningless, and the whole past and future are unconceived. To man, on the other hand, millionths of a second and millions of light years are units of physical measurement. But having created time, man by his imagination can also destroy it. The vast passages of history and the remotest periods of past or future evolution he can speak of with as much easy confidence as the passing hour. To such an animal, indeed, immortality may be said to have been achieved, in an intellectual sense that is more convincing than that of the picturesque myths of only a few hundred years ago.

In the matter of so fundamental an illusion as immortality, private is more important than public reality. Those who wish to believe with Epicurus that death is annihilation are free to do so. And those who admit a continuity of interest between the Now and the Then, which hardly goes with annihilation, are free to assume an immortality of the four-dimensional existence, the mind extended in space and time, which we call the soul. The difference between the two points of view is genetically determined and both are useful to society. From the public and social point of view, therefore, we no longer care if one organized sect of believers, or disbelievers, contradicts another or threatens them with the frightful consequences of their opinions. For these opinions have no consequences that are incompatible with social life.

FREE WILL

We describe as irrational what is beyond those limits of reason to which we are accustomed or which we consciously accept. The matters which Kant excluded from the field of reason, matters of which our senses give us no evidence, are, however, diminishing in scope. They are, we may now begin to feel, without by any means wishing to erase them from our thoughts, approaching zero. At the same time the possibility that one mind might comprehend all that is within the grasp of the general reason has already vanished.

As the bounds of our understanding expand, what has hitherto been regarded as irrational becomes classifiable. To one who has been known as a rationalist its classification might seem to be easy. The alternative, he would say, is between sense and nonsense. By considering the development of social and sexual instincts we are led to doubt this. We begin to see that certain human opinions and beliefs may be untrue by scientific standards, or mutually inconsistent. Or, above all, they may not be capable of being justified by those who hold them. But nevertheless they may be the necessary consequences of processes of natural selection acting in the evolution of the human mind. A number of almost universal illusions come to mind in this connexion, and it is worth seeing how they fit into the picture of knowledge as a whole.

The conflict between individual and social or sexual instincts is responsible, as it now seems, for an inconsistency in human thought and conduct. The direct effects of this apparent or first-instance irrationality are observable in many directions. Those which concern us now, if we are to apply what we have learnt of the facts of life to the understanding of nature, are concerned with intuitive beliefs. Intuition has been used, equally by philosophers and by believers in common sense, as a basis of argument, a foundation for otherwise indefensible propositions. We have an important one in the belief in the immortality of the soul. We may now examine the most important of all, the belief in free will.

The question of free will has been brought before us again owing to the discussion of indeterminacy by physicists and mathematicians. The deduction of free will from 'indeterminacy' has seemed so simple that the properties, and even, apart from the person of the author, the existence, of living organisms have often seemed unnecessary to consider. Thus for Eddington there are two bodies of valid information, two sources of truth: physics derived from the universe and metaphysics derived from his own intuition, his own feelings. Biology does not come in. He asks, 'How can I cause an event in the absolute future, if the future was predetermined before I was born?' It seems that Eddington looks upon himself as having sprung into the world, not only like Athene from the head of Zeus, but absolutely without origin and without cause. He assumes that he himself has arisen undetermined. He is able in this way to confirm the principle of indeterminacy and to conclude that 'science thereby withdraws its moral opposition to free-will'. The Old Testament failure to distinguish between biology and morals is thus still with us in *The Nature of the Physical World*.

There is irony in these question-begging arguments. It is hard to imagine any physical measurement that could surpass the precision of the predictions we make with living organisms on a genetic basis. The behaviour of one-egg twins was merely one instance of this accuracy as seen in human beings. Biological prediction is in some sense of a higher level of accuracy than physical prediction. One pinhead of sperm determines half the heredity of England.

But more ironical still in Eddington's argument is the process by which he infers free will in the human mind from the uncertainty in the observation or measurement of the smallest particles of physics. The inference depends on the assumption that physics (or at least recent discoveries in physics) is fundamental, and underlies biology. This in turn depends on the assumption that the properties of large and complex bodies must be *determined* by those of their smaller and simpler components. Thus

Eddington carries forward into biology the principle of indeterminacy along the very path that has earlier been cut by the principle of determinacy.

Fisher likewise has related indeterminacy and free will, but his reasoning is different. He argues that the instantaneous state of a physical system following a predetermined course

must be related to its subsequent state by equations identical with those which relate it to its previous states. That this is not the case with the human mind is, like the existence of the power of effective choice, universally verified by subjective experience.

Two related questions, both of them fundamental, arise from this argument. The first question is: Can we suppose that the human mind corresponds with any physical system, however elaborate? It is not isolated from its physical environment. It is not even isolated from the body which carries it. Nor is it always isolated from other bodies. It is a part of a system of continually changing units and relationships. And the future of this system is never, therefore, predictable from the inside alone.

A classical instance will illustrate the point. The Archbishop of Granada asked his young secretary, Gil Blas, to tell him when his homilies seemed to be losing their grip. When Gil Blas gave him the news that he was indeed going downhill anybody might have told the young man how violently the Archbishop was bound to react – anybody, that is, except the Archbishop. The only mind, the only will, whose action we can never predict, and whose nature therefore appears free, is our own. Our subjective experience is therefore the least valid of all. But even here, if a choice has been long discussed and our interests are only mildly engaged – as in a parliamentary election – with increasing certainty as the time approaches, we can predict how we shall make the choice and others can predict accordingly.

The second question is: Can there be subjective experience without flaw? Or can we rely on intuition to provide evidence of the laws of nature? To this question we have also seen the answer. Intuition and biology often disagree. But whereas intuition cannot explain the errors of biology, biology can explain the errors of intuition.

In discussing free will we have to separate two aspects of the will. We have to separate what we may call the continuous state of mind from the discontinuous actions arising from that state of mind. In regard to the state of mind we formerly believed that we might control our attitude of love, or hate, or anxiety, or hope, by an effort of the will. We now know, owing to Freud, and it is his chief discovery, that our will may be used to distort our state of mind. It may be used to regulate the relations of the conscious and the unconscious and to enable us to deceive ourselves and others with regard to our state of mind. It may be used to upset the proper working of our bodies through the distress of our minds, causing what are called, in medical jargon, psychosomatic disturbances. But control is what we can never achieve. We merely have an interaction between different parts of the mind or personality. Each of these parts is genetically determined. And the whole in turn determines how we shall exercise our choice when from time to time alternative courses of action are open to us.

On a biological view we can also see free will more clearly. The human mind, the brain in action, is the result of evolution. What man learns is not inherited. But his capacity to learn is inherited. During his last 20,000 generations, with increasing effect, an increased capacity to learn has favoured the survival of men and women. Their capacity to learn has therefore been increased by natural selection. What has made this increase in capacity to learn possible? It has depended on the increased development of the roof of man's forebrain. This organ, with its ten or fifteen thousand million cells, has become capable of keeping count of events. What it perceives through its means of sensation, in the nervous system, it remembers. It remembers things in almost unlimited number. Between these things remembered it establishes connexions of an almost unlimited complexity and it can hold them in mind for an almost unlimited time. In a word, man possesses a memory of the past. And this has given him an expectation of the future.

The possession of this expectation has the most revolutionary consequences for man. It leads him to exercise choice and to institute purpose. The necessity for assuming indeterminacy in human action is thought to arise, not from the discovery of uncertainty in physics (which is an afterthought) but from our consciousness of this choice and purpose.

We are continually throughout life being confronted with situations in which memory and expectation guide us in making the choice between alternative courses of action. Our personality and judgement are used to weigh the advantages and disadvantages and decide which course is better. Those who believe in free will believe that our decisions can never be predicted with certainty. The experimental procedures of genetics and psychology are equally based, and with gradually increasing justification, on the assumption that they can be predicted with certainty. In genetics we can predict, with as high an expectation of success as the asymmetries of eggs and the accidents of environment will allow, what one twin will have done from what his identical brother is known to have done. In psychology we can explain the most trivial details of behaviour, errors of speech, slips of the tongue, by circumstances of which the speaker is unconscious at the time, circumstances which the speaker's intuition would repudiate.

In the light of what we have seen of genetic determinism it is not necessary to depart seriously from the conceptions of Spinoza and Locke on the subject of free will. Every individual is self-determining. He is free to be himself. He is not free to be anyone else. He is in fact bound to be himself and to obey the natural laws which govern the development and behaviour of such an individual in such an environment.

Genetics, however, enables us to split up the propositions of Spinoza and Locke on free will. Division of determination into two separate systems – genotype and environment – entails as a corollary the successive interaction of these systems and the introduction of one into the other. It is this interaction which gives the illusion of free will, of uncertainty, when seen from one side alone, the inside, whose past appears to be internally determined but whose future will be in part externally determined. In every choice we make we test a reaction of genotype and environment which, if it seems a choice to us, does so because in every fresh contingency it is a new reaction of genotype and environment. The two channels of determination meet in our minds. The neurologist Sherrington put the same view in another way when he said:

If free will means a series of events in which at some point the succeeding is not conditioned by reaction with the preceding, such an anomaly in the brain's series of events is scientifically unthinkable. When I 'choose' a book from a bookcase I react fundamentally as does my microscopic acquaintance, amoeba, confronted by two or more particles when it takes one of them. A difference between us is that my fancy conjures up several courses to take. Subsequently I experience my act as doing one of them.... It leaves me an impression of a decision....

Man on his Nature, p. 230

Step by step we move towards the goal of a completely deterministic explanation and prediction of human behaviour. Our instincts may revolt at the conclusion but that is no evidence of its falsehood: our instincts revolt at all new conclusions and many old ones. And we are assisted in this revolt by all the apparatus of self-deception.

Our instincts and our means of intuition are, so genetics teaches us, products of natural selection operating to favour not the judgement of scientists or philosophers or prophets but the survival of quite ordinary men. An intuition of free will, whether it comes to a scientist, a philosopher, or a prophet, is not therefore the kind of witness to which biology will allow us to listen with any degree of faith.

As Sherrington puts it,

from the human standpoint, the important thing is less that man's will should be free than that man should think it is free.

From the genetic standpoint it would be even better to say: the important thing is that man's will should *not* be free, but at the same time that he should think it free. For, if it were free, human society would crumble in the dust.

The question of free will is bound to seem recondite, and remote from ordinary people, yet in fact the assumption that they make, or that is made for them by their pastors and masters – following decisions in the earlier history of the Christian Churches – decides the course of their everyday lives. If you suppose that good will, assisted by prayer, will remedy the forms of character which determine whether a life is good or a marriage is happy or not, then you will miss the chances you have for making your life good or your marriage happy. Refusing to believe in free will, by a paradox, you will be able to make the right choice. You will also be likely, by changing your mind and admitting a mistake to yourself, to make a new choice.

Socially, as we saw, the admission of determinism requires us to take an entirely heretical view of crime and punishment. It is, however, a view so contrary to the instinctive beliefs of mankind in general that we need not expect it to be seriously entertained, this side of *Erewhon* – that is, without an improbable revolution in thought.

RELIGIOUS TEACHING

During the last 5,000 years the success of the great and complex societies which have arisen has always been connected with certain religious beliefs and moral rules. The beliefs have been inculcated by teachers whose teachings have survived by virtue of the survival of those who faithfully followed them. The basis of their success was always twofold: social and biological. The social basis lay in the creation of harmonious relations between the individual and a complex community, one involving a hierarchical or stratified arrangement of classes. The biological basis lay in the establishment of rules for successful propagation depending on the care of the young, and the avoidance of disease, the control of inbreeding and outbreeding, and above all the encouragement of fertility.

Teaching which was to advance these varied objects had to be well conceived socially and biologically. It had also to exploit the available resources of superstition and magic. For only by this means could it recommend itself to a large part of a heterogeneous community as conforming with their instincts and satisfying their illusions. Many of these illusions are now obvious. Some are obviously dangerous. Beliefs that man's will is unconditionally free, his soul unconditionally immortal and his life unconditionally sacred may not seem to do much harm. But the belief, so admirable 2,000 years ago, that his fertility is unconditionally desirable, an end to be pursued without limit, now faces us with certain penalties. And the belief, at the back of all these, that man differs utterly from his animal relatives and must not be related to them in any scientific inquiry, this is a belief in darkness which can lead only to disaster.

One augur, the Romans said, could not look at another augur without smiling. And a little deception in these matters will no doubt always be politic. But the world needs someone to explain what he believes to be true without any deception and without regard for the applause which is the easy reward of deception. This somewhat ungrateful task is clearly today beyond the capacity of either the statesman or the mystic. It is the business of science, more precisely the science of life, to explain not only what has been needed for the survival of man in the past but what will be needed in the future.

18

Matter, Life and Science

LEVELS OF BIOLOGY

THE determinants of life, genes and chromosomes, plasmagenes and viruses, are now within our reach. We can now understand their modes of action in the cell, in heredity and development, in infection and immunity, in the animal body and even in the human mind. These varied aspects of genetic discovery compel us to look at nature as a whole with fresh eyes. We are faced with a need for revaluing our ideas as urgent as that which faced the men of the seventeenth century. The earlier upheaval required them to think in terms of laws of nature. The present upheaval requires us to look into the relationships of these laws, and indeed of separate systems of laws, and of the principles by which these systems are maintained, and enlarged. We can compare the biological and physical compartments of science for the first time.

It is not an accident that the microscope was needed to enable us to put life on a basis of cause and effect. It made visible the invisible small particles which determine the behaviour of the larger bodies we see with the naked eye. The living world, from being a mere finished façade, a completed shop-window, became for the first time a solid working world with interlocking and reacting parts.

The determinism of physics and chemistry could have grown without the microscope, for the kinds of atoms and the shapes of molecules could be predicted, and were actually predicted with accuracy, without the aid of a magnified vision. The reason is that in the non-living world the intervening steps between molecules and the bodies we handle are simple – not so simple as was thought but still fairly simple. In the living world, however, an immense variety of particles live and move and have their being between the molecule and the man. It was only with the help of microscopes that they could be known and that organic determinism could take shape and fill the place of purpose and essences in the understanding of nature. It was only when particles had been seen that life could diverge from beginnings instead of converging on ends.

However coherent the picture of life becomes under the influence of the concepts of matter, particles, and causes, it will therefore always recognize more levels of analysis or integration, more stages of breaking down or building up, than are known to the study of non-living matter. It is possible, but it seems unlikely, that beneath the atom there exists a world as diverse, as multitudinous, as that above the molecule. The genetic particle, the group of particles organized within its membrane, nuclear or cytoplasmic, the cell, the tissue, the individual (with a body, and sometimes with a mind and a memory as well), the family, the mating group, the class, tribe or community, the race and the species, the ecological community and the evolutionary procession of each and all of these entities with their relationships of heredity, development and infection: these all obey the laws of their own level and their own duration. They also interact or interfere with one another and suffer or enjoy the interference of non-living systems.

What is the consequence of this interference?

One part of it can probably be expressed without departure from a crudely or naïvely deterministic framework. Such are the systems comprised within the notion of physiology, including, for example, the relations between the hormones and nervous system of the animal body, by which electrical impulses affect the secretion of chemical substances and vice versa. Another part, however, concerned with the genetic system, is on quite a different footing.

In his admirable sketch *What is Life?* Schrödinger argued that uncertainty or irregularity (which he calls indeterminacy) at the atomic level is compatible with a regularity at higher levels. He looks upon the monster molecule of the chromosome as well fitted by its elaboration to control or suppress the irregularity of its atomic constituents. Thus the behaviour of living organisms can be predictable through heredity even though resting on unpredictable foundations.

Schrödinger's principle of regularization is a more important one than he implies and we have had several glimpses of its working. A variation in the individual protein molecule is obliterated under the weight of the whole cell. The mutation of a cell is subject to the constancy of the whole tissue and the regulation of the whole organism. The irregularity of an individual is reduced to rule in the normal behaviour of the herd. The discipline of society secures the obedience of an uncomfortable minority.

All this is true, at least, in a physiological sense. To some extent it is true also in a psychological or social sense. But is it true in a genetic sense? We have seen that it is not. Living organisms have made the discovery that lower-level irregularities in mutation and recombination, if not suppressed or buffered, can be exploited. In order to exploit them the organism can actually use them to boost one another. By a regulated irregularity in the recombination of mutations in the sexual alternation of diploid and halved phases of life, they are, as it were, skilfully exposed to the action of selection in changing or optional environments generation after generation. Selection acts deterministically so that the environment can appear to change the organism and change its heredity in the course of evolution. It can appear (until we have microscopes and experiments to guide us) to act directly. The intercalated uncertainty in the living systems is the means of establishing a deterministic relationship between the succession of living systems and the environment. This intercalation of uncertainty has become the key mechanism of evolution. It is perhaps the fundamental discovery of life.

The other side of this picture is that the relations of determinism and uncertainty involved in the succession of processes covered by the superficial and popular terms heredity, variation and evolution have hitherto been utterly concealed from biologists, physicists and philosophers alike. Now that they are clear in principle it is worth while to sum up the evidence.

Genetic and physiological studies have changed our views of determinism in life in the following ways:

In the first place, the limited resemblances of parents and offspring are not due to the deterministic principle of heredity directly and alone. They are due to the interference of the uncertainty not only of the environment but also of mutation and recombination, an uncertainty which can be abolished in parthenogenesis and in one-egg twinning. The Mendelian paradox that brothers differ by heredity, and on account of heredity, alters the whole explanatory scheme.

In the second place, the uncertainty of mutation and recombination is in practice irrelevant to the individual. We find it because without it evolutionary change could never have occurred and incipient life would have been snuffed out. It means that parents and offspring have an unpredictability in their genetic relationship. But, on the Schrödinger principle, populations, if they are large enough, remain genetically predictable.

Finally, the force of heredity is vastly greater than the founders of genetics thought. On the one hand, heredity itself exists in part in forms beyond Mendelian analysis, in polygenes and in the cytoplasm. On the other hand, the environment has a fluctuating role. Only its highest value achieved in a plant (and in an individual, not a population) enables us to describe the result of development as due to a simple reaction of genotype and environment. In all animals the genotype itself chooses the environment. And in man, the genotype can create the environment.

CENTRAL AND PERIPHERAL KNOWLEDGE

The biologist has grown up with the complexity we have now surveyed and with its difficulties. They have become part of his subject. So much so that he may even resent their removal. The physicist, on the other hand, has been used to a long record of diminishing error. An apparent increase in error (at the beginning of this century) came therefore to many physicists and mathematicians as a surprise. They expressed the result as due to indeterminacy.

Having done so, this school of thought have popularized their views. And, with the undoubted achievement of quantum physics behind them, they have proceeded to explain the consequences of their 'revolutionary upheaval in natural philosophy' for the understanding of the world in general, including living organisms and the human mind. In the nineteenth century chemists and physicists were often impatient with the errors arising from the study of life. Liebig and Berzelius had a better reason to understand fermentation than Pasteur; Kelvin had a better reason to know the age of the earth than Darwin or Huxley. Physicists and mathematicians of the twentieth century have likewise thought it possible to treat biology as a deduction from what used to be called (and indeed very nearly were) the exact sciences. They have been strengthened in this method by the view that living matter (as it is called) obeys the same laws as non-living matter. The extreme point of view has been expressed as follows:

> There are not, and cannot be, any hidden features in the radium atom, a knowledge of which would enable us to predict the time of its disintegration. There is a true indeterminacy in the occurrence qualified only by the knowledge of its probability.
>
> Whittaker, 1950

So far as this is a statement of our present knowledge we may willingly accept it. It is, however, something more. Here the claim is made that the limits of knowledge can be finally set and the universal negative finally asserted. This is a metaphysical conclusion. It is contrary to the principles on which scientific discovery has been attempted in the past. If successful it might represent a revolutionary upheaval in natural philosophy. But, if it proves to be unsuccessful, it will be regarded by posterity as an attempt by those who were impatient with a momentary check, to kick over the traces of scientific discipline.

In biology this irritating kind of situation has been met (as we have seen) by rubbing on the sore spot a lotion of purpose or design. The quantum physicist is too sophisticated for this remedy. His response is to claim finality for the statistical statement and to assert that the peripheral knowledge, the new experience, is more significant than the central body. For example, Eddington in 1928 says that a law which, by the advance of science, becomes deducible from a higher law is a 'truism' and is possibly not subject to indeterminacy but this 'will not convince anyone that the universe is governed by laws of deterministic type'. He thus dismisses the central and certain framework of science as irrelevant. What matters are the uncertain margins, the active margins of discovery, margins which by the process of discovery are always retreating. Hence when Eddington refers to the 'replacement in *orthodox science* of causation by causality' by orthodox science he means marginal physics.

Translating these views into terms of biology we should have to say that the three-to-one ratios of Mendel were orthodox science, and evidence of indeterminacy, so long as they were unexplained. On the other hand, they became truisms, irrelevant to the great order of nature, when they became deducible from the chromosome theory or the observations of tetrads of spores.

The metaphysical foundations of physical discovery – dealing with space, matter and cause – have changed in fifty years. It now seems that the metaphysics of discovery is a different matter from that of knowledge already discovered. The principles used in developing genetics – the determinant segregation, crossing-over, selection – come to have a different meaning when they are seen and used as part of the working mechanism of life. This contradiction is equally emphatic in the field of physics. But it has been overlooked or repudiated by physicists impressed by the reality of discovery. Discoverers are accustomed to unlimited self-indulgence. Knowledge in the process of discovery is, to be sure, more interesting than it becomes later. But interest does not add to validity.

The opinions of quantum physicists rejecting the old order of determinism are well known. The opposite point of view has been less popular or less public. It is worth noting two examples since they help to make the position of biology intelligible. Max Planck puts the matter so:

> The power of determination is as strictly valid in the world picture of quantum mechanics as in that of classical physics. The difference consists only in the symbols used and in the mathematics applied (1950).

Similarly Einstein declined to dispense with determinism.

> The great initial success of the quantum theory cannot bring me to believe in that fundamental game of dice,

he writes in 1947 (quoted by Born, 1949). And again:

> I am absolutely convinced that we shall eventually arrive at a theory in which the things connected by laws are not probabilities, but conceived facts, as we took for granted until quite recently. I cannot however offer logical grounds for this conclusion. . . .

The grounds that may be offered are perhaps not so much logical or deductive as inductive. By considering the whole framework of science (including biology) we can see the relative positions of determinacy and indeterminacy in the *method* of discovery and the *form* of explanation. We then find that the replacement of the game of dice by the conceived fact – and conversely – is characteristic of the great advances in biology. The alternation of induction and deduction has long been known. The alternation of statistical and individual observations has now become evident. It accompanies the invasion of each new level of inquiry. In consequence only the simpler biologists suppose that stable assumptions are possible about the basic ideas of, for example, heredity or environment, genes or plasmagenes. What has happened in physics is that meristematic research, the zone of inquiry, has passed from its solid central position. It has, like biology, entered the region where stable assumptions are no longer possible. It is the great achievement of modern physics to have removed itself, or rather its meristematic part, from the position in which Newton had placed it, which had become somewhat uninteresting, to a very exciting but unsteady position on the periphery of knowledge.

The consequence of this movement is that discovery in physics, while partaking of the thrills and hazards of revolutionary change, can no longer enjoy the broad-bottomed security or authority inherent in being the immovable foundation of all knowledge. It is therefore to the central, not the peripheral, body of physics that biology may well be attached.

STATISTICAL LAWS AND UNCERTAINTY

The problem of indeterminacy naturally concerns the mathematical biologist. Sir Ronald Fisher has proposed that the indeterminacy of quantum physics may be extended throughout science. In urging this view he has pointed out how the former faith in determinacy in physics gained ground:

As, in each branch of research, accuracy was increased, as disturbing causes were eliminated or allowed for, as purer materials were used, as more refined methods of measurement were discovered, so were the physical laws more and more exactly verified. The mathematical formulae were constantly found to be more accurate than the observations upon which they had first been based, or, when their form had to be modified they were found to be so much the more comprehensive (1934).

In other words *theory*, based on determinism, was always proving truer than *fact*, based on observation: a situation which continues at the present day in the main body of scientific observation. Nevertheless Fisher continues:

the man of science who is determined to abide by Descartes' precept never to accept anything for true which he does not clearly know to be such, has no option, in the absence of cogent evidence for determinism, but to set this aside as an unproved assumption, which, in spite of its familiarity, is unnecessary to a rational and coherent approach to scientific studies.

If in this argument, however, we replace determinism by indeterminacy, the same conclusion follows. But we cannot set aside both unproved assumptions. Some assumption on this question is necessary for a logically coherent approach not only to scientific studies but to life itself. We do not need 'to accept anything for true' except as a working hypothesis. But a working hypothesis we must have. A working hypothesis as a standard of reference is of course fundamental for Fisher's own experimental theory. Discovery is indeed limited by the rigour with which working hypotheses can be stated and the accuracy with which predictions can therefore be made. Conversely the hypothesis of indeterminacy cannot be stated in a form in which it can be disproved. Indeterminacy as a universal principle is not a working hypothesis: it is the absence of one. That is the prior reason why determinism became the basis of scientific inquiry.

This, however, is not all. Fisher holds that generalizations such as the gas laws, where a statistical statement is made and a probability predicted, are the perfect or normal form of natural law. This would mean that, for Fisher, Mendel's statistical laws are perfect and normal, while the chromosome theory, with the absolute statements of the linear order and physiological action of genes to which it led is imperfect and abnormal. Again, the implications of a perfect law for most people can only be that it concludes an inquiry. This is just what Mendel's law did not do: it began an inquiry. It is not, however, with perfect laws that we are ever concerned but rather with a necessary succession of imperfect ways of formulating our understanding of nature, the kind of succession we saw in the works of Darwin, Pasteur and Mendel.

The views of Eddington and Fisher both lead us into difficulties in biology. But the difficulties are contradictions. Thus for Eddington (in ignorance of Mendelism, in 1928) statistical laws 'do not rest on a basis of causality' – 'causation' having been replaced by 'causality' in the previous argument. Fisher, on the other hand (with a clear knowledge of Mendelism and the technique of experimentation which he himself has perfected), speaks of 'the statistical formulation of physical laws as reinstating the principle of causation'. This statement comes very near to describing their use, which he had already foreseen, in proving the polygene explanation of continuous variation. For, as we noticed, statistical methods were there used to reveal and establish individual relationships of cause and effect which could be shown in no other way. But the statistical formulation, as with the Mendelian ratio, was only an interim statement. The final statement was individual and deterministic.

The solution of this puzzle seems to be twofold. On the one hand, Fisher, like the quantum physicists, is not making the distinction between mere uncertainty and genuine indeterminacy. This seems especially likely since Fisher's chief contribution to biology, his *Genetical Theory of Natural Selection* and his repudiation of uncertain drift, can be put in gear only in terms of determinacy. On the other hand Fisher has forged statistical weapons for rigorous treatment over a large field of scientific inquiry. We must now suppose that this approach influences his attitude towards statistical statements in general.

Interim statements in the development of science, as we have seen, frequently take an uncertainty of form expressed by statistical laws. In biology this pseudo-indeterminacy has never led to the adoption of a fundamental indeterminacy of principle. Yet if anyone were looking for examples in living organisms, warts and sports almost cry out to be adopted by the philosopher of uncertainty. Yet the reverse is the case. Warts can now be made experimentally. And the mutation theory of sports has become the basis of a new determinism. Slips of the tongue might seem the stuff of indeterminacy. But Freud made them building blocks in a deterministic psychology.

The reason why biology has been so virtuous seems to be a simple one. The first step in understanding life has always been to replace convergence towards ends by divergence from beginnings; to replace first magic, then purpose and design, by causation – notably in the theories of natural selection and gene structure. Determinism had to be there before indeterminacy could be considered. To the biologist indeed indeterminacy, or an absence of determinacy, has no meaning except as a modification or exception or extension of determinacy. How else, he asks, can its existence be discovered?

THE RULES OF LIFE

Everywhere in the study of life for the last hundred years attempts, successful attempts, have been made to simplify the situations which it is the business of scientific inquiry to reduce to order, to put in terms of cause and effect. The attempts are usually made by specialists, by experts supreme in each field, who are bound to ignore the methods, the assumptions and the knowledge acquired in other fields. Or if they take over anything they simplify it, and they keep it as though it were alive after it is dead.

We find the documentary historian expelling the small men from his thoughts, the archaeologist expelling the big men. We find the social anthropologist, the economist and the psychiatrist reducing men to a level and mankind to a predictable pulp. We find the physician concentrating on the remedies for diseases in their diversity, and forgetting the immense diversity of men: the golden mean suppressing the normal curve. We find the systematist smothered under the multiplicity of species and varieties, and shutting his eyes to the diversity of processes by which they have come into existence and afterwards maintain themselves. We see men in all branches of inquiry clinging to some hopeful token of unity, some word like 'evolution' which promises to be a simplification but, beyond a certain point, proves to be a mystification of real processes.

There are those who will feel that the idea of genetic determinism is yet another attempt to comprehend the complexity of life under one simple formula. Indeed the formula is simple. But, in applying it, we certainly make no pretence to simplicity. It is merely, we dare to think, not beyond the wit of man to grasp.

If we are to find unifying principles for science as a whole we are justified, at least by convenience, in taking them from those which work for the static uses or maintenance of the coherent system built on Newtonian physics, Daltonian chemistry, and Mendelian genetics. These provide a central framework which is based on the tripod of matter, atomism, and determinacy. They belong, it has been said, to the region of experience where models work. The unity of our knowledge depends on the uniformity and continuity of its parts, the predictability of one from another, which these three notions underlie.

In the past our knowledge has been split in two by the great gaps between the non-living and the living and between matter and mind. It has been possible for philosophers to assert that living matter is subject to the same laws as non-living. But was the transition itself between non-living and living governed by these same laws? The answer is that life is subject to so many laws peculiar to itself that the question has only a limited value. Four chief laws of properties of life are worth noting:

First, the property of self-propagation is the foundation of what we may call the first order of determinacy of living organisms.

Secondly, the properties of mutation and sexual recombination represent the intrusion of uncertainty from outside, by interference between levels of organization. The exploitation of this uncertainty by selection, giving adaptation, yields what we may call the second order of determinacy.

Thirdly, the two properties of self-propagation and adaptation to a changing environment give the organism its irreversibility in development, its capacity to defeat the law of entropy within its own limits, and its prospect of unlimited evolutionary diversification.

Life, therefore, although its behaviour might be *understood* on the basis of a knowledge of the non-living, could never be *predicted* on such a basis. Physics and metaphysics together are not enough.

CONCLUSION

We have now surveyed man's efforts to understand heredity, especially his own heredity. After much stumbling we have seen some success, after much hesitation some confidence. Many will think too much confidence: rightly so if they imagine that the whole story has here been told. But after learning how man has discovered heredity and genetics we must now use heredity and genetics to discover man.

The wonderful recent advances in our knowledge of man's physical evolution and physical remains, and the changes in his habitat, mainly wrought by his own efforts, the exact timing by physical devices of all the new evidence brought up by the spade, these have matched the new evidence of man and society existing today. They have made it possible to re-write the history of man. The new ideas, on account of their common biological components, prove to have a generality which has often been claimed but never realized in the past. For in the last three centuries our science has usually been seen as the accumulation of Laws. But now we find ourselves continually stumbling on Paradoxes, principles which are more difficult to understand and are likely to occupy several centuries more. We shall be finding our science not as something separated from man and ethically neutral in a moral vacuum but as a part of a great continuum of human understanding with which all human activity is bound up. This new view is above all an evolutionary view. But explaining the evidence for it I must leave to another work.

Names and Dates

ARISTOTLE, 384–322 BC.
THEOPHRASTUS, 372–287 BC.
TITUS LUCRETIUS CARUS, 98–55 BC.
ROGER BACON, 1214–1292.
LEONARDO DA VINCI, 1452–1519.
WILLIAM HARVEY, 1578–1657.
JOHN RAY, 1628–1705.
NEHEMIAH GREW, 1628–1711.
ANTONY VAN LEEUWENHOECK, 1632–1723.
ROBERT HOOKE, 1635–1703.
CAROLUS LINNAEUS, 1707–1778.
GEORGE LOUIS LECLERC DE BUFFON, 1707–1788.
LAZZARO SPALLANZANI, 1729–1799.
CASPAR FRIEDRICH WOLFF, 1733–1794.
JOSEPH GOTTLIEB KOELREUTER, 1733–1806.
JEAN BAPTISTE DE LAMARCK, 1744–1829.
KARL ERNST VON BAER, 1792–1876.
CHARLES DARWIN, 1809–1882.
HERBERT SPENCER, 1820–1903.
GREGOR MENDEL, 1822–1884.
LOUIS PASTEUR, 1822–1895.
FRANCIS GALTON, 1822–1911.
AUGUST WEISMANN, 1832–1914.
EDUARD STRASBURGER, 1844–1912.
HUGO DE VRIES, 1848–1935.
EDMUND BEECHER WILSON, 1856–1939.
WILHELM LUDVIG JOHANNSEN, 1857–1927.
WILLIAM BATESON, 1861–1926.
THEODOR BOVERI, 1862–1915.
FRANS-ALFONS JANSSENS, 1863–1924.
THOMAS HUNT MORGAN, 1866–1945.

References by Chapters

A list of books and articles, original or translated, used in preparing the present work or acknowledged in the text or in the legends of figures.

PART ONE

(Chapters 1 to 4)

ARISTOTLE. *De Generatione Animalium.* (Trans. Arthur Platt, 1910). Oxford.

BACON, ROGER. *Opus Majus.* (Trans. R. B. Burke, 1928). Philadelphia.

BLAIR, PATRICK. 1720. *Botanick Essays.* London: Innys.

DARLINGTON, C. D. 1959. *Darwin's Place in History.* Oxford: Blackwell.

DARWIN, C. 1859. *Origin of Species.* 1st ed. Reprinted 1950: Foreword by C. D. Darlington. London: Watts.

DARWIN, C. 1868. *The Variation of Animals and Plants under Domestication.* London: Murray.

DOBELL, C. 1932. *Antony van Leeuwenhoeck etc.* London.

FISHER, R. A. 1930. *The Genetical Theory of Natural Selection.* Oxford: U.P.

GALTON, F. 1889. *Natural Inheritance.* London: Macmillan.

GLASS, B. 1947. Maupertuis and the beginnings of genetics. *Q. Rev. Biol.* **22,** 196–210.

GRANT, VERNE. 1949. Arthur Dobbs (1750) and the discovery of the pollination of flowers by insects. *Bull. Torrey Bot. Club,* **76,** 217–19.

GRAVES, R., and PATAI, R. 1963. Some Hebrew myths and legends. *Encounter* 20, (2), 3–18.

GREW, NEHEMIAH. 1682. *The Anatomy of Plants with an Idea of a Philosophical History of Plants.* 4, ii, 5, 171–3. London: Rawlins.

GUYÉNOT, E. 1941. *Sciences de la Vie aux XVII*e *et XVIII*e *Siecles.* Paris: Michel.

HAECKEL, E. 1874. *The Evolution of Man.* London: Watts. (5th ed. Trans. McCabe, 1906.)

HIPPOCRATES. *Works.* (Trans. W. H. S. Jones, 1923.) London: Heinemann.

HOFMEISTER, W. 1848. Ueber die Entwicklung des Pollens. *Bot. Ztg,* **6,** 425–34.

REFERENCES BY CHAPTERS

HUXLEY, L. 1900. *Life and Letters of T. H. Huxley.* London: Macmillan.

LAMARCK, J. B. DE. 1809. *Philosophie Zoologique.* Paris.

LAMARCK, J. B. DE. 1815. *Histoire naturelle des animaux sans vertèbres.* Paris.

LEEUWENHOECK, A. VAN. 1695. *Arcana Naturae.* Delft: Henricum a Krooneveld.

LE GROS CLARK, F., *et al.* 1951. *Four Thousand Million Mouths.* Oxford: U.P.

LOCKE, JOHN. 1690. *Essay Concerning Human Understanding.* London.

MALTHUS, ROBERT. 1798–1824. *Essay on Population.* (Last Edition in Supp. to Brit. Cf. Le Cros Clark.)

MONTAIGNE, M. DE. 1580. *Essais, II,* 37: *De la Ressemblance des Enfans aux Pères.* Paris *et alibi.*

PEARSON, KARL. 1892. *The Grammar of Science.* London: Scott.

RAY, JOHN. 1686. *Historia generalis Plantarum.* London: Smith and Walford.

ROOSEBOOM, MARIA. 1956. *Microscopium.* Leyden: Comm. 95. R. Mus. Gesch. N. Wet.

SIRKS, M. J. 1952. The earliest illustrations of chromosomes. *Genetica,* **26,** 65–76.

SPALLANZANI, LAZZARO. 1785. *Experiments pour servir à l'histoire de la génération des animaux et des plantes.* Geneva: Barthélémi Chirol.

SPENCER, HERBERT. 1863. *Principles of Biology.* London: Williams.

THEOPHRASTUS. *Inquiry into Plants.* (Trans. Arthur Hort, 1916.) London: Heinemann.

WEISMANN, A. 1892. *Das Keimplasma.* Jena: Fischer. Trans. The Germ-Plasm. 1893. London.

ZIRKLE, C. 1935. *The Beginnings of Plant Hybridization.* Philadelphia: Univ. Pen. Press.

ZIRKLE, C. 1936. Animals impregnated by the wind. *Isis,* **25,** 91–130.

ZIRKLE, C. 1946. The early history of the idea of the inheritance of acquired characters and of pangenesis. *Trans. Amer. Phil. Soc.,* **35,** (2), 91–151.

ZIRKLE, C. 1951. The knowledge of heredity before 1900. (See Dunn, 1951.)

PART TWO

(*Chapters 5 and 6*)

BATESON, B. 1929. *William Bateson, F.R.S., Naturalist, His Essays and Addresses.* Cambridge: U.P.

BATESON, W. 1909. *Mendel's Principles of Heredity.* Cambridge: U.P.

BATESON, W. 1902. *Mendel's Principles of Heredity: a Defence*. Cambridge: U.P.

BOVERI, TH. 1904. Ergebnisse über die Konstitution der chromatischen Substanz des Zellkerns. Jena.

DARLINGTON, C. D. 1937. The early hybridisers and the origins of genetics (in Darlington and Mather, 1950).

DARLINGTON, C. D. 1951. Mendel and the determinants (in Dunn 1951).

DARLINGTON, C. D. 1953. Purpose and particles in the study of heredity. In Charles Singer: *Science, Medicine and History* (2). Oxford: U.P.

DARLINGTON, C. D. 1960. Chromosomes and the theory of heredity. *Nature*, **187**, 892–5.

DARLINGTON, C. D. 1963. Fifty years of Drosophila. *Nature*, **197**, 830–31.

DARLINGTON, C. D., and MATHER, K. 1949. *The Elements of Genetics*. London: Allen and Unwin.

DUNN, L. C. 1951. *Genetics in the 20th Century*. New York: Macmillan.

EICHLING, C. W. 1942. I talked with Mendel. *J. Hered.*, **33**, 243–6.

FISHER, R. A. 1936. Has Mendel's work been rediscovered? *Ann. Sci.*, **1**, 115–37.

ILTIS, HUGO. 1932. *Life of Mendel*. (Trans.) London: Allen and Unwin.

JOHANNSEN, W. 1909. *Elemente der exakten Erblichkeit*. Jena: Fischer.

JOHANNSEN, W. 1911. The genotype conception of heredity. *Amer. Nat.*, **45**, 129–59.

MENDEL, G. 1866. Versuche über Pflanzenhybriden. Reprint, Leipzig 1911. Translation in Bateson's, 1909. See also: The Birth of Genetics, Suppl. *Genetics*, **35**, 1950, and *Experiments in Plant Hybridisation*, ed., R. A. Fisher and J. H. Bennett. Edinburgh: Oliver and Boyd.

MORGAN, T. H. 1910. Chromosomes and heredity. *Amer. Nat.*, **44**, 449–96.

MULLER, H. J. 1943. Edmund B. Wilson: An Appreciation. *Amer. Nat.*, **77**, 768–9.

PEARSON, KARL. 1897. *The Chances of Death*. London: Arnold.

PUNNETT, R. C. 1950. The early days of genetics. *Heredity*, **4**, 1–10.

ROBERTS, H. F. 1929. *Plant Hybridisation before Mendel*. Princeton: U.P.

SUTTON, W. S. 1902. On the morphology of the chromosome group in *brachystola magna*. *Biol. Bull.*, **4**, 24–39.

VRIES, H. DE. 1889. *Intracelluläre Pangenesis*. Jena: Fischer.

WILSON, E. B. 1896. *The Cell in Development and Inheritance.* 1st ed. New York: Macmillan.

WILSON, E. B., and MORGAN, T. H. 1920. Chiasmatype and crossing over. *Amer. Nat.,* **54,** 193–219.

(*Chapters 7 and 8*)

CATCHESIDE, D. G. 1951. *The Genetics of Micro-organisms.* London: Pitman.

CONTARIO, F., and CHIARELLI, B. 1962. Study of the inheritance of some daily life habits. *Heredity,* **17,** 347–59.

DARLINGTON, C. D. 1948. The plasmagene theory of the origin of cancer. *Brit. J. Cancer,* **2,** 118–26.

DARLINGTON, C. D. 1959. Plasmagene theory and cancer genesis. *Genetics and Cancer,* Texas, 1959: 9–24.

DARLINGTON, C. D. 1960. Origin and evolution of viruses. Symp. on evolution of arborvirus diseases. *R. S. Trop. Med. and Hyg.,* **54,** 89–134.

DUBOS, RENÉ J. 1951. *Louis Pasteur.* London: Gollancz.

FALCONER, D. S., and BLOOM, J. L. 1962. A genetic study of lung-tumours in mice. *Brit. J. Cancer,* **16,** 665–85.

FENNER, F. 1959. Myxomatosis. *B. Med. Bull.,* **15,** 240–45.

FILDES, PAUL. 1951. The evolution of microbiology. *Proc. Roy. Soc., B.* **138,** 65–74.

GOWEN, J. W. 1948. Inheritance of immunity in animals. *An. Rev. Microbiol.,* 1948, 215–54.

GOWEN, J. W. 1951. Genetics and disease resistance. (See Dunn, 1951.)

HADDOW, A. (ed.) 1952. *Biological hazards of atomic energy.* Oxford: U.P.

HUXLEY, JULIAN. 1958. *Biological Aspects of Cancer.* London: Allen and Unwin.

LARGE, E. C. 1940. *The Advance of the Fungi.* London: Cape.

LATARJET, R. 1959. Radiation in cancerogenesis etc. *Symp: Genetics and Cancer.* Texas: U.P.

LIEBERMAN, M., and KAPLAN, H. S. 1959. Leukemogenic activity of filtrates from radiation – induced lymphoid tumours of mice. *Sci.,* **130,** 387–8.

MACFARLANE BURNET, J. 1962. *Natural History of Infectious Disease.* 3rd ed. Cambridge: U.P.

MICHAELIS, A. 1962. The geography of cancer. *New Sci.,* **16,** 253–5.

MOTULSKY, A. G. Metabolic polymorphisms and the role of infectious diseases in human evolution. *Processes of Ongoing Human Evol.* (ed. G. W. Lasker). Detroit: Wayne U.P.

PARRY, H. B. 1962. A transmissible and hereditary disease of sheep (scrapie). *Heredity*, **17**, 75–105.

PLATT, SIR ROBERT, *et al.* 1962. *Smoking and Health*. London: Pitman.

REID, G. ARCHDALL. 1905. *The Principles of Heredity*. London: Chapman and Hall.

ROBERTS, J. A. FRASER. 1957. Blood groups and susceptibility to disease. *Brit. J. Prev. & Social Med.*, **11**, 107–25.

ROTHSCHILD, MIRIAM. 1961. The flea vector of myxomatosis in Britain. *Ent. Monthly Mag.*, **96**, 106–9.

SMITH, KENNETH. 1952. The production of new virus diseases. *Biol. Rev.*, **27**, 347–57.

ZINSSER, HANS. 1934. *Rats, Lice and History*. New York: Little, Brown.

PART THREE

(*Chapters 9 and 10*)

DARLINGTON, C. D. 1952. The cell and heredity under ionization. *Biol. Hazards of Atomic Energy*. Ed. Haddow. Oxford.

DARLINGTON, C. D. 1958. *The Evolution of Genetic Systems*. (2nd ed.) Edinburgh: Oliver Boyd.

DARLINGTON, C. D. 1963. *Chromosome Botany and the Origins of Cultivated Plants*. London: Allen and Unwin.

DARLINGTON, C. D. and MATHER, K. 1950. *Genes, Plants and People*. London: Allen and Unwin.

GEIGY, R. 1941. Die Metamorphose als Folge gewebsspezifische Determination. *Rev. suisse Zool.*, **48**, 483–94.

HUXLEY, J. S. 1963. *Evolution: the Modern Synthesis*. (2nd ed.) London: Allen and Unwin.

KETTLEWELL, H. B. D. 1955. Selection experiments on industrial melanism in the lepidoptera. *Heredity*, **9**, 323–47.

LUSCHER, M. 1944. Die Larvale und die imaginale Determination im Ei der Kleidermotte. *Rev. suisse Zool.*, **51**, 531–627.

MATHER, K. 1951. *Biometrical Genetics*. (2nd ed.) London: Methuen.

MATHER, K., and WIGAN, L. G. 1942. The selection of invisible mutations. *Proc. Roy. Soc.*, *B.* **131**, 50–64.

MORGAN, T. H. 1934. *Embryology and Genetics*. New York: Columbia U.P.

MULLER, H. J. 1922. Variation due to change in the individual gene. *Amer. Nat.*, **56**, 32–50.

SCHRÖDINGER, E. 1944. *What is Life?* Cambridge: U.P.

REFERENCES BY CHAPTERS

INTERLUDE

(Chapter 11)

CRANE, M. B. 1949. Soviet biology. *Heredity*, **3**, 254.

EWART, J. COSSAR. 1901. Address to British Association. *Nature*, **64**, 482.

GOLDSCHMIDT, R. 1960. *In and Out of the Ivory Tower.* (Autobiography). Seattle: U.W.P.

HALDANE, J. B. S. 1949. In defence of genetics. *Modern Quarterly*, **4**, 194–202.

LYSENKO, T. D. 1943. *Heredity and Its Variability.* (Trans. 1946. Th. Dobzhansky. New York: King's Crown Press.)

LYSENKO, T. D. 1950. New developments in the science of biological species. *Agrobiologia*. 6. (Trans. Moscow: Foreign Pub. Ho.)

LYSENKO, T. D. 1951. *Agrobiologie: Arbeiten über Fragen der Genetik, u.s.w.* Berlin (670 pp.)

MICHURIN, I. V. 1936. *Selected Works.* Moscow: Foreign Publishing House.

ZIRKLE, C. 1959. *Evolution, Marxism and the Social Scene.* Philadelphia: U.P.

(Chapter 12)

PART FOUR

BEAGLEHOLE, E., *et al.* 1950. *Statement by Experts on Race Problems.* Paris: UNESCO.

FORTES, MEYER. 1951. *The Social Sciences: Scientific Thought in the 20th Century.* London: Watts.

TOYNBEE, A. 1935. *A Study of History.* Vol. i, 2nd ed. Oxford: U.P.

TYLOR, E. B. 1871. *Primitive Culture.* London: Macmillan.

UNESCO. 1950. *Statement by Experts.* (See Beaglehole.)

(Chapter 13)

BLACKER, C. P. 1952. *Eugenics: Galton and After.* London: Duckworth.

DARLINGTON, C. D. 1963. The genetics of man (review). *Heredity*, **18**, 113–18.

GALTON, FRANCIS. 1869. *Hereditary Genius.* (Introduction by C. D. Darlington, Fontana, 1962). London: Murray.

GALTON, F. 1853. *Tropical South Africa.* London: Murray.

GALTON, F. 1876. The history of twins as a criterion of the relative powers of nature and nurture. *J. Anthrop. Inst.*, **5**, 391–406.

GALTON, F. 1883. *Inquiries into Human Faculty and Its Development.* London: Macmillan.

LANGE, JOHANNES. 1929. *Verbrechen als Schicksal*. Liepzig: Thieme. (*Crime as Destiny*. Eng. Trans. 1931. London: Allen and Unwin.)

LAWRENCE, E. M. 1931. Relation between intelligence and inheritance (foster children). *B. J. Psych.* Supp. 16. (80 pp.)

LEWIS, AUBREY. 1936. A case of apparent dissimilarity of monozygotic twins. *Ann. Eug.*, **7**, 58–64,

NEWMAN, H. H. 1942. *Twins and Super Twins*. London: Hutchinson.

PEARSON, KARL. 1914–1930. *Life, Letters and Labours of Francis Galton*. Cambridge: U.P.

SHIELDS, J. 1962. *Monozygotic Twins brought up apart and together*. Oxford: U.P.

SONDERN, F. 1958. *Brotherhood of Evil: the Mafia*. London: Gollancz.

STOCKS, PERCY. 1952. Multiple births in England and Wales. *Acta Gen. Med. Gem.*, **1**, 8–12.

VERSCHUER, O. VON. 1939. Twin research from the time of Francis Galton to the present day. *Proc. Roy. Soc., B.* **128**, 62–81.

WILLIAMS, A. B. 1955. *Biochemical Individuality*. Texas: U.P.

WILLIAMS, ROGER J. 1956. *Biochemical individuality*. New York: Wiley.

(*Chapter 14*)

ALLISON, A. C. 1954. Protection afforded by sickle-cell trait against subtertian malarial infection. *Brit. Med. J.*, **4857**, 298.

ALLISON, A. C. 1961. Abnormal haemoglobin and erythocyte enzyme-deficiency traits. In G. A. Harrison 1961.

BRIDGES, E. LUCAS. 1948. *Uttermost Part of the Earth*. London: Hodder and Stoughton.

BROSNAHAN, L. F. 1961. *The Sounds of Language*. Cambridge: Heffer.

CARTER, CEDRIC O. 1956. Changing patterns in the causes of death at the hospital for sick children. *Gt. Ormond St. J.*, **11**, 65–8.

CLARKE, A. M. and A. D. B. (ed.) 1958. *Mental Deficiency*. London: Methuen.

COON, CARLETON S. 1963. *The Origin of Races*. London: Cape. New York: Knapp.

CUÉNOT, L. 1925. *L'Adaptation*. Paris: G. Doin.

DARLINGTON, C. D. 1954. Heredity and environment. *Caryologia*, **6**, 370–81.

DARLINGTON, C. D. 1958. The control of evolution in man. *Eug. Rev.*, **50**, 169–78. *Nature*, **182**, 14–17.

DARLINGTON, C. D. 1964. *The Genetics of Society*. Symposium on Race, (ed. A. J. Gregor). Hawaii: U.P.

DAVENPORT, C. B. 1903. The animal ecology of the cold spring sand spit. *Univ. Chicago Dec. Pub.*, **10**, 157–76.

DARWIN, C. 1871. *Descent of Man*. London: Murray.

DARWIN, F. 1887. *Life and Letters of Charles Darwin*. London: Murray.

DARWIN, F., and SEWARD, A. C. 1903. *More Letters of Charles Darwin*. London: Murray.

FISHER, R. A. 1927. Triplet children in Great Britain and Ireland. *Proc. Roy. Soc.*, *B*. **102**, 286–311.

HARRISON, G. A. (ed.) 1961. Genetical variation in human populations. Oxford: Pergamon.

KROPOTKIN, P. 1904. *Mutual Aid*. London.

MOTULSKY, A. G. 1961. Metabolic polymorphisms and the role of infectious diseases in human evolution. In Lasker: *Processes of Human Evol.*, 28–62. Detroit: Wayne U.P.

MOURANT, A. E., and WATKIN, I. M. 1952. Blood groups, anthropology and language of Wales and the western counties. *Heredity*, **6**, 13–26.

NEEL, JAMES V. 1961. The hemoglobin genes. *Blood*, **18**, 769–75.

PLATO. *The Republic*.
    (i) Trans. H. Spens, 1763. London: Dent.
    (ii) Trans. P. Shorey, 1930. London: Heinemann.

POST, R. H. 1962. Population differences in red and green colour vision deficiency. *Eugenics Q.*, **9**, 131–46.

UNITED NATIONS. 1962. Report of the United Nations Scientific Committee on the effects of atomic radiation. General Assembly official records, 17th session. Supplement No. 16 (a/5216). New York: United Nations.

(Chapter 15)

BULLOUGH, W. S. 1951. *Vertebrate Sexual Cycles*. London: Methuen.

CARTER, C. O. 1958. A life-table for mongols with the causes of death. *J. Ment. Def. Res.*, **2**, 64–75.

CLARKE, C. A. 1962. *Genetics for the Clinician*. Oxford: Blackwell.

DARLINGTON, C. D. 1965. *Cytology*. London: Churchill.

FULLER, J. L., and THOMPSON, R. W. 1961. *Behavior Genetics*. New York: Wiley.

HALDANE, J. B. S. 1924. *Daedalus, or Science and the Future*. London: K. Paul.

HAMERTON, J. L. (ed.) 1961. *Chromosomes in Medicine*. London: Heinemann.

MARSHALL, F. H. A., *et al.* 1952. *The Physiology of Reproduction*. (3rd ed.) London: Longmans.

REFERENCES BY CHAPTERS

MULLER, H. J., LITTLE, C. C. and SNYDER, L. H. 1947. *Genetics, Medicine, and Man.* Ithaca, New York: Cornell U.P.

PETTERSSON, G., and BONNIER, G. 1937. Inherited sex mosaic in man. *Hereditas*, **23**, 49–69.

ROBERTS, J. A. FRASER. 1952. The genetics of mental deficiency. *Eug. Rev.*, **44**, 71–83.

STOCKARD, C. R. 1941. The genetic and endocrine basis of differences in form and behaviour. *Amer. Anat. Memoirs*, **19**, Philadelphia: Wistar Institute.

VOGEL, F. 1961. *Allgemeiner Humangenetik.* Berlin: Springer.

(Chapter 16)

ARCHER, W. G. (ed.) 1963. *The Kama Sutra of Vatsyayana.* (Trans. Burton and Arbuthnot 1883). London: Unwin.

CARR SAUNDERS, A. M. 1922. *The Population Problem: a study in human evolution.* Oxford: U.P.

COOK, R. C. 1951. *Human Fertility: the Modern Dilemma.* London: Gollancz.

DARLINGTON, C. D. 1958. *Evolution of Genetic Systems.* Edinburgh: Oliver and Boyd.

DARLINGTON, C. D. 1960. Cousin marriage and the evolution of the breeding system in man. *Heredity*, **14**, 297–332.

DARLINGTON, C. D. 1961. Cousin marriage and population structure. *Eug. Rev.*, **53**, 139–44.

EATON, J. W., and MAYER, A. J. 1954. Man's capacity to reproduce. (Hutterites). *Hum. Biol.* 25 (3). Baltimore.

EDWARDS, JOSEPH. 1940. The effect of unilateral castration on spermatogenesis. *Proc. Roy. Soc.*, B. **128**, 407–21.

GARROD, A. E. 1902. The incidence of alkaptonuria: a study in chemical individuality. *Lancet*, 1902, (2), 1616–20.

HAMMOND, JOHN. 1941. Fertility in mammals and birds. *Biol. Rev.*, **16**, 165–90.

KINSEY, A. C., POMEROY, W. B., and MARTIN, C. E. 1948. *Sexual Behaviour in the Human Male.* Philadelphia: Saunders.

NEWSOM, J. 1945. *The Education of Girls.* London: Faber.

PEARL, RAYMOND. 1939. *The Natural History of Population.* Oxford.

PEARSON, K., and LEE, A. 1899. On the inheritance of fertility in mankind. *Phil. Trans. R. S. (A)* **192**, 279–90.

SORSBY, A. (ed.) 1951. *Genetics in Ophthalmology.* London: Butterworth.

PART FIVE

(Chapters 17 and 18)

CLARK, G. 1961. *World Prehistory.* Cambridge: U.P.

REFERENCES BY CHAPTERS

CRICHTON-MILLER, H. 1945. *Psycho-Analysis and its Derivatives.* 2nd ed. Oxford: U.P.

DARLINGTON, C. D. 1961. Instincts and morals. *Rationalist Ann.* 23–34. London.

DARLINGTON, C. D. 1963. Psychology, genetics and the process of history. *Brit. J. Psychol.* **54**, 293–8.

EDDINGTON, A. 1928. *The Nature of the Physical World.* Cambridge: U.P.

EYSENCK, H. J. 1952. *The Scientific Study of Personality.* London: Routledge.

EYSENCK, H., and PRELL, D. B. 1951. The inheritance of neuroticism (twins). *J. Mental Sci.,* **97**, 441–65.

FISHER, R. A. 1934. Indeterminism and natural selection. *Phil. Sci.,* **1**, 99–117.

FREUD, SIGMUND. 1931. *Theoretische Schriften* (1911–25). Vienna: Int. Psychoanal. Verlag.

GINSBURG, B. E. 1958. Genetics as a tool in the study of behavior. *Persp. Biol. & Med.,* **1**, 397–424.

PENROSE, L. S. 1954. *Biology of Mental Defect.* London: Sedgwick.

PLANCK, MAX. 1951. *Scientific Autobiography and other Papers.* London: Williams and Norgate.

SHERRINGTON, C. 1940. *Man on His Nature.* Cambridge: U.P.

TROTTER, W. 1915. *Instincts of the Herd in Peace and War.* London: Allen and Unwin.

WESTERMARCK, E. 1908. *The Origin and Development of the Moral Ideas.* London: Macmillan.

WHITAKER, E. 1950. Review of Born: 1949. *Scientific American* (Jan.) 56–8.

WHYTE, L. L. 1962. *The Unconscious before Freud.* London: Tavistock Pubns.

Index

401

More about Penguins and Pelicans

If you have enjoyed reading this book you may wish
to know that *Penguin Book News* appears every month.
It is an attractively illustrated magazine containing
a complete list of books published by Penguins and
still in print, together with details of the month's
new books. A specimen copy will be sent free on
request.

Penguin Book News is obtainable from most bookshops;
but you may prefer to become a regular subscriber at
3s. for twelve issues. Just write to Dept EP, Penguin
Books Ltd, Harmondsworth, Middlesex, enclosing
a cheque or postal order, and you will be put on the
mailing list.

Another book published by Penguins is described
on the following page.

Note: *Penguin Book News* is not available in the U.S.A.,
Canada or Australia

The Chemistry of Life

Steven Rose

The molecular structure of a protein (insulin) was described in detail for the first time in 1956: today such procedures are routine. Not only has the pace of biochemistry accelerated in recent years: with the perfection of the electron microscope and the development of cybernetics, the science has also widened and grown more complex.

The Chemistry of Life outlines the scope and achievement of a science which began as the study of the chemical constituents of living matter. Dealing successively with the chemical analysis of the living animal cell, the conversions induced between chemicals by the enzymes acting as catalysts, and the self-regulating nature of cells, Dr Rose explains how the design of particular cells influences their functions within the living organism as a whole.

Biochemistry is a difficult subject. But it is presented here as simply as accuracy will permit by a young research chemist who conveys much of the adventure of discovery implicit in a science which may one day answer the eternal question: 'What is life?'